OCR Advanced FSMQ Additional Mathematics

Stephen Doyle

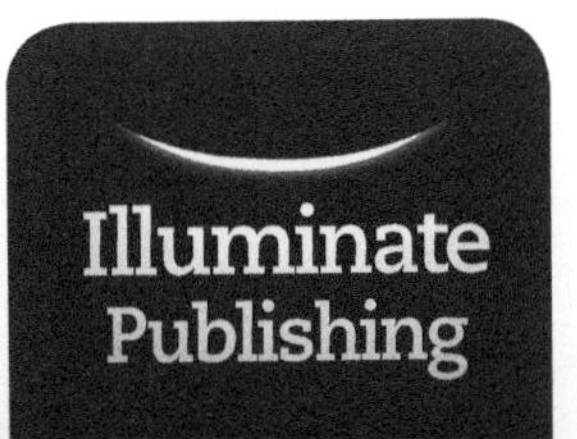

Published in 2015 by Illuminate Publishing Ltd, P.O. Box 1160,
Cheltenham, Gloucestershire GL50 9RW

Orders: Please visit www.illuminatepublishing.com
or email sales@illuminatepublishing.com

British Library Cataloguing in Publication Data

A catalogue record for this book is available from the British Library

ISBN 978-1-908682-47-5

Printed and bound by Ashford Colour Press, Great Britain

12.18

The publisher's policy is to use papers that are natural, renewable and recyclable products made from wood grown in sustainable forests. The logging and manufacturing processes are expected to conform to the environmental regulations of the country of origin.

Editor: Geoff Tuttle
Design: Greengate Publishing Services
Page make-up and diagrams: John Dickinson

Cover photograph: Shutterstock.com

Acknowledgements

I am very grateful to Peter, Geoff and the team at Illuminate Publishing for their professionalism, support and guidance throughout this project. It has been a pleasure to work so closely with them.

The publisher and author would like to thank the following for their help and advice in reviewing this book:

Margaret Shepherd

Alison Warburton

This resource is endorsed by OCR for use with specification OCR Freestanding Mathematics Qualification (Advanced): Additional Mathematics 6993. In order to gain OCR endorsement this resource has undergone an independent quality check. OCR has not paid for the reproduction of this resource, nor does OCR receive any royalties from its sale. For more information about the endorsement process please visit the OCR website www.ocr.org.uk.

Contents

Introduction

This book provides complete coverage and support for the OCR Free Standing Mathematics Qualification (FSMQ) in Additional Mathematics. Some students will be attempting this qualification with limited teacher input, so this book is ideal as it provides an interactive study path through the material by providing knowledge and testing throughout.

It is hoped that this book will encourage an interest in mathematics and mathematical techniques and a desire to study mathematics further at AS- or A-Level standard.

The structure of the book

Knowledge and understanding

Topics start with a short list of the material covered in the topic and each topic will give the underpinning knowledge and skills you need to perform well in your exams.

Formulae not included in the formula sheet should be learnt. Formulae used will be highlighted and will be included in a Topic summary at the end of each topic.

The knowledge section contains easy to understand notes which are then reinforced by detailed explanation of examples. Guidance will be given to the theory, examples and questions that will help you understand the thinking behind the steps. You will also be given detailed advice when it is needed.

Exam practice and technique

Helping students to answer examination questions lies at the heart of this book. This means that we have included questions throughout the book that will build up your skills and knowledge until you are at a stage to answer full exam questions on your own. **Examples** are included, some of which are based on recent examination questions. These are annotated with notes and general advice about the knowledge, skills and techniques needed to answer them. It is important to work through all of the examples as there are some new techniques that are only covered in the examples. There is an **Exam practice** section in each topic that provides actual examination questions with commentary so you can see how the questions should be answered.

There is a **Test yourself** section where you are encouraged to answer questions on the topic and then compare your answers with the ones given at the back of the book. You can also look at the **Worked solutions** on the website which give full detailed answers. You should, of course, work through complete examination papers as part of your revision process.

We advise that you look at the OCR website www.ocr.org.uk where you can download materials such as the specification, past examination papers and mark schemes to help you with your studies. When you have completed your course you should download the examination papers and mark schemes and work through each paper, checking your answers with the mark scheme.

The features of the book and how to use them

There are a number of features used throughout the book to assist you in the learning process. What they are and how they should be used is outlined here.

Formulae

There are many formulae used in this book and they will be identified in the following way.

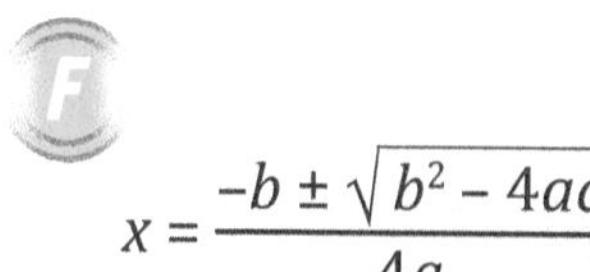

$$x = \frac{-b \pm \sqrt{b^2 - 4ac}}{4a}$$

There will also be a note mentioning whether the formula will need to be remembered or whether it will be included in the examination paper.

Tips

Tips are pieces of advice aimed at maximising your marks when answering questions.

TIP

The examiner should not have to hunt for your answer amongst your workings, so you need to state your answer clearly.

Take note

These are warnings about typical mistakes students make. Hopefully by identifying them, you are less likely to make them.

TAKE NOTE!

Note that only the x-coordinates are asked for here, so do not waste time finding the corresponding y-coordinates.

Notes

These provide additional guidance on mathematical concepts.

You should give answers in descending powers (i.e. x^3, then x^2, then x and finally ordinary numbers, e.g. 2).

Progress check

These are a very important aid to assessing your progress through the material in each topic. Progress checks occur after a section of explanation and examples and they enable you to check your progress by attempting the questions and then checking your answers with either the answers in the book or the worked solutions on the website.

Exam practice

This section provides actual examination questions on the topic from previous examination papers. Worked solutions are provided so you can follow through the various steps in the answers. If you feel really confident, you could avoid looking at the answers and provide your own answer and compare it with the worked solution. Alternatively, you may prefer to treat these as examples to be worked through.

Test yourself

Test yourself questions are included towards the end of each topic. These questions are of an equivalent standard of complexity to the questions you will encounter in the final exam.

You should attempt these questions and assess you mastery of the topic by comparing your answers with the answers provided at the back of the book or the worked solutions on the website.

Topic summary

At the end of each topic there is a topic summary which gives details of formulae and a brief summary of the topic content.

Good luck with your course.

Stephen Doyle

1 Algebra

Revision of the basics

Algebra is used throughout this course so you need a good grasp of it before you start the new material. You will have come across most of the material in this topic during your GCSE course but you may have forgotten some of this, so this material is presented here as a refresher. You should work your way through the material and check you have a thorough understanding. If you think you already understand this material then it is still worth checking your knowledge by doing the Progress checks and Test yourself and checking your answers with those provided.

This topic covers the following:

1.1 The use of brackets in algebraic expressions
1.2 Simplifying algebraic expressions
1.3 The solution of linear equations
1.4 Changing the subject of an algebraic expression
1.5 The solution of linear simultaneous equations
1.6 Use and manipulation of surds

1.1 The use of brackets in algebraic expressions

Brackets are used in maths to show which arithmetic operations need to be carried out first. In algebra you must be able to multiply out brackets and simplify the result by collecting the like terms. Here you will learn how to remove brackets and collect like terms.

Collecting like terms

Like terms are terms such as x and $4x$ or $5x^2$ and $-3x^2$. By adding or subtracting like terms we can simplify algebraic expressions as the following example shows.

Example

1 Simplify each of the following algebraic expressions.

(a) $4x^2 + 6x - x + 6x^2$

(b) $6a - b - c + a - 4a + c$

(c) $4yx + x^2 + 6xy - 4x^2$

(d) $x^3 - 6x^2 - 4x + 1 + 2x^3 + 8x^2 + 3x - 6$

Answers

You should give answers in descending powers (i.e. x^3, then x^2, then x and finally ordinary numbers, e.g. 2).

1 (a) $4x^2 + 6x - x + 6x^2 = 10x^2 + 5x$

(b) $6a - b - c + a - 4a + c = 3a - b$

You will be dealing a lot with directed numbers (plusses and minuses) in this book so always consider the sign and the value of a letter or number.

(c) $4yx + x^2 + 6xy - 4x^2 = 10xy - 3x^2$

The order of the letters in a term does not matter, so $4yx$ is the same as $4xy$. When writing terms such as this we put the number first and then the letters in alphabetical order. So, we would write $4xy$ rather than $4yx$.

(d) $x^3 - 6x^2 - 4x + 1 + 2x^3 + 8x^2 + 3x - 6 = 3x^3 + 2x^2 - x - 5$

Removing brackets

As part of the simplification process brackets are multiplied out before collecting like terms.

Any numbers or letters outside the brackets must multiply each term inside the bracket. You have to be careful when there is a negative outside the bracket as it will change the sign of all the terms inside the bracket when multiplying out the bracket. The following example shows these techniques.

Example

2 Multiply out the brackets for each of the following and simplify your answer.

(a) $3(x + 4)$

(b) $4(2x - 8)$

(c) $-6(x - 1)$

(d) $5(2x - 3) + 4(x - 1)$

(e) $-(4 - x)$

Answers

2 (a) $3(x + 4) = 3x + 12$

> Each term in the bracket is multiplied by the number outside the bracket (i.e. 3).

(b) $4(2x - 8) = 8x - 32$

(c) $-6(x - 1) = -6x + 6$

(d) $5(2x - 3) + 4(x - 1) = 10x - 15 + 4x - 4$

$= 14x - 19$

> Multiply out the brackets and then collect like terms.

(e) $-(4 - x) = -4 + x = x - 4$

> The minus can be considered to be a -1. Hence we simply change the sign of the contents of the bracket.

TAKE NOTE !

Be careful when there is a minus sign outside the brackets as this will change the sign of all the terms inside the bracket.

Progress check

Progress check

1 Multiply out the following brackets:

(a) $3(2x + 5)$

(b) $-2(x + 6)$

(c) $8(x^2 + 3x + 4)$

(d) $6(3x - 7x + 9)$

(e) $-3(5x - 9)$

(f) $-4(x^2 + x + 2)$

(g) $-(3x + 5)$

(h) $-(6x + 8)$

(i) $-(x^2 - 4x + 8)$

(j) $-4(5 - x)$

(k) $-7(2 - 4x + x^2)$

2 Simplify the following algebraic expressions:

(a) $2(3x - 4) + 2(x - 3)$

(b) $5(4 - 2x) - (x - 4)$

(c) $12(x - 8) - 4(x - 8)$

(d) $4(2x - 3y) + 6(x + 2y)$

(e) $2x(x + 4) - x(x + 6)$

(f) $4x(3x + 1) - 3x(x - 4)$

(g) $2x^2(x - 6) + x^3 + 2x^2$

(h) $4x(x + y) - y(x + y)$

Multiplying pairs of brackets

As part of this course you will regularly need to multiply two pairs of brackets together such as $(x + 2)(x - 3)$. There are various methods for this and the 'face' method is one of them.

 TIP

Using the face method, the curved lines show the terms that are multiplied together.

$(x + 2)(x - 3)$

Notice the shape of the face. The curved lines show which terms need to be multiplied together in order to multiply out the brackets.

We usually start from the top first and work from left to right. So, the x multiplies by the x to give x^2, the 2 multiplies by the -3 to give -6. We now deal with the curved lines under the brackets. The x multiplies the -3 to give $-3x$ and the $+2$ multiplies the x to give $+2x$.

Notice the way the answer is given in descending powers of x.

Hence we can write $(x + 2)(x - 3) = x^2 - 6 - 3x + 2x$

$$= x^2 - x - 6$$

An alternative method to the 'face method' for multiplying out brackets

Here is the method I prefer for multiplying out brackets. Let's look at multiplying out the same brackets we used above.

$$(x + 2)(x - 3) = x(x - 3) + 2(x - 3)$$

The first term in the first bracket (i.e. the x) multiplies the contents of the second bracket. We then take the second term in the first bracket along with its sign (i.e. $+2$) and multiply it by the contents of the second bracket. Note that the second bracket appears twice.

We then multiply the contents in the brackets by the outside letter or number like this.

We then simplify this by collecting terms in x.

$$x(x - 3) + 2(x - 3) = x^2 - 3x + 2x - 6$$

$$= x^2 - x - 6$$

The method shown here for multiplication of brackets is a good one and it is the method we will use in this book for multiplying out pairs of brackets but you should use the method you are happiest with.

Examples

3 Multiply out the following brackets.

$(x + 5)(x - 2)$

Answer

3 $(x + 5)(x - 2) = x(x - 2) + 5(x - 2)$

$= x^2 - 2x + 5x - 10$

We collect like terms in x to give the final answer.

$= x^2 + 3x - 10$

Notice the way this is set out. The second bracket appears twice whilst the term in x in the first bracket multiplies the second bracket and the term without x in the first bracket multiplies the second bracket.

4 Multiply out the following brackets.

$(x - 3)(x - 5)$

Answer

4 $(x - 3)(x - 5) = x(x - 5) - 3(x - 5)$

$x^2 - 5x - 3x + 15$

$= x^2 - 8x + 15$

With experience, you need not write this step down as you should be able to complete it mentally to give the line below.

5 Multiply out the following brackets.

$(2x - 7)(4x - 2)$

Answer

5 $(2x - 7)(4x - 2) = 2x(4x - 2) - 7(4x - 2)$

$= 8x^2 - 4x - 28x + 14$

$= 8x^2 - 32x + 14$

6 Multiply out the following brackets.

$(a + b)(a + b)$

Answer

6 $(a + b)(a + b) = a(a + b) + b(a + b)$

$= a^2 + ab + ab + b^2$

$= a^2 + 2ab + b^2$

7 Multiply out the brackets and simplify and give your answer in the form

$x^2 + y^2 + ax + by + c = 0$.

(a) $(x + 1)^2 + (y + 2)^2 = 0$

(b) $(x + 3)^2 + (y + 4)^2 - 10 = 0$

(c) $(x - 3)^2 - (y + 1)^2 = 8$

Answers

7 (a) $(x + 1)^2 + (y + 2)^2 = 0$

$(x + 1)(x + 1) + (y + 2)(y + 2) = 0$

$x^2 + 2x + 1 + y^2 + 4y + 4 = 0$

$x^2 + y^2 + 2x + 4y + 5 = 0$

(b) $(x + 3)^2 + (y + 4)^2 - 10 = 0$

$(x + 3)(x + 3) + (y + 4)(y + 4) - 10 = 0$

$x^2 + 6x + 9 + y^2 + 8y + 16 - 10 = 0$

$x^2 + y^2 + 6x + 8y + 15 = 0$

(c) $(x - 3)^2 - (y + 1)^2 = 8$

$(x - 3)(x - 3) - (y + 1)(y + 1) - 8 = 0$

$x^2 - 6x + 9 - (y^2 + 2y + 1) - 8 = 0$

$x^2 - 6x + 9 - y^2 - 2y - 1 - 8 = 0$

$x^2 - y^2 - 6x - 2y = 0$

TAKE NOTE !

Remember to give the answer with the terms in the same order as asked for in the question.

Remember that a minus sign outside the bracket will change the sign of all the terms inside the bracket when multiplied out.

Progress check

3 Multiply out the following brackets:

(a) $(x + 5)(x + 2)$

(b) $(x - 7)(x + 1)$

(c) $(x + 4)(x - 4)$

(d) $(3x + 1)(5x + 3)$

(e) $(4x - 1)(2x - 5)$

(f) $(5x - 1)(5x + 1)$

(g) $(2x - 8)(x + 4)$

(h) $(3a + b)(4a + 2b)$

(i) $(5x - y)(4x + y)$

(j) $(6x - 5y)(x - 3y)$

4 Multiply out the brackets and simplify and give your answer in the form

$x^2 + y^2 + ax + by + c = 0$.

(a) $(x + 2)^2 + (y + 1)^2 = 0$

(b) $(x + 5)^2 + (y + 3)^2 = 0$

(c) $(x - 7)^2 + (y + 2)^2 = 0$

(d) $(x - 4)^2 + (y + 6)^2 = 0$

(e) $(x - 6)^2 + (y + 7)^2 = 12$

(f) $(x + 2)^2 + (y - 5)^2 + 7 = 0$

(g) $(x - 1)^2 + (y - 9)^2 - 10 = 0$

(h) $(x + 3)^2 + (y - 8)^2 - 27 = 0$

(i) $(x + 1)^2 + (y - 1)^2 = 18$

1.2 Simplifying algebraic expressions

You have already come across how algebraic expressions can be simplified by collecting like terms. Here you will look at how algebraic fractions can be simplified by cancelling like terms on the top and bottom of the fraction.

Simplifying algebraic fractions

The top part (called the numerator) and the bottom part (called the denominator) of an algebraic fraction can be simplified by seeing if there is anything that is common to the top and bottom. Once this has been identified, you cancel them out by dividing the top and the bottom of the fraction by the terms that are common to each in order to find what is left. The following examples show this simplification process.

Examples

8 Simplify $\dfrac{2x^2}{x}$

Answer

8 $\dfrac{2x^2}{x} = 2x$

> x is common to the top and bottom. Hence, you can cancel the x on the top and bottom. This can be regarded as dividing the top and bottom by x.
> Another approach is to use the laws of indices. When you divide by the same letter raised to different powers, you subtract the indices. So $\dfrac{x^2}{x^1}$ becomes $x^{2-1} = x^1 = x$.

9 Simplify $\dfrac{25x^3y}{5xy}$

Answer

9 $\dfrac{25x^3y}{5xy} = 5x^2$

> The factor $5xy$ is common to both the top and the bottom so we divide the top (the numerator) and the bottom (the denominator) by this factor to give the answer.

10 Simplify $\frac{24x^2y}{6xy^2}$

Answer

6*xy* is a factor of both the top and the bottom so we divide both the numerator and the denominator by this to give the simplified answer.

10 $\frac{24x^2y}{6xy^2} = \frac{4x}{y}$

11 Simplify $\frac{(x+1)(x-5)}{(x-2)(x+1)}$

Answer

11 $\frac{(x+1)(x-5)}{(x-2)(x+1)} = \frac{(x-5)}{(x-2)}$

$(x + 1)$ is a factor of the numerator and the denominator and can therefore be cancelled to give the answer.

Progress check

5 Simplify the following expressions:

(a) $\frac{4x^2y}{xy}$

(b) $\frac{12x^2y^3}{4xy}$

(c) $\frac{16a^3b^2c}{24a^2b}$

(d) $\frac{24x^2y^4}{8xy^5}$

6 Simplify the following algebraic fractions:

(a) $\frac{15abc}{5c}$

(b) $\frac{4x^3}{4xy}$

(c) $\frac{6pq^3r}{3pqr}$

(d) $\frac{10x^4y^3}{2x^2y}$

(e) $\frac{45a^3bc^2}{9ab^2c}$

(f) $\frac{(x+7)(x+5)}{(x+5)(x+3)}$

(g) $\frac{(x+3)(x+5)}{(x+5)(x+3)}$

7 Factorise fully the following expressions:

(a) $12x^2y + 8xy^2$

(b) $4a^2b + 2ab$

(c) $24x^2y + 6x$

(d) $25a^3b^2c^5 + 5a^2b^3$

8 Simplify the following algebraic expressions:

(a) $\frac{x^2(x-1)}{x(x-1)}$

(b) $\frac{xy^3}{xy}$

(c) $\frac{15x^3y^3}{5x^3y^2}$

(d) $\frac{5(x-4)}{10(x-2)}$

(e) $\frac{(x+1)(x-2)}{(x-5)(x+1)}$

(f) $\frac{x-3}{(x-3)(x-1)}$

1.3 The solution of linear equations

Linear equations are equations containing one unknown and this unknown can be easily found. Remember that an equation is like a balance. If you apply a process to one side of the equation (such as add a certain number), then for the equation to remain in balance, the same process (adding the certain number) must be applied to the other side of the equation. The following examples illustrate this technique.

Examples

12 Solve the equation $x + 5 = 7$

Answer

12 $x + 5 = 7$

$x + 5 - 5 = 7 - 5$

$x = 2$

Note we normally do this step in our head.

We can remove the +5 by subtracting 5 from both sides of the equation. This will leave x on its own and immediately give the required solution of the equation.

13 Solve the equation $x - 7 = -4$

Answer

13 $x - 7 = -4$

$x = 3$

The − 7 is removed by adding 7 to both sides.

14 Solve the equation $4x = 24$

Answer

14 $4x = 24$

$x = 6$

To remove the 4 in front of the x, we divide both sides by 4.

15 Solve the equation $\frac{x}{5} = 4$

Answer

15 $\frac{x}{5} = 4$

$x = 20$

To remove the 5 in the denominator of the fraction we multiply both sides of the equation by 5. This will leave the x on its own on the left-hand side of the equation.

16 Solve the equation $4x - 7 = 21$

Answer

Add 7 to both sides of the equation.

16 $4x - 7 = 21$

$4x = 28$

Divide both sides by 4.

$x = 7$

17 Solve the equation $\frac{2x}{3} = 12$

Answer

Remove the denominator 3 by multiplying both sides by 3.

17 $\frac{2x}{3} = 12$

$2x = 36$

Divide both sides of the equation by 2.

$x = 18$

18 Solve the equation $\frac{3x}{5} + 4 = 16$

Answer

You must remove the 4 first before dealing with the fraction. Hence we subtract 4 from both sides of the equation.

18 $\frac{3x}{5} + 4 = 16$

$\frac{3x}{5} = 12$

Multiply both sides by 5 to remove the 5 in the denominator.

$3x = 60$

Divide both sides by 3 to remove the 3 in front of the x.

$x = 20$

19 Solve the equation $\frac{x - 7}{3} = 8$

Answer

Remove the denominator by multiplying both sides by 3.

19 $\frac{x - 7}{3} = 8$

$x - 7 = 24$

Add 7 to both sides.

$x = 31$

20 If $\frac{9 + x}{2} = -2$, find the value of x.

Answer

Multiply both sides by 2 to remove the denominator.

20 $\frac{9 + x}{2} = -2$

$9 + x = -4$

Subtract 9 from both sides.

$x = -13$

Linear equation involving brackets

When solving linear equations containing brackets, first multiply out the brackets and collect any like terms and then solve in the way outlined in the previous examples.

Examples

21 Solve the following equation.

$4(2x - 3) = 4$

Answer

21 $4(2x - 3) = 4$

Multiply out the brackets.

$8x - 12 = 4$

Add 12 to both sides in order to eliminate the −12.

$8x = 16$

Divide both sides by 8.

$x = 2$

22 Find the value of x if $5(1 - x) = 15$

Answer

22 $5(1 - x) = 15$

Multiply out the brackets.

$5 - 5x = 15$

Subtract 5 from both sides.

$-5x = 10$

Divide both sides by − 5.

$x = -2$

23 Solve the equation $5(x - 3) - 3(x + 1) = 0$

Answer

23 $5(x - 3) - 3(x + 1) = 0$

Multiply out the brackets.

$5x - 15 - 3x - 3 = 0$

Collecting like terms.

$2x - 18 = 0$

Add 18 to both sides.

$2x = 18$

Divide both sides by 2.

$x = 9$

Equations where the unknown quantity appears on both sides of the equation

If the unknown quantity (i.e. the quantity you are asked to find) appears on both sides of the equation, you must get it on just one side as the following examples show.

It is easier to rearrange the equation in such a way that the unknown quantity is positive.

Examples

24 Solve the equation $2x - 1 = x + 4$

Answer

24 $2x - 1 = x + 4$

You could subtract $2x$ from both sides but in doing so you would produce a $-x$ on the right-hand side. It is easier if we always try to keep the unknown (i.e. x in this case), positive. Subtracting x from both sides is a better option as this solution shows.

Subtracting x from both sides.

$x - 1 = 4$

$x = 5$

Adding 1 to both sides.

25 Solve the following equation

$2m - 4 = m - 3$

Notice that terms in m appear on both sides of the equation. We need to get terms in m on one side of the equation and it is easier if we keep m positive. This is why it is best to subtract m from both sides rather than $2m$.

Answer

25 $2m - 4 = m - 3$

$m - 4 = -3$

$m = 1$

Add 4 to both sides to eliminate the - 4 on the left-hand side.

26 Solve the equation $9(4x - 3) = 3(2x + 3)$

Answer

Multiply out the brackets on both sides of the equation

26 $9(4x - 3) = 3(2x + 3)$

$36x - 27 = 6x + 9$

Subtract $6x$ from both sides.

Add 27 to both sides.

$30x - 27 = 9$

$30x = 36$

Divide both sides by 30.

$x = \frac{36}{30} = \frac{6}{5}$, $1\frac{1}{5}$ or 1.2

TAKE NOTE!

Always cancel fractions so that they are in their lowest terms. Here both top and bottom can be divided by 6.

27 Solve the equation $3(3x - 5) = 12(x - 7)$.

Multiply out the brackets first.

Answer

27 $3(3x - 5) = 12(x - 7)$.

$9x - 15 = 12x - 84$

Subtract $9x$ from both sides.

$-15 = 3x - 84$

Add 84 to both sides.

$69 = 3x$

Divide both sides by 3.

$23 = x$

$x = 23$

28 Solve the equation $\frac{1}{4}(2x - 1) = 3(2x - 1)$

Answer

28 $\frac{1}{4}(2x - 1) = 3(2x - 1)$

Multiply both sides by 4.

$2x - 1 = 12(2x - 1)$

Multiply out the brackets.

$2x - 1 = 24x - 12$

Subtract $2x$ from both sides.

$-1 = 22x - 12$

Add 12 to both sides.

$11 = 22x$

Divide both sides by 22.

$x = \frac{11}{22}$

Cancel the fraction by dividing top and bottom by 11.

$x = \frac{1}{2}$

Progress check

9 Solve the following equation:

$x - 7 = 7$

10 Solve the equation:

$x + 7 = -3$

11 Solve the equation:

$\frac{4x}{5} = 12$

12 Solve the equation:

$$\frac{x}{5} - 1 = 7$$

13 Solve the equation:

$$\frac{2x}{3} - 1 = 5$$

14 Find the value of x if $2(2x + 1) = 18$

15 If $\frac{-6 + x}{2} = -1$, find the value of x.

16 Solve each of the following equations:

(a) $2 - x = 4 + x$

(b) $4(x - 7) = 3(2x - 10)$

(c) $5(6x - 3) = 6(2x - 1)$

(d) $\frac{1}{3}(x - 1) = 2x + 4$

17 Solve each of the following equations:

(a) $\frac{x - 5}{4} = 4x$

(b) $6x - 1 = 3(x - 4) + 7$

TAKE NOTE!

You can only add or subtract algebraic fractions if their denominators are the same.

Linear equations involving fractions

Suppose we want to solve the equation

$$\frac{x}{3} - \frac{x}{8} = 4$$

The first step is to find the smallest number that 3 and 8 divide into exactly. This number is 24. We then multiply both sides by this number.

So we have $\frac{24x}{3} - \frac{24x}{8} = 96$

We then cancel the fractions and obtain

$$8x - 3x = 96$$

$$5x = 96$$

$$x = \frac{96}{5}$$

$$x = 19.2$$

Alternative method

As in lots of maths questions, there are different ways to solve a problem.

You may prefer to use this approach where you find the common denominator of 3 and 8 which is 24.

Hence $\frac{x}{3} - \frac{x}{8} = 4$

$$\frac{8x}{24} - \frac{3x}{24} = 4$$

$$\frac{5x}{24} = 4$$

Multiply both sides by 24.

$$5x = 96$$

Divide both sides by 5.

$$x = 19.2$$

Example

29 Solve the following equation $\frac{2x}{5} - \frac{x}{4} = 3$

Answer

29 $$\frac{2x}{5} - \frac{x}{4} = 3$$

Multiplying both sides by 20 (because the denominators 5 and 4 both divide into 20 exactly) gives

$$\frac{40x}{5} - \frac{20x}{4} = 60$$

Cancelling the fractions we obtain

$$8x - 5x = 60$$

$$3x = 60$$

$$x = 20$$

Progress check

18 Solve

(a) $\frac{x}{4} + \frac{x}{2} = 15$

(b) $\frac{x}{3} + \frac{x}{4} = 49$

(c) $\frac{x}{9} + \frac{2x}{3} = 42$

19 Solve the equation $\frac{x-3}{2} + \frac{x+1}{3} = 3$

20 Solve $\frac{x}{2} - \frac{x}{5} = 3$

21 Solve $\frac{1}{4}(x-1) = \frac{1}{3}(x-2)$

22 Solve $\frac{2x}{3} - \frac{x}{4} = 5$

1.4 Changing the subject of an algebraic expression

You will frequently have to rearrange a formula or change the subject of a formula. The subject of the formula is the quantity that needs to be found and it will appear on its own on the left of the equation/formula.

Take the following example:

$$n = \frac{m}{M}$$

TIP

Notice the use of upper case and lower case letters to mean different things in this formula. Do not swap upper and lower case letters.

As n is on its own on the left-hand side, it is the subject of the formula. Suppose we want to change the subject of the formula to m. We need to get rid of M on the right of the equation and we do this by multiplying both sides of the equation by M.

The equation now appears as follows:

$$Mn = \frac{Mm}{M}$$

We normally write the letters in an equation in alphabetical order. So here we would write Mn rather than nM.

We can now cancel the M in the top and bottom of the fraction on the right-hand side to give

$$Mn = m$$

This equation can be swapped around so that the left part appears on the right and vice versa to give

$$m = Mn$$

The equation has now been transposed so that m is the subject.

If $n = \dfrac{m}{M}$ and we want to make M the subject we first multiply both sides by M to give $Mn = m$

Now, we need to remove the n and this is done by dividing both sides by n.

So, $M = \dfrac{m}{n}$ and M is now the subject.

Note that if the required subject of the equation is in the denominator, then multiply both sides by it.

Example

30 Rearrange the following equations to make the bracketed letter the subject of the equation.

(a) $y = \dfrac{1}{x}$ (x)

(b) $y = 2x + 6$ (x)

(c) $r^2 = a^2 + b^2$ (b)

Answers

30 (a) $y = \dfrac{1}{x}$ — Multiply both sides by x.

$xy = 1$ — Divide both sides by y.

$x = \dfrac{1}{y}$

(b) $y = 2x + 6$ — Subtract 6 from both sides.

$y - 6 = 2x$ — Divide both sides by 2.

$x = \dfrac{y-6}{2}$

(c) $r^2 = a^2 + b^2$ — Subtract a^2 from both sides.

$r^2 - a^2 = b^2$

$b^2 = r^2 - a^2$ — Square root both sides.

$b = \sqrt{r^2 - a^2}$

Progress check

23 Make r the subject of the formula in each of the following:

(a) $A = \pi r^2$

(b) $A = 4\pi r^2$

(c) $V = \dfrac{4}{3}\pi r^3$

24 Make the bracketed symbol the subject of the equation: e.g. in question (a), write the equation in the form $u = \dots$.

(a) $v = u + at$ (u)

(b) $v = u + at$ (a)

(c) $v^2 = 2as$ (s)

(d) $v^2 = u^2 + 2as$ (a)

(e) $v^2 = u^2 + 2as$ (u)

(f) $s = ut + \frac{1}{2}at^2$ (a)

(g) $y = mx + c$ (c)

(h) $y = mx + c$ (m)

(i) $s = \frac{1}{2}(u + v)t$ (t)

(j) $E = \frac{1}{2}mv^2$ (v)

(k) $V = \pi r^2 l$ (l)

(l) $V = \pi r^2 l$ (r)

1.5 The solution of linear simultaneous equations

To draw a line with a given equation on a graph, substitute $x = 0$ into the equation and this will give where the line cuts the y-axis. Then substitute $y = 0$ into the equation and this gives where the line cuts the x-axis. The line is then drawn passing through the two points.

Linear simultaneous equations are a pair of equations both of which represent a straight line.

Take, for example, the following equations both representing straight lines:

$$2x + y = 6$$

$$y = \frac{1}{2}x + 1$$

These can be plotted on the same graph to give the following:

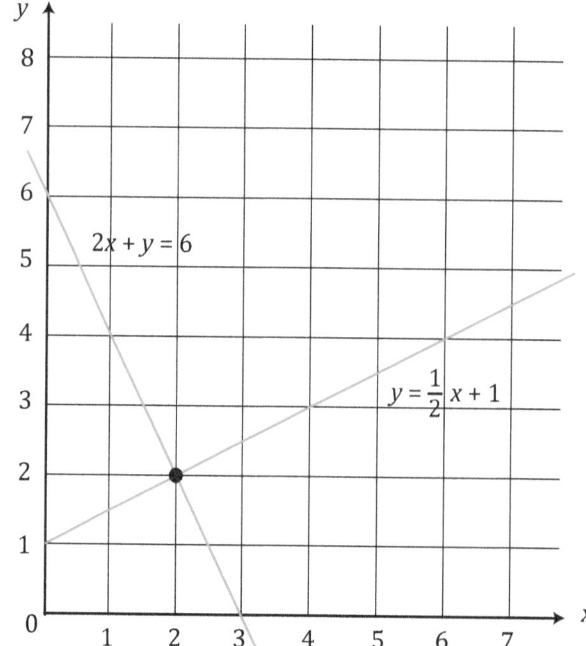

Where the two lines intersect, the coordinates of the point of intersection will be the same for both lines. The x-value will be the same for both lines as will the y-value. This point will be the only point on both lines where this is so. Not all simultaneous equations can be solved. If the lines were parallel to each other there would be no point of intersection as the lines do not cross.

The solution of a pair of simultaneous equations gives the two values (usually x and y) where the values of x and y will satisfy both of the linear equations.

There are three methods that can be used to solve a pair of simultaneous equations:

1 Graphically – both equations are used to plot two lines and their point of intersection is the solution.

2 By elimination – we eliminate one of the unknowns by adding or subtracting the two simultaneous equations together. This is the method you were probably taught for your GCSE work.

3 By substitution – we find the expression for y from one of the equations and substitute it for y into the other equation.

Solving simultaneous equations by elimination

This method of solving simultaneous equations involves eliminating one of the variables in the equations by either adding or subtracting both equations. This is the method you are most likely to have used when solving these equations at GCSE level.

The elimination method is best understood by looking at the following examples.

Examples

31 Solve the simultaneous equations.

$$2x + 3y = 8$$

$$x + 4y = 9$$

Answer

31 The first step is to look at the coefficients of x and y in both of the equations.

You need to make the coefficients of either x or y the same for both equations and we multiply one or both of the equations by numbers in order to achieve this.

In this case it is easiest to make the coefficients of x the same as we only have to multiply the second equation by 2.

TIP

The coefficients are the numbers in front of the x and the y. In the first equation the coefficient of x is 2 and that for y is 3 and in the second equation the coefficient of x is 1 and that for y is 4.

We first number the given equations so it is easier to refer to them.

$2x + 3y = 8$ .... (1)

$x + 4y = 9$ .... (2)

Multiplying both sides of equation (2) by 2 gives

$2x + 8y = 18$ .... (3)

$2x + 3y = 8$ .... (4)

Subtracting (4) from (3) gives

$5y = 10$

$y = 2$

Substituting $y = 2$ into equation (1) we obtain

$2x + 3y = 8$

$2x + 3(2) = 8$

$2x + 6 = 8$

$2x = 2$

$x = 1$

Both sides of the equation are equal, showing that the values of x and y satisfy the second equation.

Substituting $x = 1$ and $y = 2$ into LHS of equation (2) we obtain

$1 + 4(2) = 9$

$9 = \text{RHS}$

Hence solutions are $x = 1$ and $y = 2$.

---

32 Solve the simultaneous equations.

$y = 3x - 7$

$y = 3 - 2x$

Answer

32 Firstly write the second equation so that the x is aligned with the first equation and number both equations.

$y = 3x - 7$ .... (1)

$y = -2x + 3$ .... (2)

Notice that the coefficient of y (i.e. 1) is the same for both equations. We can eliminate y by subtracting equation (2) from equation (1).

Subtracting (1) – (2) we obtain

$$0 = 5x - 10$$

$$10 = 5x$$

This is the equivalent of $5x = 10$.

$$x = 2$$

Substituting $x = 2$ into equation (1) we obtain

$$y = 3x - 7$$

$$y = 3(2) - 7$$

$$y = -1$$

Substituting $x = 2$ and $y = -1$ into equation (2) we obtain

$$-1 = -2(2) + 3$$

$$-1 = -1$$

Both sides of the equation are equal, showing that the values of x and y satisfy the second equation.

Hence solutions are $x = 2$ and $y = -1$.

Solving simultaneous equations by substitution

This method of solving simultaneous equations involves removing y by substituting the y-value from one of the equations into the other equation. This is best understood by looking at the following example.

Example

33 Solve the following simultaneous equations.

$$y = 2x - 6$$

$$y = -3x + 14$$

Answer

33 Equating the y-values we obtain

$$2x - 6 = -3x + 14$$

Add $3x$ to both sides.

$$5x - 6 = 14$$

Add 6 to both sides.

$$5x = 20$$

Divide both sides by 5.

$$x = 4$$

Substituting the value $x = 4$ into the equation $y = 2x - 6$ we obtain

$$y = 2(4) - 6$$

$$y = 2$$

Substituting $x = 4$ and $y = 2$ into equation $y = -3x + 14$ we obtain

$$2 = -3(4) + 14$$

$$2 = 2$$

Both sides of the equation are equal, showing that the values of x and y satisfy the second equation.

Hence the solutions are $x = 4, y = 2$.

Whether to use the elimination or the substitution method for solving simultaneous equations

The elimination method is more popular when solving two linear equations but the substitution method is preferred when finding the points of intersection between a quadratic equation and a linear equation.

You will be looking at this in greater detail in the next topic.

Problems involving simultaneous equations

In some questions you will have to form the two simultaneous equations from information given in the question before solving them. The following example shows how to answer these types of question.

Example

34 The sum of two numbers is 14 and the difference of the same numbers is 2. Find the two numbers.

Answer

34 Let the larger of the two numbers = x and the smaller of the two numbers = y.

The sum of two numbers is 14, so we have $x + y = 14$

The difference of the two numbers is 2, so we have $x - y = 2$

Hence, we have two simultaneous equations.

$x + y = 14$ .... (1)

$x - y = 2$ .... (2)

Adding equations (1) and (2) we have

$2x = 16$

$x = 8$

Substituting $x = 8$ into equation (1) we have

$x + y = 14$

$8 + y = 14$

$y = 6$

Checking by substituting $x = 8$ and $y = 6$ into equation (2) we obtain

$x - y = 2$

$8 - 6 = 2$

$2 = 2$

Both sides of the equation are equal, showing that the values of x and y satisfy the second equation.

Hence solutions are $x = 8$ and $y = 6$.

Progress check

25 Solve the following pairs of simultaneous equations by using the elimination method:

(a) $x + y = 5$

$5x + 2y = 11$

(b) $2x - 3y = -5$

$5x + 2y = 16$

26 Solve the following pairs of simultaneous equations by using the substitution method:

(a) $y = 3x - 5$

$y = x - 1$

(b) $2x + 3y = 8$

$5x + 3y = 11$

1.6 Use and manipulation of surds

Numbers like $\sqrt{18}$ are called surds. Surds are irrational numbers. This means that they cannot be expressed as fractions, recurring decimals or terminating decimals. Surds can be simplified like this:

$$\sqrt{18} = \sqrt{9 \times 2} = 3\sqrt{2}$$

> **TIP**
>
> Always try to find the largest square factor. For example, $\sqrt{80}$ could be written as $\sqrt{16 \times 5} = 4\sqrt{5}$ or $\sqrt{4 \times 20}$ but this still needs further simplification to $\sqrt{4 \times 4 \times 5} = 4\sqrt{5}$. It is quicker to spot that 16 is the highest square factor of 80, so we have $\sqrt{80} = \sqrt{16 \times 5} = 4\sqrt{5}$.

Here the number 18 is broken down into two factors that include a square number; 9 is a perfect square so can be square rooted to give a whole number answer. So $\sqrt{18} = 3\sqrt{2}$

Suppose we are asked to simplify the expression $\sqrt{8} + \sqrt{18}$

Look for square numbers that are factors of the numbers inside the square root sign.

$\sqrt{8}$ can be written as $\sqrt{4 \times 2}$ and square rooting the 4 gives $2\sqrt{2}$. In a similar way we can write $\sqrt{18} = \sqrt{9 \times 2} = 3\sqrt{2}$

Hence we have $\sqrt{8} + \sqrt{18} = 2\sqrt{2} + 3\sqrt{2} = 5\sqrt{2}$

The following examples show the use of this technique:

1 $\sqrt{18} + \sqrt{32} = \sqrt{9 \times 2} + \sqrt{16 \times 2}$
$$= 3\sqrt{2} + 4\sqrt{2}$$
$$= 7\sqrt{2}$$

2 $7\sqrt{3} - \sqrt{48} = 7\sqrt{3} - \sqrt{16 \times 3}$
$$= 7\sqrt{3} - 4\sqrt{3}$$
$$= 3\sqrt{3}$$

Simplifying surds

Here are some general rules when manipulating surds:

F

$$\sqrt{a} \times \sqrt{a} = a$$
$$\sqrt{a} \times \sqrt{b} = \sqrt{ab}$$
$$\left(\sqrt{a} + \sqrt{b}\right)\left(\sqrt{a} - \sqrt{b}\right) = a - b$$

The following examples show ways in which surds can be simplified:

1 $\left(\sqrt{3}\right)^2 = \sqrt{3} \times \sqrt{3} = 3$

2 $\left(5\sqrt{2}\right)^2 = 5\sqrt{2} \times 5\sqrt{2} = 25 \times 2 = 50$

3 $\left(3\sqrt{2}\right) \times \left(4\sqrt{2}\right) = 12 \times 2 = 24$

4 $3\sqrt{2} + 2\sqrt{2} = 5\sqrt{2}$

5 $\left(2+\sqrt{7}\right)\left(2+\sqrt{7}\right) = 2\left(2+\sqrt{7}\right) + \sqrt{7}\left(2+\sqrt{7}\right) = 4 + 2\sqrt{7} + 2\sqrt{7} + 7 = 11 + 4\sqrt{7}$

6 $\left(1+\sqrt{3}\right)\left(5-\sqrt{12}\right) = 1\left(5-\sqrt{12}\right) + \sqrt{3}\left(5-\sqrt{12}\right)$

$$= 5 - \sqrt{12} + 5\sqrt{3} - \sqrt{3 \times 12}$$

$$= 5 - 2\sqrt{3} + 5\sqrt{3} - \sqrt{36}$$

$$= -1 + 3\sqrt{3}$$

Rationalising surds

If you have a fraction with a surd on the bottom, then it needs to be removed (i.e. rationalised). This is done by multiplying the top (i.e. numerator) and bottom (i.e. denominator) of the fraction by the surd. Rationalising makes sure that the denominator is no longer an irrational number.

$\frac{1}{\sqrt{3}} = \frac{1}{\sqrt{3}} \times \frac{\sqrt{3}}{\sqrt{3}} = \frac{\sqrt{3}}{3}$ The fraction is simplified when there are no surds in the denominator.

When there is a fraction containing a denominator like this $\frac{1}{1-\sqrt{2}}$, to remove the irrational number in the denominator, both the numerator (i.e. top) and denominator (i.e. bottom) of the fraction are multiplied by the conjugate of the denominator which in this case is $1 + \sqrt{2}$. The conjugate is the same as the denominator except the sign is the opposite.

Hence $\frac{1}{1-\sqrt{2}} = \frac{1}{\left(1-\sqrt{2}\right)} \times \frac{\left(1+\sqrt{2}\right)}{\left(1+\sqrt{2}\right)} = \frac{1+\sqrt{2}}{1-2} = \frac{1+\sqrt{2}}{-1} = -1-\sqrt{2}$

Examples

In both of these questions you have been asked to simplify. In each case this is done by rationalising the denominator (i.e. by removing the surds from the denominator) and simplifying the result.

35 Simplify

$$\frac{10}{\sqrt{5}}$$

Answer

35 $\frac{10}{\sqrt{5}} = \frac{10}{\sqrt{5}} \times \frac{\sqrt{5}}{\sqrt{5}} = \frac{10\sqrt{5}}{5} = 2\sqrt{5}$

36 Simplify

$$\frac{1}{2-\sqrt{5}}$$

Rationalise the denominator by multiplying the numerator and denominator by the conjugate of the denominator.

Answer

36 $\frac{1}{(2-\sqrt{5})}\frac{(2+\sqrt{5})}{(2+\sqrt{5})} = \frac{2+\sqrt{5}}{4-5} = \frac{2+\sqrt{5}}{-1} = -2-\sqrt{5}$

Progress check

27 Simplify

$\sqrt{45} + \sqrt{80} + \sqrt{125}$

28 Simplify

$$\frac{3\sqrt{3}-\sqrt{2}}{\sqrt{3}-\sqrt{2}}$$

29 Simplify

$$\frac{3}{\sqrt{3}} + \sqrt{75} + (\sqrt{2} \times \sqrt{6})$$

» TIP

Remember to spot those factors that are perfect squares.

Exam practice

1 (a) (i) Factorise the expression $x^2 - 9x + 20$.

(ii) Factorise the expression $x^2 - x - 12$.

(b) Hence, simplify the algebraic fraction $\dfrac{x^2 - 9x + 20}{x^2 - x - 12}$.

Answer

1 (a) (i) $x^2 - 9x + 20 = (x - 4)(x - 5)$

(ii) $x^2 - x - 12 = (x + 3)(x - 4)$

(b) $\dfrac{x^2 - 9x + 20}{x^2 - x - 12} = \dfrac{(x - 4)(x - 5)}{(x + 3)(x - 4)} = \dfrac{(x - 5)}{(x + 3)} = \dfrac{x - 5}{x + 3}$

---

2 Make the bracketed letter the subject of each of the following equations.

(a) $c + 2ab = e \quad (a)$

(b) $y - \dfrac{1}{x} = c \quad (x)$

(c) $a - x^2 = 16 \quad (x)$

(d) $4x^2 + y^2 = 16 \quad (x)$

Answer

2 (a) $c + 2ab = e$

Subtract c from both sides.

$2ab = e - c$

Divide both sides by $2b$.

$a = \dfrac{e - c}{2b}$

(b) $y - \dfrac{1}{x} = c$

Remove the denominator in the fraction by multiplying both sides by x.

$xy - 1 = cx$

Collect all the terms in x on left by subtracting cx from both sides and also add 1 to both sides.

$xy - cx = 1$

Take x out as a factor.

$x(y - c) = 1$

Divide both sides by the contents of the bracket.

$x = \dfrac{1}{y - c}$

(c) $a - x^2 = 16$

Add x^2 to both sides in order to make the x^2 term positive.

$$a = 16 + x^2$$

Subtract 16 from both sides.

$$a - 16 = x^2$$

Square root both sides.

$$x = \sqrt{a - 16}$$

(d) $4x^2 + y^2 = 16$

Subtract y^2 from both sides.

$$4x^2 = 16 - y^2$$

Divide both sides by 4.

$$x^2 = \frac{16 - y^2}{4}$$

Square root both sides.

TIP

Do not be tempted to square root the $16 - y^2$ to give $4 - y$

This could be simplified further to the following

$$x = \tfrac{1}{2}\sqrt{16 - y^2}$$

---

3 (a) Expand $(\sqrt{3} + 1)^2$ and fully simplify your answer.

(b) Using your answer to part (a) expand and fully simplify the following expression.

$(\sqrt{3} + 1)^3$

Answer

3 (a)

$$\left(\sqrt{3} + 1\right)^2 = \left(\sqrt{3} + 1\right)\left(\sqrt{3} + 1\right)$$
$$= 3 + \sqrt{3} + \sqrt{3} + 1$$
$$= 4 + 2\sqrt{3}$$

(b)

$$(\sqrt{3} + 1)^3 = \left(\sqrt{3} + 1\right)\left(\sqrt{3} + 1\right)^2$$

Use the answer from (a) to substitute $\left(4 + 2\sqrt{3}\right)$ for $\left(\sqrt{3} + 1\right)^2$.

$$= \left(\sqrt{3} + 1\right)\left(4 + 2\sqrt{3}\right)$$
$$= 4\sqrt{3} + 2\sqrt{3}\sqrt{3} + 4 + 2\sqrt{3}$$
$$= 6\sqrt{3} + 10$$

---

4 Simplify each of the following expressions.

(a) $\sqrt{50} + 4\sqrt{2} - \dfrac{6}{\sqrt{2}}$

(b) $\dfrac{1}{5 + \sqrt{2}}$

Answer

4 (a) $\sqrt{50} + 4\sqrt{2} - \frac{6}{\sqrt{2}} = \sqrt{25}\sqrt{2} + 4\sqrt{2} - \frac{6}{\sqrt{2}}$

$$= 5\sqrt{2} + 4\sqrt{2} - \frac{6}{\sqrt{2}} \times \frac{\sqrt{2}}{\sqrt{2}}$$

$$= 5\sqrt{2} + 4\sqrt{2} - 3\sqrt{2}$$

$$= 6\sqrt{2}$$

Spot any square numbers inside the square root sign.

Remove the surd from the denominator by multiplying the top and bottom of the fraction by $\sqrt{2}$.

(b) $\frac{1}{5+\sqrt{2}} = \frac{1}{5+\sqrt{2}} \times \frac{(5-\sqrt{2})}{(5-\sqrt{2})} = \frac{5-\sqrt{2}}{25-2} = \frac{5-\sqrt{2}}{23}$

Multiply the top and bottom of the fraction by the conjugate of $5 + \sqrt{2}$ which is $5 - \sqrt{2}$.

---

5 This year John is 4 times as old as his son Paul, in 5 years' time John will only be 3 times as old as Paul.

Let the age of Paul now be x years.

By forming an equation in x and solving it, find Paul's age now.

(OCR FSMQ June 2013 q3)

Answer

5 This year John's age = $4x$

John's age in 5 years = $4x + 5$

Paul's age in 5 years = $x + 5$

TIP

Spend a little time methodically writing the information in terms of algebra as shown below.

In 5 years' time John will be 3 times as old as Paul. Hence we can write

$$4x + 5 = 3(x + 5)$$

$$4x + 5 = 3x + 15$$

$$x + 5 = 15$$

$$x = 10$$

TAKE NOTE!

Always check your result by working through the question using your answer. Initially John is 4 times older than Paul so John is 40. In five years' time John will be 45 and his son will be 15. You can see that John is 3 times older now so the answer is correct.

Test yourself

1 Solve each of the following equations:

(a) $2x + 11 = 25$
(b) $3x - 5 = 10$
(c) $15x = 60$
(d) $\frac{x}{4} = 8$
(e) $\frac{4x}{5} = 20$
(f) $\frac{2x}{3} = -6$
(g) $5 - x = 7$
(h) $\frac{x}{7} - 9 = 3$

2 Simplify the following algebraic fractions:

(a) $\frac{35x^3y^2}{7xy^2}$
(b) $\frac{15ab^3c}{3ab}$
(c) $\frac{(x-4)(x-7)}{(x-1)(x-4)}$
(d) $\frac{(x+3)^2}{(x-6)(x+3)}$

3 Multiply out the following brackets and simplify your answer:

(a) $4(2x - 3) + 5(2x + 1)$
(b) $-2(x + 4)$
(c) $-(x - 5)$
(d) $4(2x - 6) - (5x - 4)$
(e) $3(5x - 9) - 4(2x - 6)$
(f) $4(2x - 7) + 5x - 9$
(g) $-(3x^2 + 4x - 2)$
(h) $x(x^2 - 4x + 8)$
(i) $3a(a + b) + 2b(a + b)$
(j) $4a(2a - b) - 3b(2a - b)$
(k) $5x^2(x - 3) + 3x(x + 4)$
(l) $2x(x - 1) - (x^2 - 3x)$

4 Multiply out the brackets and simplify your answer:

(a) $(x - 5)(x + 3)$
(b) $(4x - 1)(x - 5)$
(c) $(2x - 7)(3x + 5)$
(d) $(9x - 1)(9x + 1)$
(e) $(4a - b)(2a + 4b)$
(f) $(5y - 1)(2y + 5)$

5 Here is an equation: $pV = nRT$.

Rearrange this equation so that each of the following is the subject of the equation:

(a) V
(b) n
(c) T
(d) p

6 Rearrange the equation below, to make f the subject of the equation.

$$E = hf$$

7 All straight lines have equations which can be written in the following form:

$$y = mx + c$$

Rearrange the above equation so that m is the subject of the equation.

8 Make the bracketed symbol the subject of the equation: e.g. in part (a), write the equation in the form $\lambda = \ldots$.

(a) $c = f\lambda \quad (\lambda)$

(b) $c = \frac{n}{V} \quad (V)$

(c) $Q = mcT \quad (T)$

(d) $n = \frac{V}{1000} \times c \quad (V)$

(e) $n = \frac{V}{1000} \times c \quad (c)$

(f) $E = hf \quad (h)$

9 Simplify each of the following, expressing your answers in surd form:

(a) $\sqrt{48} + \frac{12}{\sqrt{3}} - \sqrt{27}$

(b) $\frac{2 + \sqrt{5}}{3 + \sqrt{5}}$

10 Simplify the following:

(a) $\frac{5}{\sqrt{2}}$

(b) $\frac{1}{3 + \sqrt{5}}$

(c) $\sqrt{32} + 3\sqrt{2}$

(d) $(2\sqrt{5})^2$

11 Solve the following pair of simultaneous equations:

$7x + 4y = 2$

$3x - y = 9$

Topic summary

Almost every subsequent topic will involve some use of algebra and the best way to learn algebra is by continual use.

Multiplying out brackets

$(a + b)(c + d) = a(c + d) + b(c + d) = ac + ad + bc + bd$

$(x + 5)(x - 4) = x(x - 4) + 5(x - 4) = x^2 - 4x + 5x - 20 = x^2 + x - 20$

Solving linear equations

The main point to remember here is that an equation is like a balance. Whatever you do to one side of the equation, you should make the identical change to the other side of the equation in order to keep the equation balanced. This means that you can add, subtract, multiply or divide an equation by any quantity as long as the change is made to both sides of the equation.

So if we had to solve $\frac{3x}{4} - 1 = 5$

we first remove the denominator by multiplying both sides by 4 to give $3x - 4 = 20$.

We then add 4 to both sides to give $3x = 24$ and finally divide both sides by 3 to give the answer $x = 8$.

Surds

Simple manipulation of surds

$\sqrt{a} \times \sqrt{a} = a$

$\sqrt{a} \times \sqrt{b} = \sqrt{ab}$

$\left(\sqrt{a} + \sqrt{b}\right)\left(\sqrt{a} - \sqrt{b}\right) = a - b$

Rationalisation of surds

We avoid having surds in the denominator and removing them is called rationalising the denominator.

$$\frac{a}{b\sqrt{c}} = \frac{a}{b\sqrt{c}} \times \frac{\sqrt{c}}{\sqrt{c}} = \frac{a\sqrt{c}}{bc}$$

(Here the denominator is rationalised by multiplying the top and bottom by $\sqrt{c}$.)

$$\frac{a}{\sqrt{b} \pm \sqrt{c}} = \frac{a}{\left(\sqrt{b} \pm \sqrt{c}\right)} \times \frac{\sqrt{b} \mp \sqrt{c}}{\left(\sqrt{b} \mp \sqrt{c}\right)} = \frac{a\sqrt{b} \mp a\sqrt{c}}{b - c}$$

(Here the denominator is rationalised by multiplying the top and bottom of the expression by the conjugate of the denominator.)

Manipulation of algebraic expressions

Some of the material will be familiar to you because you will have covered it in your GCSE mathematics course. This topic looks at some of the techniques for factorising and solving quadratic equations. It also looks at certain techniques that will help you to draw a sketch of a quadratic function. At the end of this topic you will be able to solve quadratic equations and be able to draw graphs of quadratic functions.

This topic covers the following:

2.1 Completing the square

2.2 Solving quadratic equations

2.3 The discriminant of a quadratic equation

2.4 Sketching a quadratic function

2.5 Solving simultaneous equations where one is linear and the other is a quadratic

2.1 Completing the square

A quadratic expression $ax^2 + bx + c$ can be written in the form $(x + p)^2 + q$ and this is called completing the square. Note that the values of p and q can be positive or negative.

For example, suppose you were asked to express $x^2 + 6x + 11$ in the form $(x + a)^2 + b$, where the values of a and b are to be determined.

Provided there is no number other than 1 in front of the x^2 (called the coefficient of x^2), a is half the number in front of the x (the coefficient of x). Here there is a 6 in front of the x so halving this gives $a = 3$. If there is a minus sign, then this will need to be included.

When $(x + 3)^2$ is expanded it gives $x^2 + 6x + 9$. So we have the first two terms and also a number 9 which we remove by subtracting out of the bracket like this:

$(x + 3)^2 - 9$

It is now necessary to add the 11, so we have

$x^2 + 6x + 11 = (x + 3)^2 - 9 + 11 = (x + 3)^2 + 2$

The answer can be compared with $(x + a)^2 + b$

Hence $a = 3$ and $b = 2$.

Examples

1 Express $x^2 + 8x + 2$ in the form $(x + a)^2 + b$ where a and b are to be determined.

Answer

1 $x^2 + 8x + 2 = (x + 4)^2 - 16 + 2 = (x + 4)^2 - 14$

2 Write $x^2 - 4x - 2$ in the form $(x + a)^2 + b$ where a and b are to be determined.

Answer

2 $x^2 - 4x - 2 = (x - 2)^2 - 4 - 2 = (x - 2)^2 - 6$

3 Express $x^2 + 5x - 1$ in the form $(x + a)^2 + b$ where a and b are to be determined.

Answer

3 $x^2 + 5x - 1 = \left(x + \frac{5}{2}\right)^2 - \frac{25}{4} - 3 = \left(x + \frac{5}{2}\right)^2 - \frac{37}{4}$

4 Express $2x^2 + 12x + 3$ in the form $a(x + b)^2 + c$, where a, b and c are to be determined.

Answer

Before completing the square, take 2 out as a factor because the coefficient of x^2 needs to be one when completing the square.

4 $2x^2 + 12x + 3$

$= 2\left[x^2 + 6x + \frac{3}{2}\right]$

$= 2\left[(x + 3)^2 - 9 + \frac{3}{2}\right]$

We now complete the square inside the square bracket.

$= 2\left[(x + 3)^2 - \frac{15}{2}\right]$

$= 2(x + 3)^2 - 15$

Now multiply by the two outside the square bracket to give the required format.

Hence $a = 2$, $b = 3$, $c = -15$

Progress check

1. Expand and simplify each of the following expressions:

   (a) $(x + 1)^2$

   (b) $(x + 11)^2$

   (c) $(x + 13)^2$

   (d) $(x - 6)^2$

   (e) $(x - 11)^2$

   (f) $(x + 7)^2$

2. Copy and complete each of the following expansions:

   (a) $(x + 3)^2 = x^2 +$ .... $+ 9$

   (b) $(x + 4)^2 = x^2 +$ .... $+ 16$

   (c) $(x + 1)^2 = x^2 +$ .... $+ 1$

   (d) $(x + 6)^2 = x^2 +$ .... $+ 36$

   (e) $(x + 8)^2 = x^2 +$ .... $+$ ....

   (f) $(x + 5)^2 = x^2 +$ .... $+$ ....

   (g) $(x - 4)^2 = x^2 -$ .... $+ 16$

   (h) $(x - 5)^2 = x^2 -$ .... $+ 25$

   (i) $(x - 9)^2 = x^2 -$ .... $+ 81$

   (j) $(x - 7)^2 = x^2 -$ .... $+$ ....

   (k) $(x - 10)^2 = x^2 -$ .... $+$ ....

   (l) $(x + 12)^2 = x^2 +$ .... $+$ ....

3. For each of the following quadratic expressions, complete the square by giving your answer in the form $(x + a)^2 + b$ where a and b are integers to be determined.

   (a) $x^2 + 4x + 8$

   (b) $x^2 + 2x + 6$

   (c) $x^2 - 6x + 4$

   (d) $x^2 - 2x - 10$

   (e) $x^2 - 10x - 2$

   (f) $x^2 - 8x + 4$

   (g) $x^2 - 6x + 12$

2.2 Solving quadratic equations

Quadratic equations are equations that can be written in the form:

$$ax^2 + bx + c = 0$$

where a, b and c are numbers.

There are three ways to solve quadratic equations:

1 By factorising. You should be familiar with this from your GCSE work.

2 By completing the square.

3 By using the quadratic formula.

Solving a quadratic equation by factorising

TAKE NOTE!

Factorisation was covered at GCSE. Check that you can multiply out two brackets such as $(x + 3)(x - 2)$, or more complicated brackets such as $(3x - 8)(4x + 7)$ quickly. If you can't remember how to do this, refer back to your GCSE notes or a revision book. Incidentally, the correct answers are $x^2 + x - 6$ and $12x^2 - 11x - 56$ respectively.

Factorising quadratic expressions

Factorising is the reverse process to multiplying out brackets. So, for example, if we start with the quadratic expression $x^2 - 3x + 2$ when it is factorised it becomes $(x - 1)(x - 2)$.

There are many different methods for factorisation but the method shown here is a good one and is particularly useful when the numbers in the quadratic expression become large.

Suppose you are asked to factorise the following:

$$x^2 - x - 30$$

You need to find two factors which multiply together to give -30 and add together to give the coefficient of x (-1 in this case).

Start with factors that give -30:

1 and -30
-1 and 30
-3 and 10
3 and -10
6 and -5
-6 and 5
15 and -2
-15 and 2

We then look for the pair of numbers in the above list which will add together to give -1. The pair of numbers we need from the list is -6 and 5. With practice you do not need to write the list out and you can do all this mentally.

Now we include the two factors we have found as the coefficients of the x-terms like this:

$$x^2 - x - 30 = x^2 - 6x + 5x - 30$$

You then factorise the first two terms by taking a term in x out and also the last two terms by taking a number out like this:

$$x^2 - 6x + 5x - 30 = x(x - 6) + 5(x - 6)$$

The terms inside the brackets have to be identical.

Notice that the term (x – 6) is common in this expression so it may be taken out as a factor in the following way:

$$x(x - 6) + 5(x - 6) = (x - 6)(x + 5)$$

It is always advisable to multiply out the brackets to check that you obtain the original expression.

This may seem long winded, but it works with all quadratic expressions that can be factorised, as the following examples show.

Examples

5 Factorise the quadratic expression

$x^2 - 9x + 18$.

The factors of 18 which add together to give –9 are –6 and –3. These are added as the coefficients of both x-terms.

Answer

5 $x^2 - 9x + 18 = x^2 - 6x - 3x + 18$

Hence $x^2 - 6x - 3x + 18 = x(x - 6) - 3(x - 6)$

$x(x - 6) - 3(x - 6) = (x - 6)(x - 3)$

Notice that we need to take –3 out as a factor in the second bracket. This means that the terms in both the brackets are the same.

Again multiply out the brackets to check you produce the expression to be factorised.

6 Factorise the expression $6x^2 - 17x + 12$.

Answer

6 As there is a number in front of the x^2 this must be multiplied by the number independent of x (i.e. the ordinary number). So here we have $6 \times 12 = 72$. We now need two factors which add to give – 17. By investigation these numbers are –9 and –8.

Hence we have

$$\begin{aligned} 6x^2 - 17x + 12 &= 6x^2 - 9x - 8x + 12 \\ &= 3x(2x - 3) - 4(2x - 3) \\ &= (2x - 3)(3x - 4) \end{aligned}$$

Notice the way the sign for the number outside the bracket is negative. This is necessary to make the contents of both brackets identical.

7 Factorise the expression $8x^2 + 14x - 9$.

Answer

We need to find two factors of $8 \times (-9) = -72$ with a sum of 14. These numbers are 18 and -4.

7 $8x^2 + 14x - 9 = 8x^2 + 18x - 4x - 9$

$= 2x(4x + 9) - (4x + 9)$

When you have $-(4x + 9)$ the multiplier of the bracket is -1.

$= (4x + 9)(2x - 1)$

Remember to check that you get back to the original expression when you multiply out the brackets.

Progress check

4 Factorise each of the following expressions.

(a) $x^2 + 3x + 2$

(b) $x^2 + 6x + 8$

(c) $x^2 + 10x + 21$

(d) $x^2 + 3x - 4$

(e) $x^2 - 2x - 3$

(f) $x^2 - 3x + 2$

(g) $x^2 - 4x - 5$

(h) $x^2 + 5x - 14$

(i) $x^2 - 5x + 4$

(j) $x^2 + 3x - 10$

5 Factorise each of the following expressions.

(a) $2x^2 - x - 3$

(b) $2x^2 + 9x + 4$

(c) $3x^2 + 4x + 1$

(d) $5x^2 + 19x - 4$

(e) $5x^2 - 7x + 2$

(f) $4x^2 - 3x - 1$

(g) $3x^2 + 8x + 5$

(h) $2x^2 + 3x - 14$

(i) $4x^2 - 21x + 20$

(j) $x^2 - 3x - 10$

6 Factorise each of the following expressions:

(a) $x^2 + 3x + 2$

(b) $x^2 + 6x + 5$

(c) $x^2 + 11x + 24$

(d) $x^2 + 10x + 9$

(e) $x^2 + 8x + 15$

(f) $x^2 - 2x + 1$

(g) $x^2 + 5x - 6$

(h) $x^2 + 4x - 21$

(i) $x^2 - 5x + 6$

(j) $x^2 + 7x - 30$

(k) $x^2 + 2x - 15$

7 Factorise each of the following expressions:

(a) $2x^2 + x - 1$

(b) $2x^2 + 13x + 6$

(c) $4x^2 - 3x - 1$

(d) $3x^2 + 19x - 14$

(e) $5x^2 + 18x - 8$

(f) $8x^2 + 30x - 27$

(g) $12x^2 + 28x - 5$

(h) $12x^2 - 7x + 1$

Solving quadratic equations

A quadratic equation is an equation that can be expressed in the following format:

$$ax^2 + bx + c = 0$$

where a, b and c are numbers.

To solve a quadratic using the method of factorisation you must first get the equation into the above format and then factorise it.

For example, if we had to solve $2x^2 = 5 - 9x$, we would first rearrange it as $2x^2 + 9x - 5 = 0$ and then factorise it to give

$$(2x - 1)(x + 5) = 0$$

For the above to equal zero, either one of the brackets must equal zero. So we equate the contents of each bracket to zero.

Hence $2x - 1 = 0$ or $x + 5 = 0$,

giving $x = \frac{1}{2}$ or -5.

Examples

8 Solve $2x^2 + 7x - 4 = 0$

Answer

8 $(2x - 1)(x + 4) = 0$

Putting each bracket equal to 0, gives $2x - 1 = 0$ or $x + 4 = 0$

Hence $x = \frac{1}{2}$ or $x = -4$

9 If the rectangle shown below has an area of 60, find the value of x.

6x

2x + 1

» TIP

With some equations it is not immediately obvious they are quadratic equations. For example, the equation $6x^2 = 2 - x$; we need to rearrange it so it is in the more familiar format (i.e. $6x^2 + x - 2 = 0$). Always look to see if an equation can be rearranged to form a quadratic equation.

If you are asked to solve a quadratic equation like this, where the number in front of the x^2 is negative, rearrange the equation so that the number in front of the x^2 is positive as this example shows.

Solve the equation $-2x^2 + x + 3 = 0$.

Rearrange the equation making the coefficient of the x^2 term positive we obtain $2x^2 - x - 3 = 0$

Factorising gives $(2x - 3)(x + 1) = 0$

Hence $x = \frac{3}{2}$ or $x = -1$

Answer

9 Area of rectangle = length × width

$$= 6x(2x + 1)$$

Now length = 60 so we have

$$60 = 6x(2x + 1)$$

$$60 = 12x^2 + 6x$$

$$0 = 12x^2 + 6x - 60$$

$$0 = 2x^2 + x - 10$$

Divide both sides by 6. This will make factorisation easier as the numbers will be smaller.

$$(2x + 5)(x - 2) = 0$$

Solving gives $x = -\frac{5}{2}$ or $x = 2$

Always check to see if both values are possible or only one of them.

Now $x = -\frac{5}{2}$ would give a length of $6 \times \left(-\frac{5}{2}\right) = -15$ which is impossible, so this value of x is ignored.

Hence $x = 2$

TAKE NOTE!

Pythagoras' theorem states that, for any right-angled triangle, if you square the length of the hypotenuse it will be equal to the squares of each of the two other sides added together. Remember that the hypotenuse is the longest side of a right-angled triangle which is always opposite the largest angle, which is the right-angle.

10

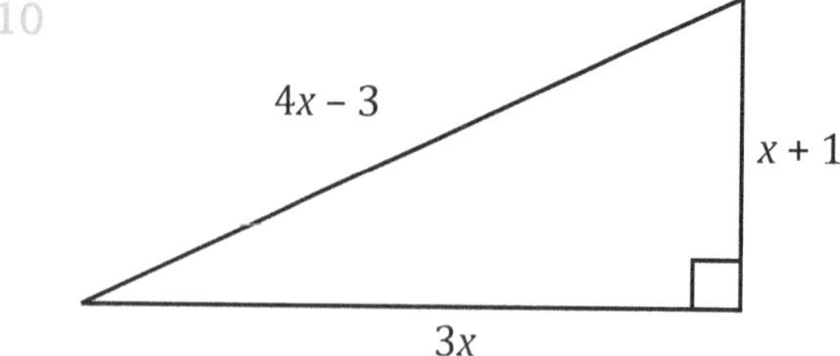

A right-angled triangle with sides $4x - 3$, $x + 1$ and $3x$ is shown above.

Use Pythagoras' theorem to find the value of x and hence find the lengths of the sides of the triangle.

Answer

10 Using Pythagoras' theorem we obtain

$$(4x - 3)^2 = (x + 1)^2 + (3x)^2$$

$$16x^2 - 24x + 9 = x^2 + 2x + 1 + 9x^2$$

$$6x^2 - 26x + 8 = 0$$

This needs to be rearranged so it is in the usual format for a quadratic equation.

Dividing both sides by 2 we obtain

$$3x^2 - 13x + 4 = 0$$

$$(3x - 1)(x - 4) = 0$$

$$3x - 1 = 0 \text{ or } x - 4 = 0$$

Hence $x = \frac{1}{3}$ or 4.

We need to put both values into each of the expressions for the sides to see if any of the sides end up negative.

When $x = \frac{1}{3}$ is substituted into $4x - 3$ the result is negative.

As you cannot have a negative length for a side, $x = \frac{1}{3}$ is disregarded.

Hence $x = 4$.

When x is 4 the sides are 5, 12 and 13.

Substitute $x = 4$ into the expressions for the sides to find the lengths.

The difference of two squares

If you have two perfect square terms, with a minus between them as in Example 11, this is called the difference of two squares. To factorise this you would find the square root of each term and have two brackets one with a plus and one with a minus between the square roots. The following examples show this.

TAKE NOTE!

Note that a perfect square number will have a square root that is a whole number. As $5^2 = 25$ and $1^2 = 1$, both 5 and 1 are perfect square numbers. Other perfect square numbers include 9, 16, 36, 49, etc.).

Examples

11 Factorise $a^2 - b^2$.

Answer

11 $a^2 - b^2 = (a + b)(a - b)$

The square root of a^2 is a and the square root of b^2 is b. You then write one bracket with a and b added and the other bracket with a and b subtracted.

12 Factorise $16x^2 - 1$.

Answer

12 $16x^2 - 1 = (4x + 1)(4x - 1)$

It is important to be able to recognise the difference between two squares. You must have two perfect square terms with a minus sign between them. Note that $16x^2$ is a perfect square with square root $4x$ and 1 is a perfect square with square root 1.

13 Factorise $16a^2 - 9b^2$.

Answer

13 $16a^2 - 9b^2 = (4a + 3b)(4a - 3b)$

14 Factorise $1 - x^2$.

Answer

14 $1 - x^2 = (1 + x)(1 - x)$

The order of the brackets is unimportant when we factorise, so for this answer you could equally write $1 - x^2 = (1 - x)(1 + x)$.

Solving a quadratic equation by completing the square

Quadratic equations can be solved by completing the square. When solving a quadratic equation, first ensure that you have all the terms on the left-hand side of the equation and a zero on the right-hand side. When you have this, you can then complete the square and then solve the resulting equation for x.

TAKE NOTE !

You must use completing the square to solve the quadratic equation. You will lose marks if a method is specified in the question and you use a different method.

Example

15 Show that $x^2 + 0.8x - 3.84$ may be expressed in the form $(x + p)^2$, where p is a constant whose value is to be found.

Hence solve the quadratic equation $x^2 + 0.8x - 3.84 = 0$.

Answer

15 $x^2 + 0.8x - 3.84 = (x + 0.4)^2 - 0.16 - 3.84$

$= (x + 0.4)^2 - 4$

Hence $p = 0.4$

$x^2 + 0.8x - 3.84 = 0$

So, $(x + 0.4)^2 - 4 = 0$

$(x + 0.4)^2 = 4$

Finding the square root of each sides gives

$(x + 0.4) = \pm 2$

So, $x = 2 - 0.4$ or $x = -2 - 0.4$

Hence $x = 1.6$ or $x = -2.4$

TAKE NOTE !

You must include both the positive and negative values when you find the square root of a number.

Progress check

8 Factorise each of the following expressions:

(a) $x^2 - 1$

(b) $4x^2 - 25$

(c) $4c^2 - b^2$

(d) $16x^2 - 49$

(e) $p^2 - q^2$

(f) $25x^2 - y^2$

(g) $x^2 - y^2$

(h) $y^2 - 100$

(i) $4a^2 - 1$

(k) $c^2 - 25$

9 Solve the following equations:

(a) $(x + 1)(x + 2) = 0$

(b) $(x + 4)(x + 2) = 0$

(c) $(x + 3)(x + 7) = 0$

(d) $(x + 4)(x - 1) = 0$

(e) $(x - 3)(x + 1) = 0$

(f) $(x - 1)(x - 2) = 0$

(g) $(x - 5)(x + 1) = 0$

(h) $(x + 7)(x - 2) = 0$

(i) $(x - 1)(x - 4) = 0$

(j) $(x + 5)(x - 2) = 0$

10 Solve the following equations by using factorisation:

(a) $x^2 - 10x + 21 = 0$

(b) $a^2 - a - 42 = 0$

(c) $3x^2 + 11x - 4 = 0$

11 Using the method completing the square, solve the following quadratic equations giving your answers correct to two decimal places.

(a) $x^2 + 4x + 1 = 0$

(b) $2x^2 + 4x - 5 = 0$

12 Solve the following quadratic equation by completing the square and give your answers to two decimal places.

$x^2 + 8x - 12 = 0$

Solving a quadratic equation using the formula

Quadratic equations, when in the form $ax^2 + bx + c = 0$, can be solved using the formula:

$$x = \frac{-b \pm \sqrt{b^2 - 4ac}}{2a}$$

Important note: This formula will not be given so you will need to remember it.

TAKE NOTE !

Be careful with signs when you are entering numbers into this equation.

Example

16 Solve the equation $2x^2 - x - 6 = 0$

Answer

16 Comparing the equation given, with $ax^2 + bx + c = 0$ gives $a = 2$, $b = -1$ and $c = -6$.

Substituting these values into the quadratic equation formula gives:

$$x = \frac{1 \pm \sqrt{(-1)^2 - 4(2)(-6)}}{2(2)}$$

$$= \frac{1 \pm \sqrt{1 + 48}}{4} = \frac{1 \pm 7}{4} = \frac{1 + 7}{4} \text{ or } \frac{1 - 7}{4} = 2 \text{ or } -1.5$$

The +1 at the front of the equation is because of the minus sign in the formula multiplying the value of b which is also − 1. Two minuses multiplied together give a plus.

2.3 The discriminant of a quadratic equation

No real roots means that the curve $y = ax^2 + bx + c$ does not cut the x-axis so there are no real solutions to the equation $ax^2 + bx + c = 0$. When the formula is used to find the values of x it is found that in part of the formula there is the square root of a negative number which cannot be found. Note if you have a square root of a negative number such as $\sqrt{-9}$ there are no solutions because you cannot have two numbers the same that multiply together to give -9.

The roots of the quadratic equation are the same as the solutions and are also the x-coordinates of the points where the curve with the equation $y = ax^2 + bx + c$ cuts the x-axis.

$ax^2 + bx + c$ is a quadratic function. The quantity $b^2 - 4ac$ is called the discriminant and it gives the following information about the roots of a quadratic equation:

If $b^2 - 4ac > 0$, then there are two real and distinct (i.e. different) roots.

If $b^2 - 4ac = 0$, then there are two real and equal roots.

If $b^2 - 4ac < 0$, then there are no real roots.

The three situations can be shown graphically:

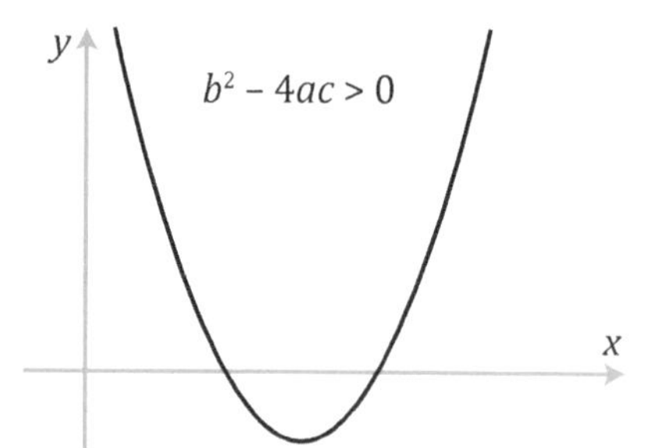

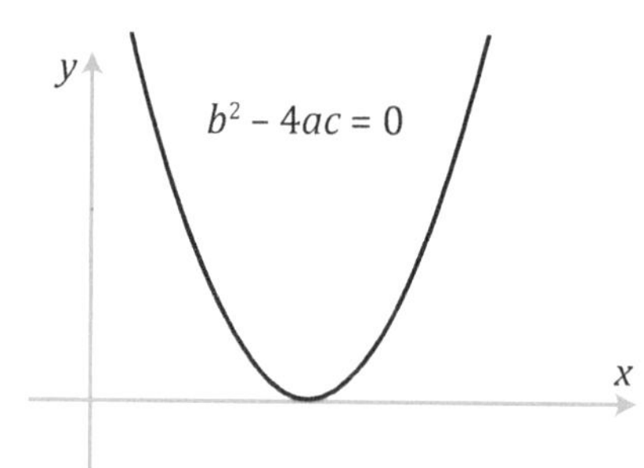

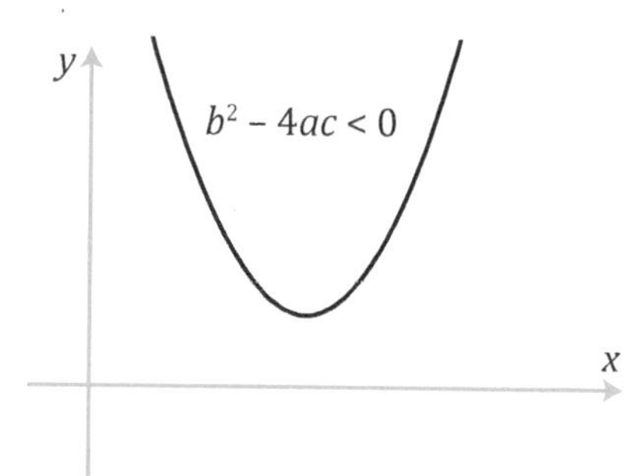

Example

17 (a) Express $f(x) = x^2 + 6x + 100$ in the form $(x + a)^2 + b$ where a and b are integers.

(b) Hence show that the equation $f(x) = 0$ has no real roots.

Answer

17 (a) Completing the square, we obtain

$$x^2 + 6x + 100 = (x + 3)^2 - 9 + 100$$
$$= (x + 3)^2 + 91$$

(b) If $f(x) = 0$, then $(x + 3)^2 + 91 = 0$

Hence, $(x + 3)^2 = -91$.

$$\text{So } x + 3 = \sqrt{-91}$$
$$x = \sqrt{-91} - 3$$

The square root of the negative number means that the roots of the equation are not real.

Progress check

13 (a) Explain why the following equation has no real roots.

$3x^2 - 4x + 6 = 0$

(b) Solve the quadratic equation $3x^2 + 6x + 2 = 0$ using the formula and giving your answer to two decimal places.

2.4 Sketching a quadratic function

The quadratic equation having the form $y = ax^2 + bx + c$ has a graph which is a parabola.

Depending on the sign of a in the above equation, the parabola is ∪-shaped if a is positive or ∩-shaped if a is negative.

> The maximum value of a curve is the largest y-value reached by a ∩-shaped curve and the minimum value is the smallest y-value reached by a ∪-shaped curve. They are often referred to as the maximum and minimum of the curves.

To find the points where the parabola intersects the x-axis, you can solve the equation

$ax^2 + bx + c = 0$

If the question started by asking you to complete the square and then later the question asked you to sketch the curve and/or find the maximum or minimum value then there is a quick way of finding them.

When the square has been completed, the equation for the curve will be in this format:

$y = a(x + p)^2 + q$

If a is positive and $x = -p$, the value of the bracket is zero and, since the bracket is squared, this is its minimum value (since it cannot be negative), hence the minimum value of y is q. If a is negative and $x = -p$, the maximum value of y is q.

From the equation $y = a(x + p)^2 + q$

If a is positive (i.e. $a > 0$) the curve will be ∪-shaped.

If a is negative (i.e. $a < 0$) the curve will be ∩-shaped.

The vertex (i.e. the maximum or minimum point) will be at $(-p, q)$.

The axis of symmetry will be $x = -p$

Note that the maximum and minimum points of curves are called stationary points. They are called stationary points because if a tangent is drawn to the curve at these points the gradient of the tangent is zero as the tangent is parallel to the x-axis.

For example the curve with the equation $y = 2(x + 3)^2 - 1$ can be compared with $y = a(x + p)^2 + q$. This gives $a = 2$, $p = 3$ and $q = -1$.

The curve will be U-shaped with a minimum point at $(-3, -1)$ (i.e. $(-p, q)$) and an axis of symmetry of $x = -3$.

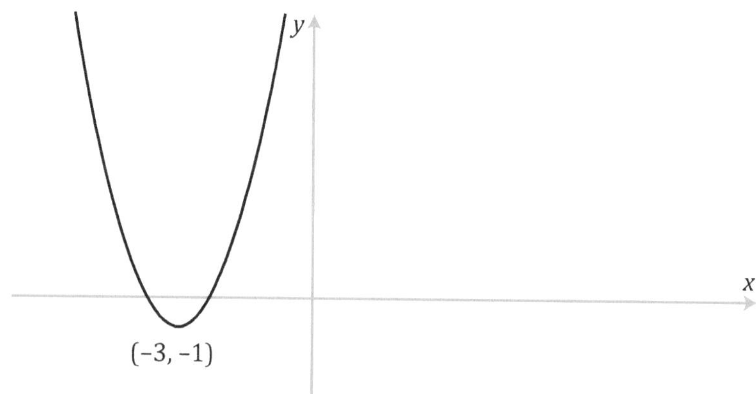

Example

18 Express $4x^2 - 12x + 9$ in the form $a(x + b)^2 + c$ where the values of b and c are to be determined.

Hence, sketch the graph of $4x^2 - 12x + 9$, including the coordinates of the stationary point.

Answer

18 $$4x^2 - 12x + 9 = 4\left[x^2 - 3x + \frac{9}{4}\right]$$
$$= 4\left[\left(x - \frac{3}{2}\right)^2 - \frac{9}{4} + \frac{9}{4}\right]$$
$$= 4\left(x - \frac{3}{2}\right)^2$$

Comparing the above expression with $a(x + b)^2 + c$, gives a = 4, $b = -\frac{3}{2}$ and $c = 0$.

The graph of $4\left(x - \frac{3}{2}\right)^2$ is U-shaped because the coefficient of x^2 is positive.

$y = 4\left(x - \frac{3}{2}\right)^2$ has its minimum point when $x = \frac{3}{2}$. When $x = \frac{3}{2}$, $y = 0$.

Hence the coordinates of the stationary point are $\left(\frac{3}{2}, 0\right)$

Maximum and minimum points are stationary points because the gradient at these points is zero.

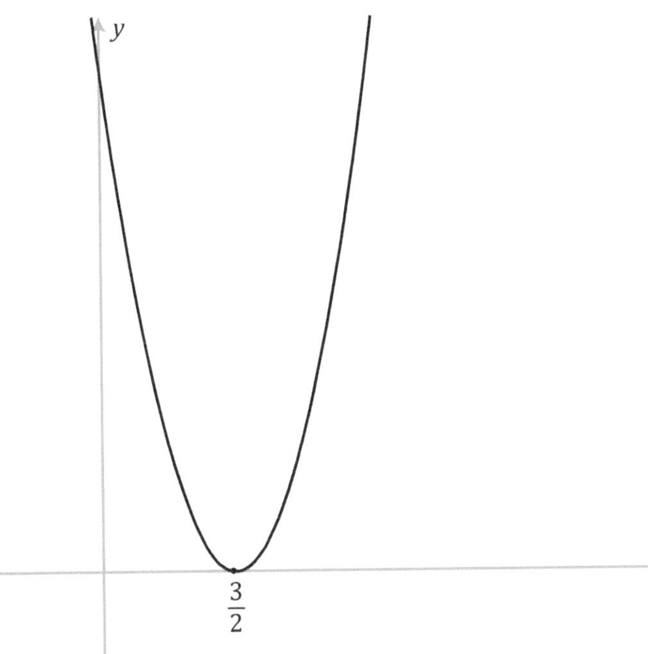

2.5 Solving simultaneous equations where one is linear and the other is a quadratic

For this course you need to find the solution of one linear equation and one quadratic equation. Here you will be finding the points of intersection or the point of contact of a straight line and a curve.

Example

19 Solve the simultaneous equations $y = 10x^2 - 5x - 2$ and $y = 2x - 3$ algebraically. Write down a geometrical interpretation of your results.

Here we are using the substitution method for solving simultaneous equations. The y-value for the linear equation is substituted in for the y-value of the quadratic.

Answer

19 Equating expressions for y gives

$$10x^2 - 5x - 2 = 2x - 3$$

$$10x^2 - 7x + 1 = 0$$

At the points of intersection, the y-coordinates of the curve and straight line will be the same.

Factorising this quadratic gives

$$(5x - 1)(2x - 1) = 0$$

$$\text{Hence } x = \frac{1}{5} \text{ or } x = \frac{1}{2}$$

It is easier to substitute the x-coordinate into the equation of the straight line rather than the curve.

Substituting $x = \frac{1}{5}$ into $y = 2x - 3$ gives

$$y = -2\tfrac{3}{5}$$

Substituting $x = \frac{1}{2}$ into $y = 2x - 3$ gives

$$y = -2$$

There are two places where the line and curve intersect.

The points of intersection of the line with the curve are $\left(\frac{1}{5}, -2\frac{3}{5}\right)$ and $\left(\frac{1}{2}, -2\right)$.

Exam practice

1. Solve simultaneously the equations $y = x + 6$ and $y = x^2 - x + 3$. [4]

(OCR FSMQ June 2003 q1)

Answer

1. Equating the y-values, we obtain

$$x + 6 = x^2 - x + 3$$

$$\text{Hence, } x^2 - 2x - 3 = 0$$

Factorising we obtain

$$(x - 3)(x + 1) = 0.$$

Solving $x - 3 = 0$ or $x + 1 = 0$

Hence $x = 3$ or -1

When $x = 3, y = 3 + 6 = 9$

When $x = -1, y = -1 + 6 = 5$

Hence the solutions are $x = 3, y = 9$ and $x = -1, y = 5$.

2. Find the x-coordinates of the points of intersection of the line $y = 5 - 2x$ with the curve $y = x^2 - 4x - 11$, giving your answers correct to two decimal places.

Answer

2. To find the x-coordinates of the points of intersection, the equations of the straight line and the curve are solved simultaneously.

At the points of intersection, the y-values will be equal.

Equating the y-values, we obtain

$$x^2 - 4x - 11 = 5 - 2x$$

$$x^2 - 2x - 16 = 0$$

Comparing the equation above, with $ax^2 + bx + c = 0$ gives $a = 1$, $b = -2$ and $c = -16$.

Substituting these values into the quadratic equation formula

$x = \dfrac{-b \pm \sqrt{b^2 - 4ac}}{2a}$ gives the following

$$x = \frac{2 \pm \sqrt{(-2)^2 - 4(1)(-16)}}{2(1)}$$

$$x = \frac{2 \pm \sqrt{4 + 64}}{2} = \frac{2 \pm \sqrt{68}}{2} = \frac{2 + \sqrt{68}}{2} \text{ or } \frac{2 - \sqrt{68}}{2} = 5.12 \text{ or } -3.12$$

TAKE NOTE !

This is a quadratic equation which will have two solutions. As the question asks for the coordinates to be given to two decimal places, it would be almost impossible to factorise. Hence we need to either use the method of completing the square or use the formula to solve this quadratic equation.

---

3 Use the method of completing the square to solve the quadratic equation $x^2 + 6x - 2 = 0$, giving your answers to two decimal places.

Answer

3 $x^2 + 6x - 2 = 0$

Completing the square we obtain

$$(x + 3)^2 - 9 - 2 = 0$$

$$(x + 3)^2 - 11 = 0$$

$$(x + 3)^2 = 11$$

$$x + 3 = \pm\sqrt{11}$$

$$x = \sqrt{11} - 3 \text{ or } -\sqrt{11} - 3$$

$$= 0.32 \text{ or } -6.32 \text{ (2 d.p.)}$$

If a method is stated in the question you must use this method and not an alternative one.

---

4 The right-angled triangle shown has a base of $5x - 3$ and a height of $2x + 1$. If the area of the triangle is 42, find the value of x.

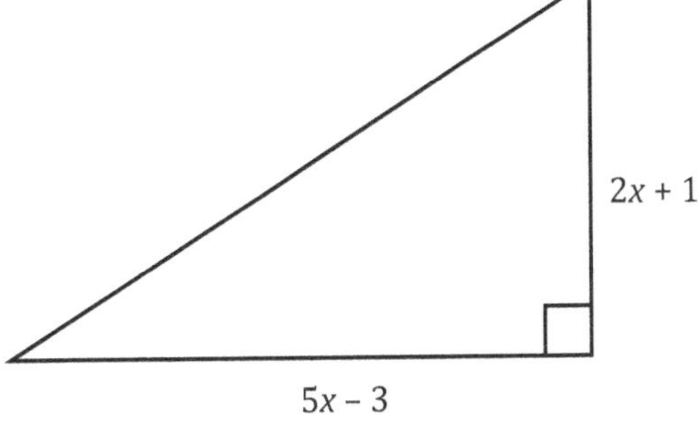

Answer

You would be expected to already know this formula.

4 Area of a triangle $= \frac{1}{2} \times \text{base} \times \text{height}$

$$= \frac{1}{2}(5x - 3)(2x + 1)$$

Now the area of the triangle is 42 so we have

$$42 = \frac{1}{2}(5x - 3)(2x + 1)$$

Multiply both sides by two.

This equation needs to be put into a quadratic equation format.

$$84 = (5x - 3)(2x + 1)$$

$$84 = 10x^2 + 5x - 6x - 3$$

$$10x^2 - x - 87 = 0$$

This quadratic equation is now factorised and solved.

This is a hard factorisation. If you cannot factorise it then use the method of completing the square or the method making use of the formula to solve the quadratic equation.

$$(10x + 29)(x - 3) = 0$$

Solving, we obtain $10x + 29 = 0$ or $x - 3 = 0$

Hence $x = -\frac{29}{10}$ or 3

Now if $x = -\frac{29}{10}$ is substituted into either of the expressions for the sides you would obtain a negative length which is impossible. Hence we disregard this answer.

Hence $x = 3$.

TAKE NOTE !

Be careful here – do not dismiss a value simply because it is negative. You need to substitute it into each expression and ask yourself if a negative value for the expression makes sense.

---

5 Show that $x^2 - 1.2x - 3.64$ may be expressed in the form $(x + p)^2 - 4$, where p is a constant whose value is to be found.

Hence solve the quadratic equation $x^2 - 1.2x - 3.64 = 0$

Answer

5 $x^2 - 1.2x - 3.64 = (x - 0.6)^2 - 0.36 - 3.64$

$$= (x - 0.6)^2 - 4$$

Hence $p = -0.6$

$$x^2 - 1.2x - 3.64 = 0$$

This is obtained by completing the square.

So $(x - 0.6)^2 - 4 = 0$

$$(x - 0.6)^2 = 4$$

$$x - 0.6 = \pm 2$$

$$x = 2 + 0.6 \text{ or } x = -2 + 0.6$$

Hence $x = 2.6$ or -1.4

6 (i) Find the value of the constants a and b such that, for all values of x

$$x^2 + 8x + 19 = (x + a)^2 + b.$$ [3]

(ii) Hence state the least value of $x^2 + 8x + 19$ and the value of x at which this occurs. [3]

(iii) Write down the greatest value of $\frac{1}{x^2 + 8x + 19}$. [1]

(OCR FSMQ June 2013 q9)

Answer

6 (i) $x^2 + 8x + 19 = (x + 4)^2 - 16 + 19 = (x + 4)^2 + 3$
Hence, $a = 4$ and $b = 3$.

(ii) The least value of $x^2 + 8x + 19$ is 3 and it will occur at $x = -4$.

(iii) The greatest value of $\frac{1}{x^2 + 8x + 19}$ will occur when the expression $x^2 + 8x + 19$ has its smallest value. The smallest value $x^2 + 8x + 19$ is 3, so the greatest value $\frac{1}{x^2 + 8x + 19}$ will take is $\frac{1}{3}$.

Because the coefficient of x^2 is +1, the graph will be U-shaped. The graph of $(x + 4)^2 + 3$ can be obtained from the graph of x^2 by a translation of 4 units to the left and a translation of 3 units upwards. Hence there will be a minimum point at (−4, 3). This makes the least value 3 and this will occur at $x = -4$.

Test yourself

1 Show that $x^2 - 3x + \frac{1}{4}$ may be expressed in the form $(x + p)^2 - 2$ where p is a constant to be determined.

2 (a) The quadratic expression $x^2 - 8x + 12$ can be expressed in the form

$(x + a)^2 + b$ where a and b are constants.

Find the values of a and b.

(b) Using your answer to part (a) find the solution of the quadratic equation $x^2 - 8x + 12 = 0$ giving each answer correct to two decimal places.

3 (a) Express $x^2 + 4x + 12$ in the form $(x + a)^2 + b$ where the values of a, b are to be determined.

(b) Hence find the least value of $x^2 + 4x + 12$ and the value of x for which this occurs.

4 (a) Express $x^2 + 8x - 9$ in the form $(x + a)^2 + b$, where the values of a, b are to be determined.

(b) Use your answers to part (a) to find the least value of $x^2 + 8x - 9$ and the corresponding value of x.

5 Factorise the following expressions:

(a) $x^2 + 2x + 1$

(b) $x^2 + 5x + 6$

(c) $2x^2 + 3x + 1$

(d) $3x^2 + 10x + 3$

(e) $x^2 - x - 2$

(f) $x^2 + 3x - 4$

(g) $x^2 + x - 12$

(h) $x^2 - 6x + 5$

(i) $x^2 - 2x - 35$

6 Factorise the following expressions:

(a) $3x^2 + 5x + 2$

(b) $4x^2 + 5x + 1$

(c) $5x^2 + 21x + 4$

(d) $20x^2 + 17x + 3$

(e) $3x^2 + 11x - 4$

(f) $5x^2 - 34x - 7$

(g) $7x^2 - 31x + 12$

(h) $6x^2 - 5x + 1$

(i) $4x^2 + 19x - 30$

(j) $8x^2 - 49x + 6$

(k) $12x^2 - 31x + 7$

(l) $9x^2 + 89x - 10$

7 Express $5x^2 - 20x + 10$ in the form $a(x + b)^2 + c$, where a, b and c are constants whose values are to be found.

8 Show that the straight line $y = x + 4$ touches the curve $y = x^2 - 7x + 20$ and find the coordinates of the point of contact.

Topic summary

This is a very important topic and although you don't get many examination questions that are restricted to this topic, you will come across this material in questions that involve material from other topics. You will need to remember the formula for the solution of a quadratic equation.

Completing the square

The quadratic expression $ax^2 + bx + c$ can be written in the form $(x + p)^2 + q$ and this is called completing the square. Completing the square can be used when a quadratic equation cannot be solved by factorisation or you want to find the maximum or minimum value of a quadratic function.

Solving/finding the roots of a quadratic equation when it cannot easily be factorised

$ax^2 + bx + c = 0$ has roots/solutions given by

$$x = \frac{-b \pm \sqrt{b^2 - 4ac}}{2a}$$

Discriminants of quadratic functions

The discriminant of $ax^2 + bx + c$ is $b^2 - 4ac$.

For the equation $ax^2 + bx + c = 0$:

If $b^2 - 4ac > 0$, then there are two real and distinct (i.e. different) roots.

If $b^2 - 4ac = 0$, then there are two real and equal roots.

If $b^2 - 4ac < 0$, then there are no real roots.

The remainder and factor theorems and solving cubic equations

This topic looks at the remainder and factor theorems and how they are used to factorise and hence solve cubic equations such as $x^3 - 6x^2 + 11x - 6 = 0$.

This topic covers the following:

3.1 Finding the remainder of a polynomial
3.2 Finding the linear factors of a polynomial
3.3 Solving a cubic equation by factorisation

3.1 Finding the remainder of a polynomial

Polynomials are expressions consisting of variables (usually called x) and coefficients (i.e. the numbers in front of terms containing x). For this course you will need to know about quadratic polynomials such as $x^2 - x - 6$ and cubic polynomials such as $x^3 - 6x^2 + 11x - 6$.

Algebraic division

When 25 is divided by 4 the quotient is 6 and the remainder is 1. The number 25 can be written in the following way:

> You can see that 4 divides into 25, 6 times with a remainder of 1.

$$25 = 4 \times 6 + 1$$

This can be applied to algebra like this:

Find the quotient and remainder when $x^2 + 5x - 8$ is divided by $x - 2$.

> The quotient is how many times $x - 2$ goes into $x^2 + 5x - 8$ exactly but in algebraic form.

$x^2 + 5x - 8 = (x - 2)(ax + b) + c$ where $ax + b$ is the quotient and c is the remainder.

$$= ax^2 + bx - 2ax - 2b + c$$

$$= ax^2 + (b - 2a)x - 2b + c$$

Comparing this with the original expression and equating the coefficients of x^2 gives

The coefficients of x, x^2, x^3, etc., are the numbers in front of these terms. The term independent of x is the number without any x's (i.e. the constant term).

$$a = 1$$

Equating coefficients of x gives $5 = b - 2a$ and since $a = 1$, solving gives $b = 7$.

Equating constant terms gives $-2b + c = -8$ and since $b = 7$, $c = 6$.

Hence the quotient (i.e. $ax + b$) is $x + 7$ and the remainder (i.e. c) is 6.

Notice that $x^2 + 5x - 8 = (x - 2)(x + 7) + 6$

An alternative method making use of long division

We can obtain the same result as the above by using algebraic long division.

The calculation would be set out like this.

The method is the same as for ordinary numbers but here we are using algebra. The steps below show how the division is done.

$$x - 2\,\overline{)\,x^2 + 5x - 8}$$

$$\begin{array}{r} x \\ x - 2\,\overline{)\,x^2 + 5x - 8} \end{array}$$

First divide the x into x^2 which goes in x times. The x is written above in the way shown. We now multiply this x by the $x - 2$ and write the answer (i.e. $x^2 - 2x$) in the way shown.

$$\begin{array}{r} x \\ x - 2\,\overline{)\,x^2 + 5x - 8} \\ \underline{x^2 - 2x} \end{array}$$

The $x^2 - 2x$ is subtracted from the term above (i.e. $x^2 + 5x$) to give $7x$ (note that the x^2 terms subtract to give zero and $5x - (-2x)$ gives $7x$. The next term is brought down (i.e. -8) so we now have $7x - 8$.

$$\begin{array}{r} x \\ x - 2\,\overline{)\,x^2 + 5x - 8} \\ \underline{x^2 - 2x} \\ 7x - 8 \end{array}$$

We now see how many times the x outside the divide sign goes into $7x$. The answer is $+7$ which is added to the top of the division like this.

$$\begin{array}{r|l} & x+7 \\ x-2 & x^2+5x-8 \\ & \underline{x^2-2x} \\ & \quad 7x-8 \end{array}$$

We then multiply the 7 by the $x - 2$ to give $7x - 14$. This is written directly under the $7x - 8$ like this.

$$\begin{array}{r|l} & x+7 \\ x-2 & x^2+5x-8 \\ & \underline{x^2-2x} \\ & \quad 7x-8 \\ & \quad \underline{7x-14} \end{array}$$

We now subtract the $7x - 14$ from the $7x - 8$ to give +6 which is the remainder.

$$\begin{array}{r|l} & x+7 \\ x-2 & x^2+5x-8 \\ & \underline{x^2-2x} \\ & \quad 7x-8 \\ & \quad \underline{7x-14} \\ & \qquad\quad 6 \end{array}$$

We can now write $x^2 + 5x - 8 = (x - 2)(x + 7) + 6$

The remainder theorem

The remainder theorem states:

If a polynomial $f(x)$ is divided by $(x - a)$ the remainder is $f(a)$.

For example, if $f(x) = x^3 + 2x^2 - x + 1$ is divided by $x - 1$ the remainder will be $f(1)$.

Remainder = $f(1) = 1^3 + 2(1)^2 - 1 + 1 = 3$

Examples

1 Find the remainder when $x^3 + x^2 + x - 2$ is divided by $x - 1$

Answer

Let $f(x) = x^3 + x^2 + x - 2$

If $f(x) = x^3 + x^2 + x - 2$ is divided by $x - 1$, the remainder is $f(1)$.

This is the remainder theorem.

$f(1) = 1^3 + 1^2 + 1 - 2 = 1$

Hence remainder = 1

The value of x to be put into the function is found by letting $3x - 1 = 0$ and then solving for x giving $x = \frac{1}{3}$.

2 Find the remainder when $27x^3 + 9x^2 - 3x + 7$ is divided by $3x - 1$.

Answer

Let $f(x) = 27x^3 + 9x^2 - 3x + 7$

$$f\left(\tfrac{1}{3}\right) = 27\left(\tfrac{1}{3}\right)^3 + 9\left(\tfrac{1}{3}\right)^2 - 3\left(\tfrac{1}{3}\right) + 7 = 1 + 1 - 1 + 7 = 8$$

Hence remainder = 8.

The factor theorem

For a polynomial $f(x)$, if $f(a) = 0$ then $(x - a)$ is a factor of $f(x)$.

For example, in a polynomial $f(x)$ if $f(5) = 0$, then $(x - 5)$ is a factor of $f(x)$.

If for the same polynomial $f(-2) = 0$, then $(x + 2)$ is also factor of $f(x)$.

Examples

3 Prove that $x + 3$ is a factor of the polynomial

$2x^3 + x^2 - 13x + 6$

Answer

Let $f(x) = 2x^3 + x^2 - 13x + 6$

If $x + 3$ is a factor, then when $x = -3$ is put into $f(x)$ there will be no remainder.

If $x + 3$ is a factor then $f(-3)$ should be zero.

$$f(-3) = 2(-3)^3 + (-3)^2 - 13(-3) + 6 = -54 + 9 + 39 + 6 = 0$$

Hence $x + 3$ is a factor.

4 Prove that $x - 2$ is **not** a factor of the function

$f(x) = 3x^3 - 2x^2 + x + 2$

» TIP

Always read the question carefully. It would be easy to miss the word 'not' in this question.

Answer

4 $f(2) = 3(2)^3 - 2(2)^2 + 2 + 2 = 20$

As $f(2) \neq 0$ then $x - 2$ is not a factor of the function.

5 (a) If $f(x) = x^3 - 2x^2 - x + 2$, find the remainder when $f(x)$ is divided by $(x - 2)$.

(b) State what the answer to part (a) tells you about the function $f(x)$.

Answer

5 (a) $f(x) = x^3 - 2x^2 - x + 2$

$f(2) = (2)^3 - 2(2)^2 - 2 + 2$

$= 8 - 8 - 2 + 2$

$= 0$

(b) It shows that $(x - 2)$ is a factor of $f(x)$.

Progress check

1. Prove that $(x - 3)$ is a factor of the function $x^3 - 7x - 6$.
2. You are given that $g(x) = 2x^3 - 7x^2 + 3x + 1$.

   Find the remainder when $g(x)$ is divided by $(x - 1)$.
3. The function $f(x)$ is defined by $f(x) = x^3 - 4x^2 + x + 8$.

   Show that when $f(x)$ is divided by $(x + 2)$ the remainder is -18.
4. If $f(x) = x^3 - 2x^2 + 6$, find the remainder when $f(x)$ is divided by $(x - 2)$.
5. Show that $(x - 1)$ is a factor of $x^3 + 4x^2 + x - 6$.

3.2 Finding the linear factors of a polynomial

The polynomial $x^3 + 4x^2 + x - 6$ can be factorised to give $(x - 1)(x + 2)(x + 3)$. $(x - 1)$, $(x + 2)$ and $(x + 3)$ are the linear factors of the polynomial. In the following section you will learn how to take a cubic expression and factorise it so that it becomes the product of three linear factors.

> To multiply the brackets $(x - 1)(x + 2)(x + 3)$ out multiply the second pair of brackets out first like this.
>
> $(x - 1)(x + 2)(x + 3)$
> $= (x - 1)(x^2 + 5x + 6)$
>
> Now multiply the second bracket by the first bracket. To do this multiply the contents of the second bracket first by x and then by -1 and simplify the answer.
>
> Hence,
>
> $(x - 1)(x^2 + 5x + 6)$
> $= x^3 + 5x^2 + 6x - x^2 - 5x - 6$
>
> $= x^3 + 4x^2 + x - 6$

Factorising a polynomial

Suppose a function $f(x)$ is defined by $f(x) = x^3 - 3x^2 - x + 3$

In order to factorise the function it is necessary first to find a factor.

Suppose we think that $(x + 1)$ is a factor. We can see if it is a factor by substituting $x = -1$ into the function. If there is no remainder then $(x + 1)$ is a factor.

$$f(-1) = (-1)^3 - 3(-1)^2 - (-1) + 3 = -1 - 3 + 1 + 3 = 0$$

Hence $(x + 1)$ is a factor.

The function can now be written in the following way:

Each term in the first bracket multiplies each term in the second bracket.

$(x + 1)(ax^2 + bx + c) = x^3 - 3x^2 - x + 3$

Equating coefficients of x^3 gives $a = 1$.

Equating constant terms gives $c = 3$.

Equating coefficients of x gives $c + b = -1$ so $b = -4$.

These values can be substituted in giving:

$(x + 1)(x^2 - 4x + 3)$

The second bracket is then factorised giving:

$(x + 1)(x - 3)(x - 1)$

TAKE NOTE!

Three of the four terms have been equated here. The fourth term could be equated as a check. Here it is the coefficients of x^2. Equating these gives $b + a = -3$. We can substitute the values in $b + a = -4 + 1$.

A slightly different method of finding the quadratic factor would be to write down the x^2 and the constant term by inspection, e.g.

$$x^3 - 3x^2 - x + 3 = (x + 1)(x^2 + ax + 3)$$

as it is clear that $x \times x^2 = x^3$ and $1 \times 3 = 3$. Then there is only one unknown coefficient to find. Equating coefficients of x^2 or x is sufficient to find this unknown coefficient of x in the quadratic factor – and doing both would act as a useful check.

3.3 Solving a cubic equation by factorisation

Once a cubic expression has been factorised and it is equal to zero it can be solved by putting each bracket in turn equal to zero and the resulting values of x found. The following examples show how cubic equations can be solved by factorisation.

Examples

6 The function f(x) is defined by $f(x) = x^3 + 8x^2 + 11x - 20$.

(a) Find the remainder when f(x) is divided by $(x - 1)$.

(b) Solve the equation $f(x) = 0$.

Answer

6 (a) $f(1) = 1^3 + 8(1)^2 + 11(1) - 20 = 0$

Hence, remainder = 0.

(b) Hence we know that $(x - 1)$ is a factor.

So, $(x - 1)(ax^2 + bx + c) = x^3 + 8x^2 + 11x - 20$

Equating coefficients of x^3 gives $a = 1$.

Equating constant terms gives $-c = -20$ so $c = 20$

Equating coefficients of x^2 gives $b - a = 8$

$$b - a = 8$$

$$b = 9$$

Putting these values into the expression gives

$$(x - 1)(x^2 + 9x + 20) = (x - 1)(x + 5)(x + 4)$$

Now $(x - 1)(x + 5)(x + 4) = 0$

Hence $x = 1, -5$ or -4

---

7 (a) Use the factor theorem to find an integer root of the equation

$x^3 - 7x - 6 = 0$.

(b) The equation $x^3 - 7x - 6 = 0$ can be written in the form

$(x + a)(x - b)(x + c) = 0$.

Determine the values of a, b and c.

(c) Hence, write down the three roots of the equation $x^3 - 7x - 6 = 0$.

Answer

7 (a) By trial and error, we put values of x into the function until the function equals zero.

Starting from f(1), f(−1), f(2), etc.

Let $f(x) = x^3 - 7x - 6$

Try $x = 1$

$f(1) = 1^3 - 7(1) - 6 = -12$ so $(x - 1)$ is not a factor.

Try $x = -1$

$f(-1) = (-1)^3 - 7(-1) - 6 = 0$ so $(x + 1)$ is a factor.

Therefore $x = -1$ is a root of the equation.

Hence we know that $(x + 1)$ is a factor.

(b) So, $(x + 1)(ax^2 + bx + c) = x^3 - 7x - 6$

Equating coefficients of x^3 gives $a = 1$.

Equating constant terms gives $c = -6$.

Equating coefficients of x gives $c + b = -7$

$$-6 + b = -7$$

$$b = -1$$

> You have to use trial and error by putting values 1, −1, 2, −2, etc., in until you find a value that gives zero when put into the function for x.

> Remember to reverse the sign of the number which gives a zero value, when stating the factor.

> With practice the values of a, b, and c can be found by inspection.

Hence $x^3 - 7x - 6 = (x + 1)(x^2 - x - 6)$

$= (x + 1)(x - 3)(x + 2)$

So $(x + 1)(x - 3)(x + 2) = 0$

Hence $a = 1, b = -1, c = -6$.

(c) Hence the three roots are $x = -1$, $x = 3$ or $x = -2$.

---

8 (a) Find the remainder when $x^3 + x^2 - x - 1$ is divided by $x + 1$.

Explain the significance of this remainder.

(b) Solve the equation $x^3 + x^2 - x - 1 = 0$.

Answer

8 (a) Let $f(x) = x^3 + x^2 - x - 1$

$f(-1) = (-1)^3 + (-1)^2 - (-1) - 1 = 0$

The remainder of zero means that $(x + 1)$ is a factor of $x^3 + x^2 - x - 1$.

(b) $(x + 1)(ax^2 + bx + c) = x^3 + x^2 - x - 1$

Equating coefficients of x^3 gives $a = 1$.

Equating constant terms gives $c = -1$.

Equating coefficients of x gives $b + c = -1$ and as $c = -1$, $b = 0$.

Hence the values of a, b and c can be substituted into

$(x + 1)(ax^2 + bx + c)$ to give $(x + 1)(x^2 - 1)$

Now $x^2 - 1$ is a difference of two squares and can be written as $(x + 1)(x - 1)$.

So we obtain $(x + 1)(x + 1)(x - 1) = 0$.

Hence the solutions of the equation are $x = 1$ or $x = -1$.

Progress check

6 Multiply out the following brackets and simplify:

(a) $(x + 2)(x^2 + x + 1)$

(b) $(x - 4)(x^2 - 3x + 1)$

(c) $(2x - 1)(x^2 + x + 1)$

(d) $(x + 1)(x + 4)(x + 5)$

(e) $(x - 1)(x + 2)(x + 1)$

(f) $(x + 3)^2(x - 2)$

(g) $(x - 1)^2(x - 3)$

7 If $f(x) = 2x^3 - 4x^2 + 2x + 1$, find the remainder when $f(x)$ is divided by $x - 2$.

8 Given that $(x + 1)$ is a factor of $x^3 - 2x^2 + ax + 6$.

Find the value of a.

9 If $f(x) = x^3 - 5x^2 + 7x - 2$

(i) Find the remainder when $f(x)$ is divided by $x - 2$.

(ii) Explain the significance of this result.

Exam practice

1 (a) Given that $(x - 2)$ is a factor of $x^3 - 6x^2 + ax - 6$, show that $a = 11$.

(b) Solve the equation $x^3 - 6x^2 + 11x - 6 = 0$

(c) Calculate the remainder when $x^3 - 6x^2 + 11x - 6$ is divided by $(x + 1)$.

Answer

1 (a)

$$\text{Let } f(x) = x^3 - 6x^2 + ax - 6$$

$$f(2) = 2^3 - 6(2)^2 + 2a - 6 = 2a - 22$$

As $x - 2$ is a factor, $f(2) = 0$.

Hence $2a - 22 = 0$ so

$$a = 11.$$

(b) $x^3 - 6x^2 + 11x - 6 = (x - 2)(ax^2 + bx + c)$

Equating coefficients of x^3 gives $a = 1$.

Equating constant terms gives $-2c = -6$, giving $c = 3$

Equating coefficients of x^2 gives $b - 2a = -6$, giving $b = -4$.

Hence, $x^3 - 6x^2 + 11x - 6 = (x - 2)(x^2 - 4x + 3)$

Factorising the second bracket gives:

$f(x) = (x - 2)(x - 3)(x - 1)$

Now $(x - 2)(x - 3)(x - 1) = 0$

So $x = 2$, $x = 3$, $x = 1$

(c) $f(-1) = (-1)^3 - 6(-1)^2 + 11(-1) - 6 = -1 - 6 - 11 - 6 = -24$

Remainder $= -24$.

TAKE NOTE!

Always look back at the previous part to see if it is relevant. Here it is because the polynomial is the same and we know that $x - 2$ is a factor.

---

2 The function $f(x) = x^3 + ax + 6$ is such that when $f(x)$ is divided by $(x - 3)$ the remainder is 12.

(i) Show that the value of a is -7. [2]

(ii) Factorise $f(x)$. [3]

(OCR FSMQ May 2012 q3)

Answer

2 (i)

$$f(x) = x^3 + ax + 6$$

$$f(3) = 3^3 + 3a + 6$$

$$= 27 + 3a + 6$$

$$= 33 + 3a$$

Now $f(3) = 12$, so $33 + 3a = 12$ giving $a = -7$

(ii) From part (i) we can now substitute the value of a in for the function so we have

$f(x) = x^3 - 7x + 6$

We now need to find values of x which when substituted in for x, give no remainder.

First start at 1 then −1, then 2, then −2, etc.

$f(1) = 1^3 - 7(1) + 6 = 0$. No remainder means that $(x - 1)$ is a factor of $x^3 - 7x + 6$.

The function can now be written in the following way:

$(x - 1)(ax^2 + bx + c) = x^3 - 7x + 6$

Equating coefficients of x^3 gives $a = 1$.

Equating constant terms gives $-c = 6$ so $c = -6$

Equating coefficients of x gives $c - b = -7$ so $b = 1$.

These values can be substituted giving:

$f(x) = (x - 1)(x^2 + x - 6)$

The second bracket is then factorised giving:

$f(x) = (x + 1)(x + 3)(x - 2)$

» TIP

If $(x - a)$ is a factor of $f(x)$ then $f(a) = 0$. If it is not a factor then $f(a)$ will not equal zero.

3 (a) Determine whether or not each of the following is a factor of the expression

$x^3 - 7x + 6$.

You must show your working.

(i) $(x - 2)$ [2]

(ii) $(x - 1)$ [1]

(b) (i) Factorise the function $f(x) = x^3 - 7x + 6$. [3]

(ii) Solve the equation $f(x) = 0$. [1]

(OCR FSMQ May 2011 q7)

Answer

3 (a) (i) Let $f(x) = x^3 - 7x + 6$

$f(2) = 2^3 - 7(2) + 6$

$= 8 - 14 + 6$

$= 0$

Hence, $(x - 2)$ is a factor of $x^3 - 7x + 6$.

(ii) Let $f(x) = x^3 - 7x + 6$

$f(1) = 1^3 - 7(1) + 6$

$= 0$

Hence, $(x - 1)$ is a factor of $x^3 - 7x + 6$.

(b) Let the third factor of the expression be $(x + a)$.

Hence $(x - 2)(x - 1)(x + a) = x^3 - 7x + 6$

Equating constant terms gives $2a = 6$ so $a = 3$.

So $x^3 - 7x + 6 = (x - 2)(x - 1)(x + 3)$

Now $x^3 - 7x + 6 = 0$

So, $(x - 2)(x - 1)(x + 3) = 0$ giving $x = 1, 2$ or -3.

Make sure you multiply out the brackets as a check.

Test yourself

Answer the following questions and check your answers before moving on to the next topic.

1 Calculate the remainder when $4x^3 + 3x^2 - 3x + 1$ is divided by $x + 1$.

2 (a) Given that $x + 2$ is a factor of $x^3 + 6x^2 + ax + 6$, show that $a = 11$.

(b) Solve the equation $x^3 + 6x^2 + 11x + 6 = 0$.

3 The polynomial $f(x)$ is defined by: $f(x) = x^3 - x^2 - 4x + 4$

(a) (i) Evaluate $f(-2)$.

(ii) Using your answer to part (i).
Write down one fact which you can deduce about $f(x)$.

(b) Solve the equation $f(x) = 0$.

Topic summary

Polynomials

Polynomials are expressions consisting of variables and coefficients.

Quadratic polynomials take the form $ax^2 + bx + c$.

Cubic polynomials take the form $ax^3 + bx^2 + cx + d$.

Quadratic equations can be expressed in the form $ax^2 + bx + c = 0$.

Cubic equations can be expressed in the form $ax^3 + bx^2 + cx + d = 0$.

The remainder theorem

The remainder theorem states:

If a polynomial $\mathrm{f}(x)$ is divided by $(x - a)$ the remainder is $\mathrm{f}(a)$.

The factor theorem

For a polynomial $\mathrm{f}(x)$, if $\mathrm{f}(a) = 0$ then $(x - a)$ is a factor of $\mathrm{f}(x)$.

Problem solving and inequalities

Letters are used to represent numbers in equations. This topic starts by looking at how problems can be solved using algebra and builds on previous material.

Sometimes we need to restrict variables in some way and we do this by using inequalities. For example, suppose a person has an age given by the letter x. Suppose we are considering whether a person is eligible to vote in a general election where you need to be at least 18 years old.

The following inequality could be used to restrict the ages that x could represent to 18 or older: $x \geq 18$.

This topic deals with how to manipulate and solve problems involving the inequalities $<$ (i.e. less than), $>$ (i.e. greater than), $\leq$ (i.e. less than or equal to) and $\geq$ (i.e. greater than or equal to). Topic 8 will expand on skills and techniques learnt in this topic.

This topic covers the following:

4.1 Setting up and solving problems

4.2 Manipulating inequalities

4.3 Solving one linear equation and one quadratic equation algebraically

4.4 Solving linear and quadratic inequalities algebraically

4.5 Solving linear and quadratic inequalities graphically

4.1 Setting up and solving problems

In this section you will learn to use algebra to produce equations and then use the techniques learnt in previous topics to solve these equations and so produce the answers to problems.

Setting up problems

One of the hardest parts when solving problems is using algebra correctly to create the equations ready for solving.

Take the following problem as an example.

A rectangle has a length of x cm and a width of y cm. If the perimeter of the rectangle is 24 cm and the area of the rectangle is 27 cm², find the length and width of the rectangle.

When there are two quantities to find, you need to obtain two equations in order to find their values.

x

y

This equation can be simplified by dividing both sides by 2.

Perimeter of rectangle, $2x + 2y = 24$

$x + y = 12$ .... (1)

Area of rectangle, $xy = 27$ .... (2)

The area of a rectangle = length × width.

We need to obtain an equation in just one of the variables.

This needs to be rearranged so that it is in the form for a quadratic equation that is ready to be factorised and solved.

From equation (1) we obtain $y = 12 - x$

Substituting this into equation (2) we obtain

$$x(12 - x) = 27$$

$$\text{So, } 12x - x^2 = 27$$

$$\text{Hence, } x^2 - 12x + 27 = 0$$

Factorising, we obtain $(x - 3)(x - 9) = 0$

So $x = 3$ or 9

Where there is a pair of answers to a problem, always check to see if both answers are acceptable in the context of the question.

Substituting each of these values into equation (1) we have

$3 + y = 12$ or $9 + y = 12$ giving $y = 9$ or 3.

Now if $y = 9$ cm this would make the width larger than the length of 3 cm. This answer is therefore discounted.

Hence the values are length, $x = 9$ cm and width, $y = 3$ cm.

Simple formulae such as that for finding the area of a triangle when the base and perpendicular height are known, must be remembered.

Examples

1 The triangle shown below has a base of $(2x + 5)$ cm and a perpendicular height of $(x - 1)$ cm. If the area of the triangle is 30 cm^2, find the value of x.

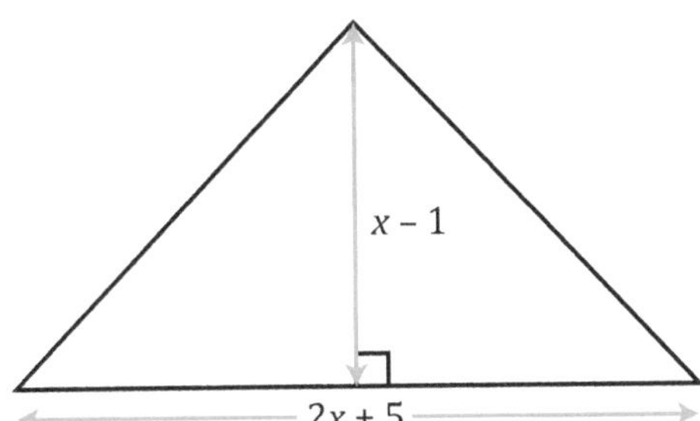

Answer

1 Area of a triangle $= \frac{1}{2} \times \text{base} \times \text{height}$

$$= \tfrac{1}{2}(2x + 5)(x - 1)$$

Now area of the triangle = 30 cm^2, so we have

$$30 = \tfrac{1}{2}(2x + 5)(x - 1)$$

$$60 = 2x^2 - 2x + 5x - 5$$

Hence $2x^2 + 3x - 65 = 0$

$$(2x + 13)(x - 5) = 0$$

$$\text{Hence } x = -\frac{13}{5} \text{ or } 5$$

The negative answer is ignored because when it is substituted in the expression for the height it gives a negative height which is impossible.

So, $x = 5$ cm

2 A rectangular sheet of metal has dimensions 16 cm by 10 cm. A square of metal is to be cut out of each corner as shown in the following diagram.

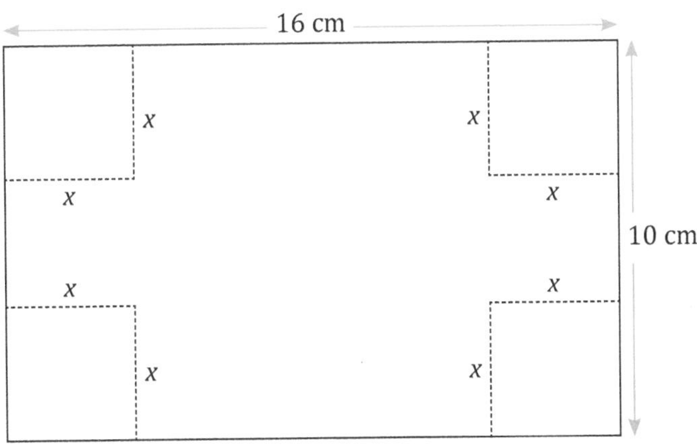

After removing the corners and folding up the flaps an open-top box is formed like that shown here:

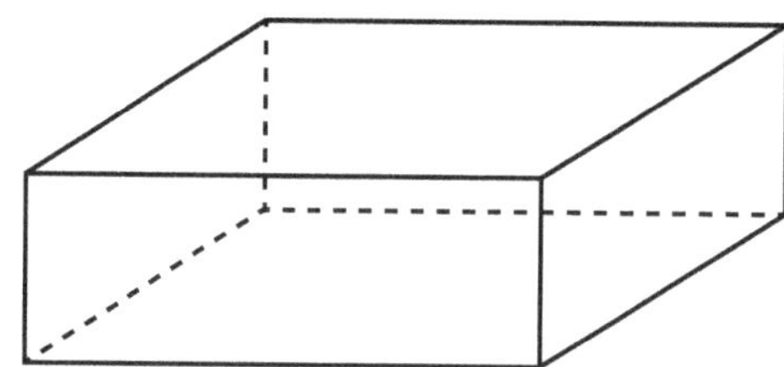

(a) Find the length, width and height of the box in terms of x.

(b) Hence show that the volume, V of the box in cm^3 is given by the following:

$4x^3 - 52x^2 + 160x$

(c) If the volume of the box is 144 cm^3, find the value of x.

Answer

2 (a) Length = $16 - 2x$, width = $10 - 2x$ and height = x.

(b) Volume of the box, $V = (16 - 2x)(10 - 2x)(x) = (160 - 52x + 4x^2)(x)$

$$= 160x - 52x^2 + 4x^3 = 4x^3 - 52x^2 + 160x$$

(c) Now $V = 144$ so $4x^3 - 52x^2 + 160x = 144$

Hence $4x^3 - 52x^2 + 160x - 144 = 0$

This is a cubic equation so the remainder theorem is used to determine one of the factors of this equation. First we try different values of x starting at 1 then −1 and so on until a value gives no remainder.

Dividing both sides by 4 we obtain

$$x^3 - 13x^2 + 40x - 36 = 0$$

Let $f(x) = x^3 - 13x^2 + 40x - 36$

Try f(1), $f(1) = 1^3 - 13(1)^2 + 40(1) - 36 = -8$

Try f(−1), $f(-1) = (-1)^3 - 13(-1)^2 + 40(-1) - 36 = -90$

Try f(2), $f(2) = 2^3 - 13(2)^2 + 40(2) - 36 = 0$, so $(x - 2)$ is a factor of the function.

Hence $x^3 - 13x^2 + 40x - 36 = (x - 2)(ax^2 + bx + c)$

Equating coefficients of x^3 we obtain $a = 1$.

Equating constant terms we obtain $-2c = -36$ giving $c = 18$.

Equating coefficients of x we obtain $c - 2b = 40$ so $18 - 2b = 40$

giving $b = -11$.

Hence we have $(x - 2)(x^2 - 11x + 18) = 0$

Factorising the second bracket we obtain $(x - 2)(x - 9)(x - 2) = 0$

Solving, we obtain $x = 9$ or 2.

Now if $x = 9$ the width would be $10 - 2x = 10 - 2(9) = -8$ which is impossible.

Hence the value of x is 2 cm.

---

3 A woman drives a distance of 40 km to work each day and her average speed for the journey is v km/h. If she increases her average speed by 5 km/h, it takes 2 minutes less time than usual to make the journey. Calculate her normal speed in km/h.

Answer

3 Speed $= \dfrac{\text{distance in km}}{\text{time in h}}$ so rearranging we have time $= \dfrac{\text{distance}}{\text{speed}}$.

Time taken at normal speed $= \dfrac{40}{v}$ hours.

Time taken at increased speed $= \dfrac{40}{v+5}$

> The denominator is $v+5$ as the speed has increased by 5 km/h.

Time taken at normal speed – time taken at increased speed $= \dfrac{2}{60}$

So we obtain $\dfrac{40}{v} - \dfrac{40}{v+5} = \dfrac{2}{60}$

Hence $\dfrac{40}{v} - \dfrac{40}{v+5} = \dfrac{2}{60} = \dfrac{1}{30}$

Multiplying both sides of the equation by $30v(v+5)$ gives

$1200(v+5) - 1200v = v(v+5)$

$1200v + 6000 - 1200v = v^2 + 5v$

Hence $v^2 + 5v - 6000 = 0$

Factorising gives

$(v - 80)(v + 75) = 0$

Solving we obtain $v = 80$ or -75. The answer -75 is ignored, as speed cannot be negative.

Hence normal speed is 80 km/h.

TIP

You must ensure that the units are consistent when forming equations. The left-hand side of this equation is in hours so the right-hand side will also need to be in hours. 2 minutes is $\frac{2}{60}$ hours.

> Note we choose $30v(v+5)$ because all the denominators will divide into it exactly. This will remove all the denominators in the equation.

TIP

Note if you have difficulty with hard quadratic equations like this do not waste too much time. Use an alternative method for solving the quadratic equation by using the formula or completing the square.

Progress check

1. Amy is one-third the age of her mother. In 12 years' time Amy will be half the age of her mother. How old is Amy and how old is her mother?

2. Two positive numbers x and y, where x is the larger of the two numbers, have a difference of one and a product of 72. Using algebra and showing your working, find the values of x and y.

3. Three consecutive positive integers are written on a piece of paper.

   The square of the largest integer is 64 greater than the square of the smallest integer. Find the value of each integer.

Problems containing inequalities

In real-life situations quantities are often limited in some way. For example, suppose you are thinking of buying a car, you will be limited by the amount you can spend. If you have a maximum budget of £5000 and x is the amount you can spend, then this can be written as

$$x \leq 5000$$

Suppose you decide that you want a car less than 5 years old. Then if y is the age of a car, then we can express this as $y < 5$.

It is very important to be able to form inequalities using the information contained in a question.

You will learn more about this in Topic 8.

Using number lines to represent inequalities

Number lines can be used to represent inequalities, with the lines themselves indicating the range of values that are allowable. The ends of the lines can be solid circles (if the value on the circle is allowed) or open circles (if the value is not allowed).

Here are some number lines and the inequalities they represent.

Notice the open circle at 25 to show you cannot have 25 itself only those numbers below 25.

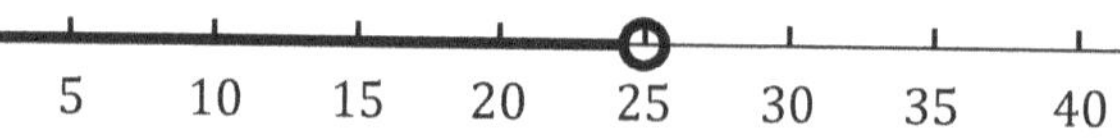

The inequality represented by the above number line is $x < 25$.

Notice the closed circle at 10 to show 10 itself is allowable.

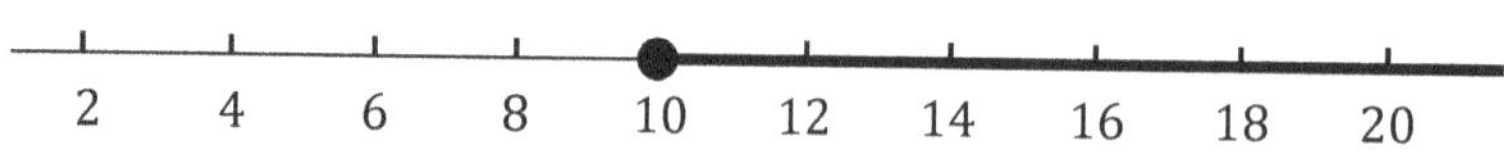

The inequality represented by the above number line is $x \geq 10$.

The above number line represents a double inequality as there are restrictions on the numbers at either end of the line. x has to be greater than or equal to -2 and less than 3. This is represented by the double inequality $-2 \leq x < 3$.

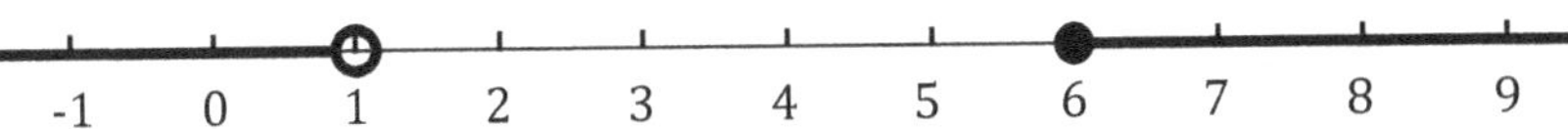

Notice in the above number line there is a gap between the two circles. When this occurs two separate inequalities are needed to represent the allowable numbers. These two inequalities cannot be combined so they must be shown separately. The two inequalities represented by the above number line are

$x < 1$ and $x \geq 6$.

Examples

4 A garage has to sell at least 10 new cars each week in order to pay all the overheads. The car manufacturer can let the garage have a maximum of 25 new cars per week. If x is the number of cars, write inequalities to represent the number of cars that can be sold each week.

Answer

4 We know that x has to be greater than or equal to 10. This can be written as $x \geq 10$. We also know that the number of cars supplied is 25 or less, which can be represented as $x \leq 25$.

This can be illustrated on the following number line.

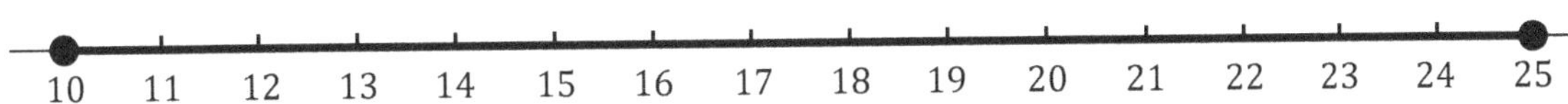

The above range can be represented by the double inequality

$10 \leq x \leq 25$.

5 A vehicle hire company hires vans and cars. The total number of vans and cars must not exceed 100. The number of vans must be at most the same as the number of cars and it must exceed half the number of cars.

If x is the number of cars and y is the number of vans and $x > 0$ and $y > 0$, write three other inequalities to represent the above information.

Answer

5 The total number of vans and cars cannot exceed 100.

> The total number of vehicles is $x + y$.

This can be written as $x + y \le 100$.

The number of vans must be at most the same as the number of cars.

This can be written as $y \le x$.

The number of vans must exceed half the number of cars.

This can be written as $y > \frac{1}{2}x$.

Progress check

4 Write down the inequality represented by each of these number lines:

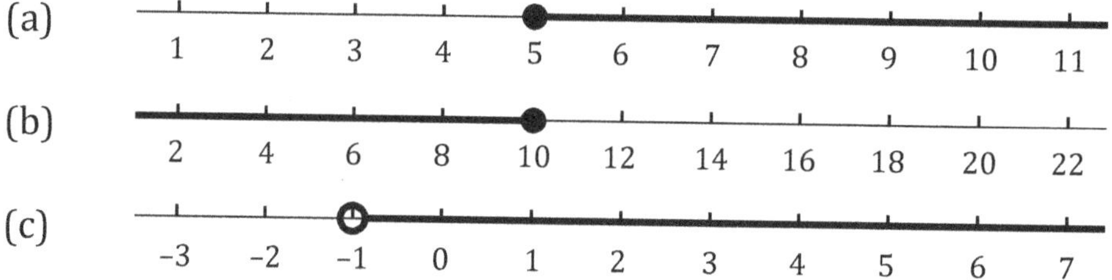

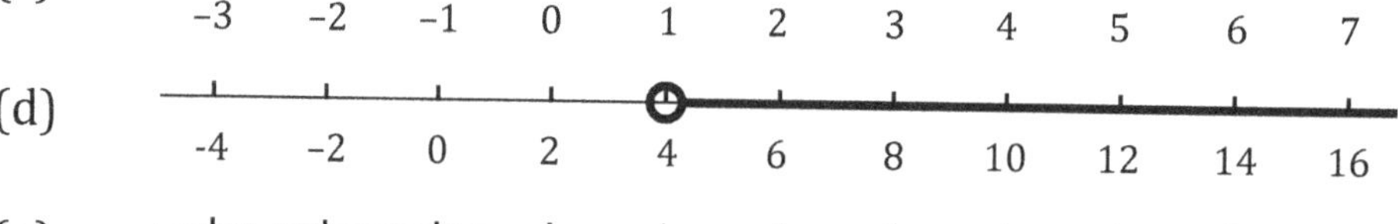

5 Write down the double inequality represented by the following number lines:

(a)

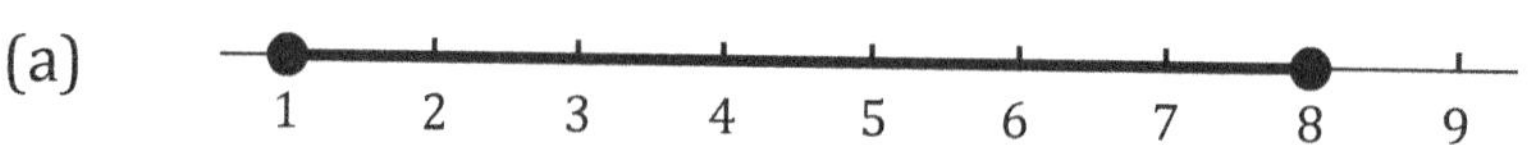

(b)

-2 -1 0 1 2 3 4 5 6

(c)

0 1 2 3 4 5 6 7 8 9

(d)

-4 -3 -2 -1 0 1 2 3 4 5

(e)

3 4 5 6 7 8 9 10 11 12

> Note that the word 'satisfy' means that each number in the list must be true for the inequalities.

6 If x is an integer, write down a list of numbers satisfied by the following inequalities:

(a) $3 \le x \le 10$

(b) $-4 \le x \le 0$

(c) $1 \le x \le 7$

(d) $15 < x \le 18$

(e) $-3 < x \le 2$

(f) $15 < x < 20$

(g) $-5 < x < 5$

(h) $3 \leq x < 10$

(i) $-1 < x \leq 5$

(j) $12 \leq x \leq 18$

7 Write the inequalities represented by the following number lines:

(a)

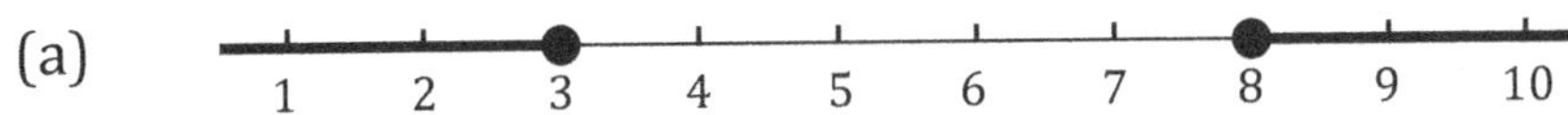

(b)

−4 −3 −2 −1 0 1 2 3 4 5 6 7 8

(c)

4 5 6 7 8 9 10 11 12 13 14 15 16

(d)

−5 −4 −3 −2 −1 0 1 2 3 4 5 6 7

(e)

2 3 4 5 6 7 8 9 10 11 12 13 14

(f)

−5 −4 −3 −2 −1 0 1 2 3 4 5 6

8 In order to be a member of a golf club a person needs to be a minimum of 14 years old and not older than 18. If the age of a person is x, write a double inequality to show this information.

4.2 Manipulating inequalities

You will already be familiar with manipulating equations. Most of the things you can do to an equation are the same with inequalities but there are some important exceptions.

Here are the meanings of certain inequalities

$<$ less than

$\leq$ less than or equal to

$>$ greater than

$\geq$ greater than or equal to

Adding and subtracting numbers or letters from both sides

As with equations you can add or subtract any number or letter from both sides of the inequality and the inequality will stay the same.

Multiplying or dividing both sides by positive numbers

Again you can multiply or divide both sides by numbers provided they are positive.

So, for example, if you have the following inequality $4x \geq 24$ you can divide both sides by 4 to give $x \geq 6$.

Multiplying or dividing both sides by negative numbers

If you multiply or divide both sides by a negative number then the inequality sign must be reversed.

Suppose you had the inequality $-3x \leq 9$. If you divided both sides by -3 you would need to reverse the inequality to give $x \geq -3$.

4.3 Solving one linear equation and one quadratic equation algebraically

In Topic 1 you solved two linear equations simultaneously to find x- and y-values fitting both equations. You were finding the coordinates of the point of intersection of two straight lines.

You also need to find the solution of one linear equation and one quadratic equation. Here you will be finding the points of intersection or the point of contact of a straight line and a curve.

Example

6 Solve the simultaneous equations $y = 10x^2 - 5x - 2$ and $y = 2x - 3$ algebraically. Write down a geometrical interpretation of your results.

Answer

> At the points of intersection, the y-coordinates of the curve and straight line will be the same.

6 Equating expressions for y gives

$$10x^2 - 5x - 2 = 2x - 3$$

$$10x^2 - 7x + 1 = 0$$

Factorising this quadratic gives

$$(5x - 1)(2x - 1) = 0$$

Hence $x = \frac{1}{5}$ or $x = \frac{1}{2}$

> It is easier to substitute the x-coordinate into the equation of the straight line rather than the curve.

Substituting $x = \frac{1}{5}$ into $y = 2x - 3$ gives

$$y = -2\tfrac{3}{5}$$

Substituting $x = \frac{1}{2}$ into $y = 2x - 3$ gives

$$y = -2$$

There are two places where the line and curve intersect.

The points of intersection of the line with the curve are $(\frac{1}{5}, -2\frac{3}{5})$ and $(\frac{1}{2}, -2)$.

4.4 Solving linear and quadratic inequalities algebraically

Solving linear inequalities algebraically

These are solved in a similar way to solving ordinary linear equations but there is one important difference. If you multiply or divide both sides by a negative quantity, then the inequality sign must be reversed since, for example, $3 > 2$, but $-3 < -2$.

Examples

7 Solve the inequality $3x - 7 < 2$

Answer

7 $3x - 7 < 2$

$3x < 9$

$x < 3$

Adding 7 to both sides.

Dividing both sides by 3.

8 Solve the inequality $1 - 2x > 5$

Answer

8 $1 - 2x > 5$

$-2x > 4$

$x < -2$

Subtracting 1 from both sides.

Dividing both sides by −2 and reversing the sign.

9 Find the integers that satisfy the inequality $13 \leq 3x + 4 < 25$.

Answer

9 $13 \leq 3x + 4 < 25$

Subtracting 4 from both sides of the inequality we obtain

$9 \leq 3x < 21$

Dividing both sides by 3 we obtain

$3 \leq x < 7$

As x has to be an integer, the possible values of x are 3, 4, 5, 6.

Integers are positive and negative whole numbers. Zero is also classed as an integer.

Solving quadratic inequalities algebraically

Quadratic inequalities can be solved algebraically using the following method.

Suppose we wish to solve the quadratic inequality $x^2 - 4x + 3 > 0$.

First factorise the quadratic. Here, this would be $(x - 1)(x - 3) > 0$.

Now if p and q are the factors of a quadratic and $pq = 0$, then either $p = 0$ or $q = 0$.

This means that if $(x - 1)(x - 3) = 0$ then $x = 1$ or 3. However, this rule does not extend to inequalities. We cannot say that if $pq > 0$ then $p > 0$ or $q > 0$ because if p and q were both negative (i.e. < 0) then $pq > 0$.

Instead we have to say that if $pq > 0$, then either $p > 0$ and $q > 0$ or $p < 0$ and $q < 0$.

Hence, for our example we can say if $(x - 1)(x - 3) > 0$, then

$x - 1 > 0$ **and** $x - 3 > 0$

giving $x > 1$ **and** $x > 3$

As both of these inequalities must be met, it means that $x > 3$

OR

$x - 1 < 0$ **and** $x - 3 < 0$

giving $x < 1$ **and** $x < 3$

As both of these inequalities must be met, it means that $x < 1$.

Hence the solution of the inequality is $x < 1$ and $x > 3$.

4.5 Solving linear and quadratic inequalities graphically

This section looks at how linear and quadratic inequalities can be solved graphically.

Solving linear inequalities graphically

Inequalities can be shown graphically. For example, the inequality $x \geq 3$ can be shown graphically by drawing a solid vertical line at $x = 3$. The line is called the boundary line and if the inequality allows you to have points on the boundary line, then it is drawn as a solid line and if you can't, then it is drawn as a dotted line. The allowable region (i.e. the region described by the inequality) is left blank and the region which is not allowed is shaded.

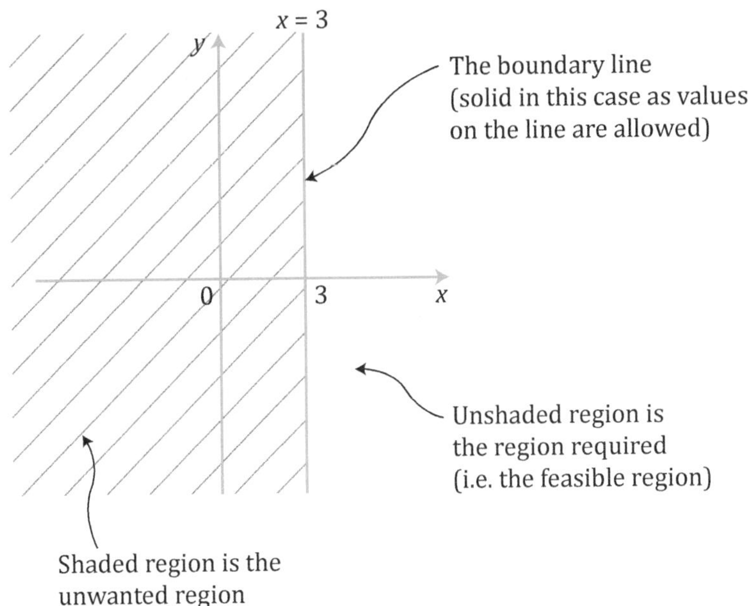

The graph below shows the inequality $x < -2$.

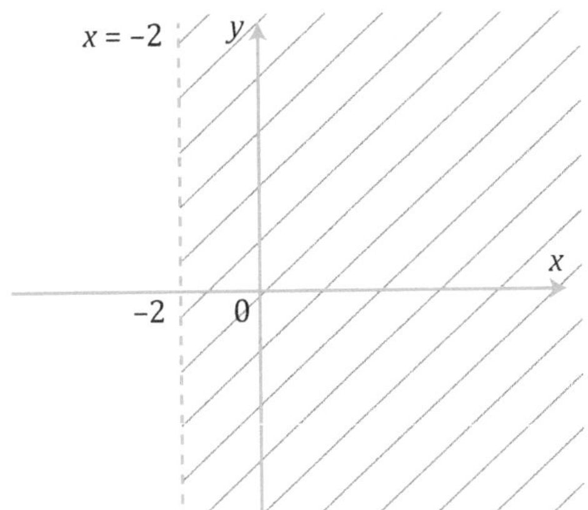

Notice that the dotted line means that values on the line are not allowable.

The graph below shows the inequality $y \leq 5$.

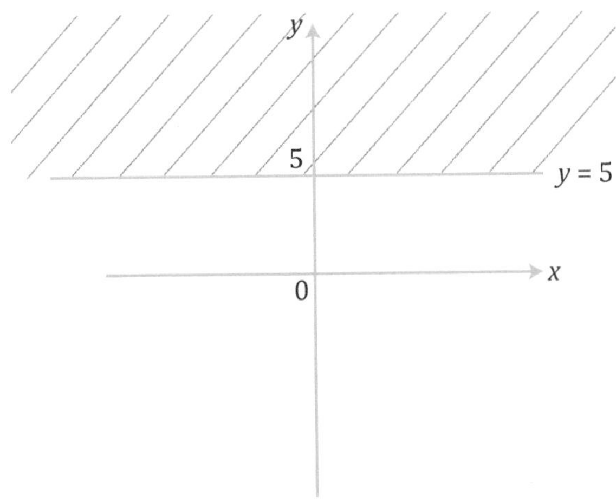

TIP

Always remember that the region that is **not allowed** is the **shaded** region. It is very common for students to get this the wrong way around.

Example

10 Illustrate the region represented by the following inequalities on a graph by shading the region that is not required.

$$y \le x$$

$$x + 3y \le 12$$

$$y \ge 1$$

Answer

10 First we need to add the following lines to the graph.

As all the inequalities have an equals component, values on the lines are allowable and hence all three lines are drawn as solid lines.

The lines we need to draw are:

$y = x$

$x + 3y = 12$

$y = 1$

> You can put any x-coordinate into the equation to find the y-coordinate.

The line $y = 1$ is a horizontal line at $y = 1$.

For the line $y = x$, when $x = 0, y = 0$ and when $x = 4, y = 4$.

For the line $x + 3y = 12$, when $x = 0, y = 4$ and when $y = 0, x = 12$.

A scale is added to both axes which will allow all the points above to be plotted.

The lines are then added to the graph.

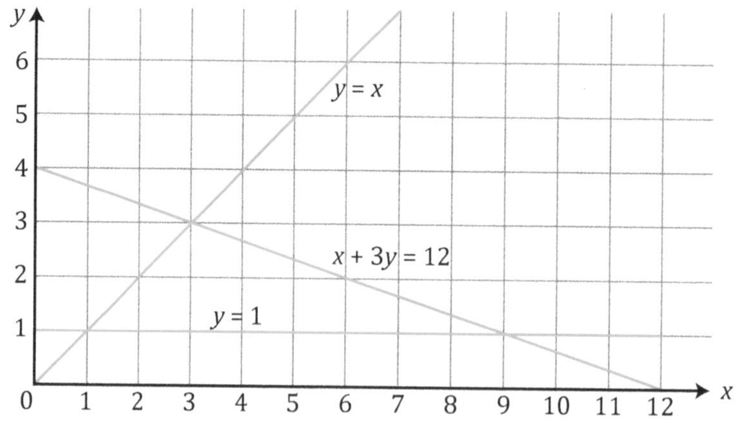

We now shade the regions **not** allowed.

> Remember to label the x- and y-axes and add the equations next to the lines.

For $y \le x$ the required region is on or below the line, so above the line is shaded.

For $x + 3y \leq 12$ the required region is on or below the line, so above the line is shaded.

For $y \geq 1$ the required region is on or above the line, so below the line is shaded.

These shadings are added.

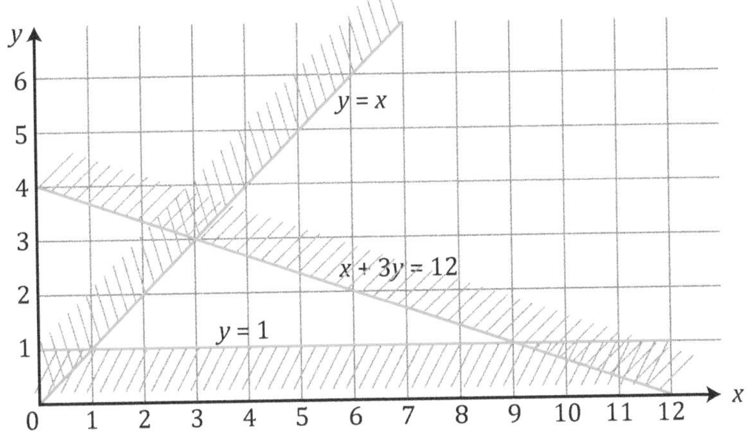

Once you have done this it is clear where the feasible (i.e. required) region is, so we should shade all the other areas on the graph like this. It is important to note that any point which is in the feasible region or on the lines that enclose this region will satisfy all the three inequalities in the question. If you look carefully at the above graph, and if x and y were integers, there would be 15 points whose coordinates would satisfy the three inequalities.

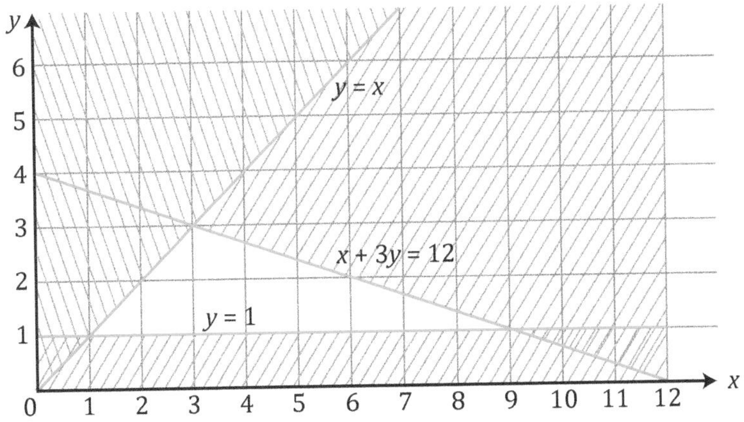

TIP

Note that we always **shade** the region that is **not required** and this will be made clear in the examination questions.

Solving quadratic inequalities graphically

To solve a quadratic inequality such as $x^2 + x \geq 6$ graphically there are a number of steps to follow:

1 Ensure that the quadratic inequality has all the terms on one side and a zero on the other side. So, if you had the inequality $x^2 + x \geq 6$ you would need to rearrange it to give $x^2 + x - 6 \geq 0$.

2 Consider the case where $x^2 + x - 6 = 0$. Factorise this quadratic equation. So here we have $(x + 3)(x - 2) = 0$. This equation is then solved. So, $x = -3$ or $x = 2$ (these are the points where the curve cuts the x-axis).

3 Now we have to decide whether the curve represented by $x^2 + x - 6$ is ∩-shaped or U-shaped. This curve is U-shaped (because the coefficient of x^2 is positive).

4 The graph can now be sketched.

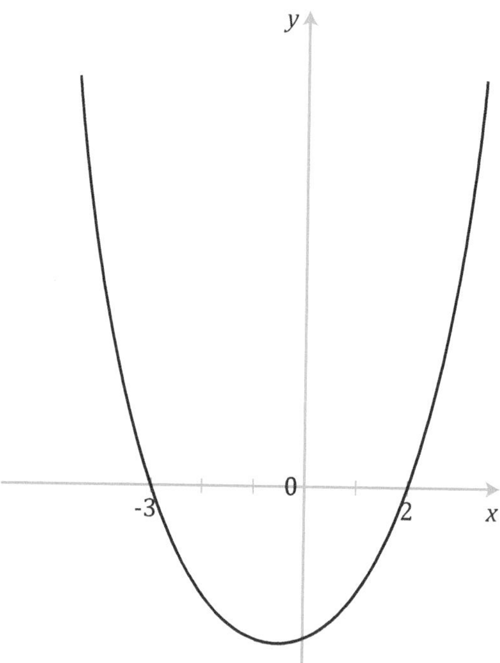

5 Now we want the values of x where the $x^2 + x - 6 \geq 0$ which will be those sections on the graph which are above or on the x-axis. Hence this will be 2 and greater than 2 and −3 and less than −3. This can be written as $x \leq -3$ and $x \geq 2$. These are now the two solutions of the inequality.

If we had the opposite inequality, i.e. $x^2 + x - 6 \leq 0$, the graph would still be the same as the one above but we just need to use the section of the graph which is on or below the x-axis. The allowable values of x would lie between −3 and 2 and also include the values −3 and 2. The solution to the inequality is therefore

$$-3 \leq x \leq 2.$$

Examples

11 Find the range of values of x satisfying the inequality

$$2x^2 + x - 6 \leq 0$$

Answer

11 $$2x^2 + x - 6 \leq 0$$

Considering the case where $2x^2 + x - 6 = 0$ and factorising gives

$$(2x - 3)(x + 2) = 0$$

Giving $x = \frac{3}{2}$ or $x = -2$ (these are the points where the curve cuts the x-axis)

Sketching the curve for $y = 2x^2 + x - 6$ gives the following:

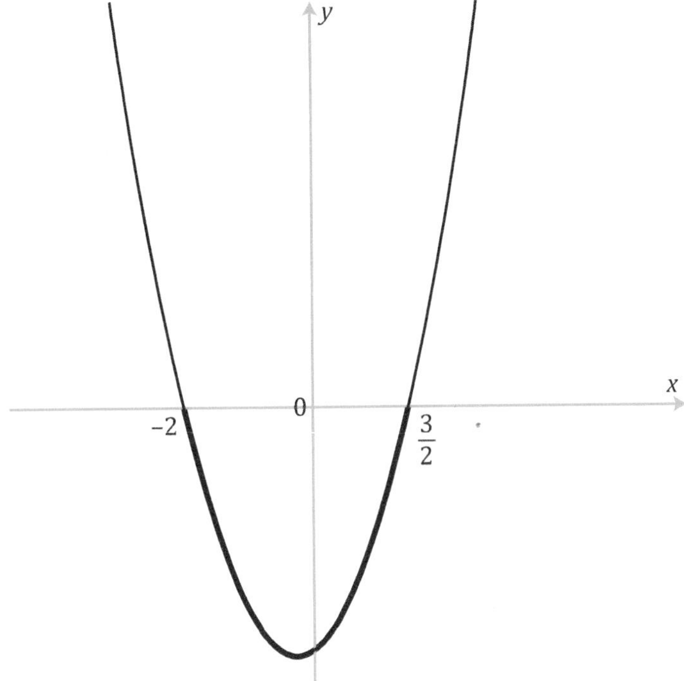

TIP

It is always worth spending the time sketching the curve as it is much easier to see the required range of values.

We want the part of the graph which is on or below the x-axis because of the $\leq$ in the inequality.

The range of values of x for which this occurs are $-2 \leq x \leq \frac{3}{2}$.

12 Find the range of values of x satisfying the inequality

$$3x^2 + 2x - 1 > 0$$

Answer

12 $3x^2 + 2x - 1 > 0$

Considering the case where $3x^2 + 2x - 1 = 0$ and factorising gives

$(3x - 1)(x + 1) = 0$

Giving $x = \frac{1}{3}$ or $x = -1$ (these are where the curve cuts the x-axis)

Sketching the curve for $y = 3x^2 + 2x - 1$ gives the following:

Remember to make the required region on the curve bolder than the rest of the curve.

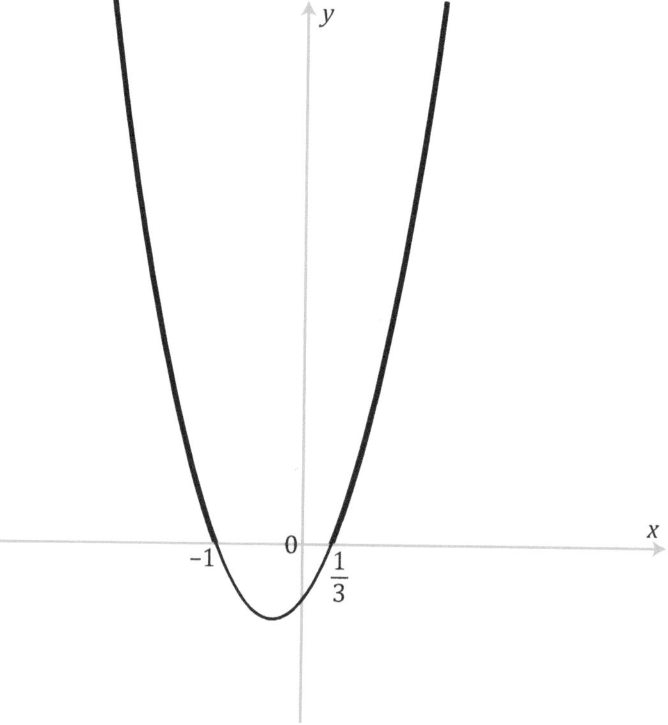

We want the part of the graph which is above the x-axis because of the > in the inequality.

The range of values of x for which this occurs are $x < -1$ or $x > \frac{1}{3}$

Progress check

9 Solve the following linear inequalities:

(a) $4x - 2 > 3 - x$

(b) $2(x + 1) > 8 - x$

(c) $2(5x - 3) \leq 4(x - 3)$

(d) $4 - x < 3x + 7$

(e) $9 - 5x \leq 4 - x$

(f) $5 - x < 3(x - 2)$

10 Solve the inequality $x^2 - 6x + 8 > 0$

11 Solve the inequality $1 - 3x < x + 7$

12 Solve the inequality $5x^2 + 7x - 6 \leq 0$

13 Show that the straight line $y = x + 4$ touches the curve $y = x^2 - 7x + 20$ and find the coordinates of the point of contact.

14 The line with the equation $y = 5x + 13$ intersects the circle with equation $x^2 + y^2 = 13$ at two points. Find the coordinates of each point.

15 The line $y = 3x + 6$ intersects the curve $y = x^2 - 2x + 1$ at two points. Find the x-coordinates for each of these two points giving your answers correct to two decimal places.

Exam practice

1 Solve the inequality $3(x + 2) > 2 - x$. [3]

(OCR FSMQ June 2007 q1)

Answer

1 $3(x + 2) > 2 - x$

$3x + 6 > 2 - x$

$4x + 6 > 2$

$4x > -4$

$x > -1$

First multiply out the bracket and collect all the terms in x on one side of the equation.

2 Solve the inequality $x^2 - 7x + 10 \leq 0$

Answer

2 Considering the case where $x^2 - 7x + 10 = 0$

and factorising gives $(x - 2)(x - 5) = 0$

Giving $x = 2$ or $x = 5$ (these are the points where the curve cuts the x-axis).

Sketching the curve for $x^2 - 7x + 10 = 0$ gives the following:

Just do a quick sketch of the curve and mark the points on the graph where the curve cuts the x-axis.

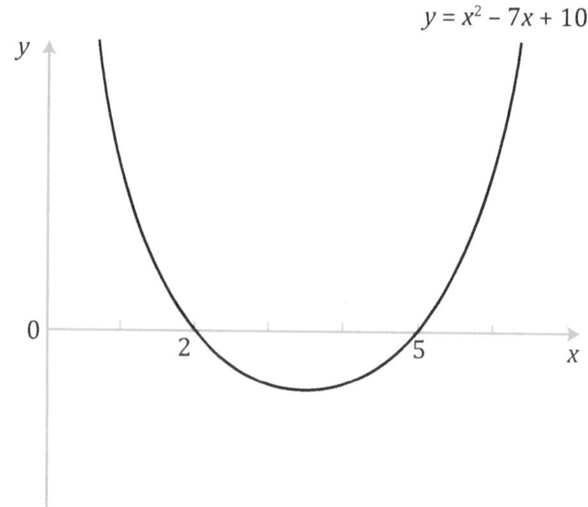

We want the part of the graph which is on or below the x-axis because of the ≤ in the inequality.

The range of values of x for which this occurs are $2 \leq x \leq 5$.

---

3 Find the integers that satisfy the inequality $-7 < 3x + 1 < 12$ [4]

(OCR FSMQ June 2013 q2)

Answer

Subtract 1 from each side.

3 $-7 < 3x + 1 < 12$

$-8 < 3x < 11$ Divide each side by 3.

$-\frac{8}{3} < x < \frac{11}{3}$

Remember that you have to give the integer values x can take.

$-2\frac{2}{3} < x < 3\frac{2}{3}$

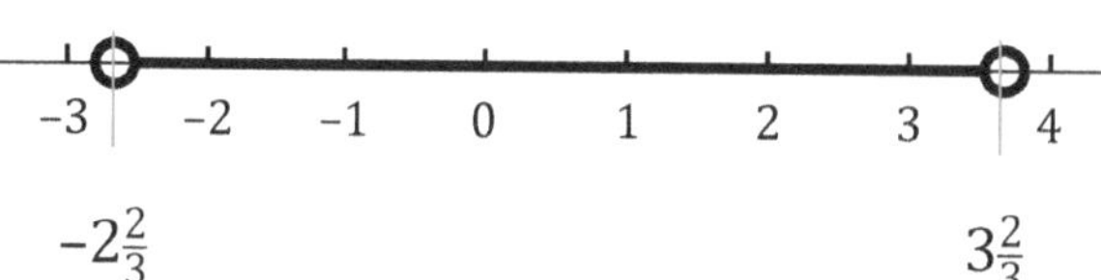

$-2\frac{2}{3}$ $3\frac{2}{3}$

It if helps, add the double inequality to a number line like this. It now makes the integer values x can take easy to spot.

Hence x can take the integer values $-2, -1, 0, 1, 2, 3$.

---

4 Solve the inequality $3 - x < 4(x - 1)$. [3]

(OCR FSMQ June 2010 q1)

Answer

Multiply out the brackets.

4 $3 - x < 4(x - 1)$

$3 - x < 4x - 4$ Subtract $4x$ from both sides.

$3 - 5x < -4$

Subtract 3 from both sides.

$-5x < -7$

Divide both sides by −5 and reverse the inequality sign.

$x > \frac{7}{5}$

$x > 1.4$

---

5 (i) Find the range of values of x satisfying $x^2 - 4x + 3 \le 0$. [3]

(ii) Show this range on the number line provided. [1]

(OCR FSMQ May 2012 q1)

Answer

Factorise and hence solve this quadratic equation.

5 (i) Considering the case where $x^2 - 4x + 3 = 0$

$(x - 3)(x - 1) = 0$

Hence, $x = 3$ or 1.

The graph of $y = x^2 - 4x + 3$ will be U-shaped (because the coefficient of x^2 is positive) and will intercept the x-axis at $x = 3$ and $x = 1$.

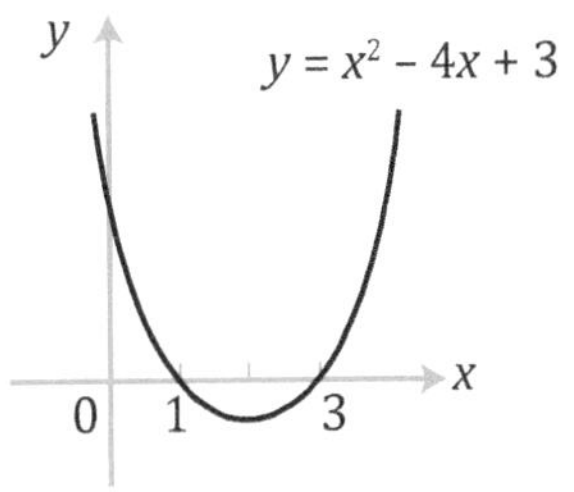

As we require $x^2 - 4x + 3 \le 0$ we want to find the range of x-values where $y \le 0$.

This is the section of the curve on and below the x-axis.

Hence $1 \le x \le 3$

(ii)

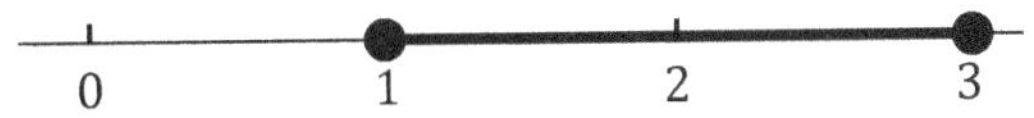

---

6 Ali and Beth make components in a factory. Ali works faster than Beth and makes 3 more components per hour. As a result he takes 2 hours less time than Beth to make 72 components.

Let t hours be the time that Ali takes to make 72 components.

(i) Write expressions for the number of components made per hour by Ali and by Beth. [3]

(ii) Hence derive the equation $3t(t + 2) = 144$. [5]

(iii) Solve this equation to find the times that Ali and Beth take to make 72 components. [4]

(OCR FSMQ June 2010 q13)

Answer

Think about an easier sum involving numbers. Suppose Ali made 72 components in 12 hours. This would be 72 divided by 12 = 6 components per hour. Now use t rather than 12 as the time.

6 (i) Number of components made per hour by Ali $= \dfrac{72}{t}$

Number of components made per hour by Beth $= \dfrac{72}{t+2}$

Beth takes 2 hours longer to make 72 components.

(ii) The number of components made per hour by Ali minus the number of components made per hour by Beth is equal to 3. Hence we can write this as

$$\frac{72}{t} - \frac{72}{t+2} = 3$$

Multiplying both sides by $t(t + 2)$ gives

$$72(t + 2) - 72t = 3t(t + 2)$$

$$72t + 144 - 72t = 3t^2 + 6t$$

$$3t^2 + 6t - 144 = 0$$

$$3t^2 + 6t = 144$$

$3t(t + 2) = 144$ which is the desired equation.

(iii) $$3t(t + 2) = 144$$

$$3t^2 + 6t - 144 = 0$$

Dividing both sides by 3.

$$t^2 + 2t - 48 = 0$$

Factorise this quadratic equation.

$$(t + 8)(t - 6) = 0$$

Hence $t = 6$ hours (note the solution $t = -8$ is ignored because it is impossible to have a negative time).

Note that you have to specifically say who takes what time.

Time taken by Ali = 6 hours

Time taken by Beth = 8 hours as Beth takes 2 hours longer than Ali.

TIP

The examiner should not have to hunt for your answer amongst your workings, so you need to state your answer clearly.

7 Calculate the x-coordinates of the points of intersection of the line $y = 2x + 11$ and the curve $y = x^2 - x + 5$. Give your answers to two decimal places. [5]

(OCR FSMQ June 2009 q8)

Answer

7 At the points of intersection the y-values will be equal. Hence equating the y-values we obtain:

$x^2 - x + 5 = 2x + 11$

$x^2 - 3x - 6 = 0$

Comparing the equation above, with $ax^2 + bx + c$ gives $a = 1$, $b = -3$ and $c = -6$.

Substituting these values into the quadratic equation formula

$x = \frac{-b \pm \sqrt{b^2 - 4ac}}{2a}$ gives:

$$x = \frac{3 \pm \sqrt{(-3)^2 - 4(1)(-6)}}{2(1)}$$

$$= \frac{3 \pm \sqrt{9 + 24}}{2} = \frac{3 \pm \sqrt{33}}{2} = \frac{3 + \sqrt{33}}{2} \text{ or } \frac{3 - \sqrt{33}}{2} = 4.37 \text{ or } -1.37 \text{ (2 d.p.)}$$

Note it is pointless trying to factorise as you are required to give the x-coordinates to two decimal places. Either use the method of completing the square or use the quadratic formula here.

TAKE NOTE !

Note that only the x-coordinates are asked for here, so do not waste time finding the corresponding y-coordinates.

Test yourself

1 Solve the following linear inequalities:

(a) $3x - 2 > 7$

(b) $3(x - 2) > 9$

(c) $\frac{x - 5}{7} \le -3$

(d) $3x - 4 < 4x + 6$

2 Solve the following inequalities:

(a) $2x - 4 > x + 6$

(b) $4 + x < 6 - 4x$

(c) $2x + 9 \ge 5(x - 3)$

3 Solve the inequality $x^2 - 3x > 18$.

4 Solve the inequality $x^2 - 2x - 15 \le 0$.

5 Solve the following inequalities.

(a) $5 < 2x - 1 \le 13$

(b) $-7 < 3x - 5 < 4$

(c) $4(x - 3) \le 3(x - 2)$

Topic summary

This contents of this topic will be built on in Topic 8 later on in the course where you will be forming lots of linear equations and using them to produce graphs to solve problems.

Solving linear inequalities

Solve them in the same way as you would solve ordinary equations but remember to reverse the inequality if you multiply or divide both sides by a negative quantity.

Manipulating inequalities

Like with equations, you can add or subtract any number or letter from both sides of the inequality and the inequality will stay the same.

You can multiply or divide both sides by numbers provided these numbers are positive.

Representing inequalities on a number line

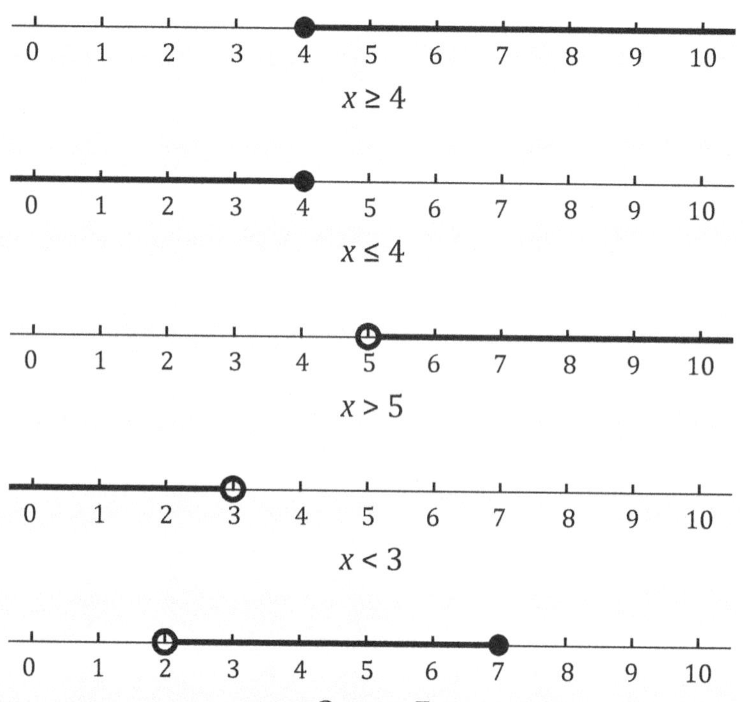

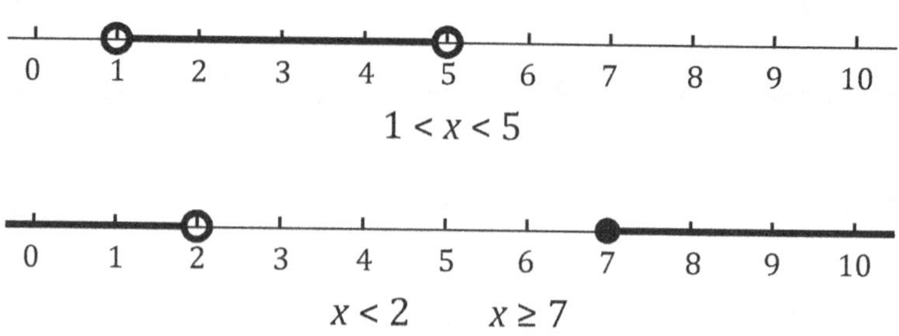

Solving quadratic inequalities

Put the quadratic function equal to zero and solve, and this gives where the curve cuts the x-axis. Draw a sketch of the graph showing the intercepts on the x-axis.

If $y < 0$ then the range of values of x covers the region below the x-axis.

If $y > 0$ then the range of values of x covers the region above the x-axis.

If the inequality includes an equals sign then the range of values of x will include the values where it cuts the x-axis.

The binomial expansion and probability

Suppose you had to expand the bracket $(x + 3)^3$ you would start by multiplying two sets of brackets to give $(x + 3)(x^2 + 6x + 9)$ and then multiply the final bracket and collect the terms to give the final answer of $x^3 + 9x^2 + 27x + 27$. The higher the power the more tedious and complex this becomes so, for example, $(x + 3)^7$ would involve a lot of work. Luckily there is an easier way of expanding brackets raised to a power called the binomial expansion using a formula. The formula is quite complicated but luckily it is included on the examination paper so you don't have to remember it. The formula for the binomial expansion can be used to expand brackets that can be expressed as $(a + b)^n$. Note that before the expansion, a binomial is a two-term expression. So, for example $(1 + x)^4$ is a binomial.

The binomial expansion can be extended to probabilities where it can be used to calculate the probability of a certain number of events happening out of a total number of events if the probability of one event happening is known.

This topic covers the following:

5.1 The binomial expansion of $(a + b)^n$

5.2 Probability situations giving rise to the binomial distribution

5.3 Calculating probabilities using the binomial distribution

5.1 The binomial expansion of $(a + b)^n$

Binomial expansion is the expansion of the expression $(a + b)^n$ where n is a positive integer.

TIP

Important note: Both formulas shown here will be given in the examination paper and need not be remembered.

The formula for the expansion is shown here:

$$(a + b)^n = a^n + \binom{n}{1} a^{n-1} b + \binom{n}{2} a^{n-2} b^2 + \ldots + \binom{n}{r} a^{n-r} b^r + \ldots + b^n$$

$$\text{where } \binom{n}{r} = {}^nC_r = \frac{n!}{r!(n-r)!}$$

$n!$ means n factorial. If $n = 5$ then $5! = 5 \times 4 \times 3 \times 2 \times 1$

Note that $0! = 1$.

You are best using a calculator to work out $\binom{n}{r}$ or ${}^nC_r$ rather than put numbers into the formula.

Factorials

Factorials can be seen as part of the formula for combinations so you need to know what they are and how they can be worked out.

Factorials are indicated by an exclamation mark after the number like this 6!

It is important to be able to work out factorials manually as it helps you understand what they are and how they are used.

$6! = 6 \times 5 \times 4 \times 3 \times 2 \times 1$ (i.e. all the numbers in descending order from 6 to 1 multiplied together).

Cancelling factorials

When factorials are divided by each other, they can be cancelled in the following way.

$$\frac{8!}{6!} = \frac{8 \times 7 \times 6 \times 5 \times 4 \times 3 \times 2 \times 1}{6 \times 5 \times 4 \times 3 \times 2 \times 1} = 8 \times 7 = 56$$

Notice the way the 6! in the denominator is cancelled with the same numbers in the numerator.

Combinations

Factorials feature in the combination formula which is part of the formula for the binomial expansion. This formula is

$$\binom{n}{r} = {}^{n}C_{r} = \frac{n!}{r!(n-r)!}$$

Suppose we want to find $\binom{9}{6} = {}^{9}C_{6}$. We can see that $n = 9$ and $r = 6$.

Substituting these values into the formula we obtain

$$\frac{n!}{r!(n-r)!} = \frac{9!}{6!(9-6)!} = \frac{9!}{6!3!}$$

Note that the 6!3! means that 6! is multiplied by 3!

Hence, $\dfrac{9!}{6!3!} = \dfrac{9 \times 8 \times 7}{3 \times 2 \times 1} = 84$

Notice the way we can cancel the 6! with the 6 × 5 × 4 × 3 × 2 × 1 part of the 9! on the top.

Examples

1 Without using a calculator, work on the following, giving your answer as an integer.

(a) 5!

(b) 7!

(c) 3!4!

(d) (5 − 3)!

(e) $\dfrac{5!}{3!}$

Answer

1 (a) $5! = 5 \times 4 \times 3 \times 2 \times 1 = 120$

(b) $7! = 7 \times 6 \times 5 \times 4 \times 3 \times 2 \times 1 = 5040$

(c) $3!4! = 3 \times 2 \times 1 \times 4 \times 3 \times 2 \times 1 = 144$

(d) $(5-3)! = 2! = 2 \times 1 = 2$

(e) $\dfrac{5!}{3!} = 5 \times 4 = 20$

2 Without using a calculator, work out each of the following using the combination formula

$$\binom{n}{r} = {}^{n}C_{r} = \frac{n!}{r!(n-r)!}.$$

(a) $\binom{4}{0}$

(b) $\binom{4}{1}$

(c) $\binom{7}{3}$

(d) ${}^{6}C_{5}$

(e) ${}^{3}C_{1}$

Note that 0! = 1.

Answer

2 (a) $\binom{4}{0} = \frac{4!}{0!(4-0)!} = \frac{4!}{4!} = 1$

(b) $\binom{4}{1} = \frac{4!}{1!(4-1)!} = \frac{4!}{3!} = 4$

(c) $\binom{7}{3} = \frac{7!}{3!(7-3)!} = \frac{7!}{3!4!} = \frac{7 \times 6 \times 5}{3 \times 2 \times 1} = 35$

(d) ${}^6C_5 = \frac{6!}{5!(6-5)!} = \frac{6!}{5!1!} = \frac{6}{1} = 6$

(e) ${}^3C_1 = \frac{3!}{1!(3-1)!} = \frac{3!}{1!2!} = \frac{3}{1} = 3$

Working out factorials and the combination formula using a calculator

On scientific calculators there is a button used for working out factorials. Usually it has the symbol $x!$ written on it and to use it on most calculators you enter the number (e.g. 5 if you want 5!) and then press the shift key and then finally the factorial button.

Check this with your calculator for 5! You should obtain 120.

Look at your calculator keyboard and you will spot a key with the symbol nCr on it.

Suppose you want $\binom{6}{3}$ which has the alternative form ${}^6C_{3.}$

On most calculators you would first press the value of n, which is 6 in this case, then press the 'shift' key and then the nCr key and finally the value of r, which is 3 in this case. You will see that 6C3 appears on the calculator display. You now need to press = to display the answer (20 in this case).

Progress check

1 Without using a calculator, work out each of the following using the formula:

$$\binom{n}{r} = {}^nC_r = \frac{n!}{r!(n-r)!}$$

(a) $\binom{8}{5}$

(b) $\binom{7}{3}$

(c) $\binom{12}{6}$

(d) ${}^7C_2$

(e) ${}^{12}C_5$

(f) ${}^4C_2$

2 Use your calculator to work out the following:

(a) $\binom{1}{0}$

(b) $\binom{2}{1}$

(c) $\binom{3}{2}$

(d) $\binom{10}{3}$

3 Work out the following using your calculator.

(a) $\binom{5}{0}$

(b) $\binom{5}{1}$

(c) $\binom{8}{5}$

(d) $\binom{10}{5}$

Example

3 Expand $(a + b)^4$.

Answer

3 First carefully copy down the formula:

$$(a + b)^n = a^n + \binom{n}{1}a^{n-1}b + \binom{n}{2}a^{n-2}b^2 + \ldots$$

You will also need this formula

$$\binom{n}{r} = \frac{n!}{r!(n-r)!}$$

Putting $n = 4$ into each formula gives:

$$(a + b)^4 = a^4 + \binom{4}{1}a^3b + \binom{4}{2}a^2b^2 + \binom{4}{3}ab^3 + \binom{4}{4}b^4$$

Now substituting the numbers 4 and 1 for n and r into $\dfrac{n!}{r!(n-r)!}$

gives $\dfrac{4!}{1!(4-1)!} = \dfrac{4 \times 3 \times 2 \times 1}{3 \times 2 \times 1} = 4$

This is repeated by substituting numbers in for $\binom{4}{2}$, $\binom{4}{3}$ and $\binom{4}{4}$ giving the numbers 6, 4 and 1 respectively.

You could have used a calculator to work out $\binom{4}{1}$, $\binom{4}{2}$, $\binom{4}{3}$ and $\binom{4}{4}$ and this should be the preferred method as it is faster and more accurate. The longer method is shown for completeness.

Hence: $(a + b)^4 = a^4 + 4a^3b + 6a^2b^2 + 4ab^3 + b^4$

TIP

Always be careful when copying down a formula from the formula sheet. With a formula as complicated as this one, it is easy to make a mistake.

Pascal's triangle

You can also find the coefficients in the expansion of $(a + b)^n$ by using Pascal's triangle.

Suppose you want to expand the expression from the previous example, $(a + b)^4$ using Pascal's triangle.

You would write down Pascal's triangle and look for the line starting 1 and then 4 (because n is 4 here). The line 1, 4, 6, 4, 1 gives the coefficients. This avoids the calculation involving the factorials for each coefficient but you will have to remember how to construct Pascal's triangle.

Notice that all the rows start and end with a 1. Notice also that the other numbers are found by adding the pairs of numbers immediately above. For example, if we have 1 3 in the line above then the number to be entered between these numbers on the next line is a 4.

1

1 1

1 2 1

1 3 3 1

1 4 6 4 1

1 5 10 10 5 1

TIP

If you intend to use Pascal's triangle, you must remember how to construct it and also how to decide which line should be used. You will not be given Pascal's triangle in the examination paper.

Suppose you wanted to find the coefficients in the expansion of $(3 + x)^6$. You would need to write Pascal's triangle until you get a 6 as the second term in one of the lines.

1

1 1

1 2 1

1 3 3 1

1 4 6 4 1

1 5 10 10 5 1

1 6 15 20 15 6 1

Highlighted is the line we need to use in the expansion.

Now $(a + b)^6 = a^6 + 6a^5b + 15a^4b^2 + 20a^3b^3 + 15a^2b^4 + 6ab^5 + b^6$

Notice the coefficients (i.e. the numbers in front of the letters) all correspond to the shaded line in Pascal's triangle.

Once you have the expansion you can then substitute numbers or letters for the values of a and b.

So for the expansion of $(3 + x)^6$, $a = 3$ and $b = x$ and we can write:

$(3 + x)^6 = 3^6 + 6(3)^5x + 15(3)^4x^2 + 20(3)^3x^3 + 15(3)^2x^4 + 6(3)x^5 + x^6$

$\quad = 729 + 1458x^2 + 1215x^2 + 540x^3 + 135x^4 + 18x^5 + x^6$

Example

4 Use the binomial expansion to expand $(2 + 3x)^3$.

Answer

4 First write the formula for the binomial expansion:

$$(a + b)^n = a^n + \binom{n}{1}a^{n-1}b + \binom{n}{2}a^{n-2}b^2 + \ldots$$

Here $a = 2$, $b = 3x$ and $n = 3$.

Substituting these values into the formula gives:

$$(2 + 3x)^3 = 2^3 + \binom{3}{1}2^2\,(3x) + \binom{3}{1}2^1\,(3x)^2 + \binom{3}{3}2^0\,(3x)^3$$

As $n = 3$ here we look for the line in Pascal's triangle which starts at 1 and then 3, etc.

You can see that the numbers in this line are: 1 3 3 1

These are the values of $\binom{3}{0}$, $\binom{3}{1}$, $\binom{3}{2}$ and $\binom{3}{3}$. So, for example, $\binom{3}{1} = 3$ and $\binom{3}{3} = 1$.

Hence we can write the expansion like this:

$$(2 + 3x)^2 = (1)2^3 + (3)2^2(3x) + (3)2^1\,(3x)^2 + (1)2^0\,(3x)^3$$

Remember that $2^0 = 1$

Hence $(2 + 3x)^3 = 8 + 36x + 54x^2 + 27x^3$

The binomial expansion where $a = 1$

When the first term in the bracket (i.e. a) is 1, the binomial expansion becomes:

$$(1 + x)^n = 1 + nx + \frac{n(n-1)x^2}{2!} + \frac{n(n-1)(n-2)x^3}{3!} + \ldots$$

This formula will not be given on the examination paper so you can either remember it or substitute $a = 1$ into the expansion of $(a + b)^n$ which will be given on the paper.

Examples

5 (a) Expand $(1 + x)^7$ in ascending powers of x up to and including the term in x^3.

(b) Using your result for part (a) find an approximation for 1.1^7. Note that you must show all your working and simply putting 1.1^7 into your calculator, will gain you no marks.

(c) Explain how the expansion could be used to find an approximate value for 0.99^7.

Answer

5 (a) The formula for the expansion of $(1 + x)^n$ is

$$(1 + x)^n = 1 + nx + \frac{n(n-1)x^2}{2!} + \frac{n(n-1)(n-2)x^3}{3!} + \ldots$$

Putting $n = 7$ into this formula gives:

$$(1 + x)^7 = 1 + 7x + \frac{7(6)x^2}{2!} + \frac{7(6)(5)x^3}{3!} + \ldots$$

Note that using the first three terms only provides an approximate value.

$$\text{Hence, } (1 + x)^7 \approx 1 + 7x + \frac{7(6)x^2}{2!} + \frac{7(6)(5)x^3}{3!}$$

$$\approx 1 + 7x + 21x^2 + 35x^3$$

(b) $(1 + x)^7 \approx 1 + 7x + 21x^2 + 35x^3$

$x = 0.1$ is substituted for x into the expansion.

Let $x = 0.1$

$$(1 + 0.1)^7 \approx 1 + 7(0.1) + 21(0.1)^2 + 35(0.1)^3$$

$$\approx 1.945$$

Note that $(1 - 0.01)^7 = (0.99)^7$.

(c) You could use the expansion and substitute $x = -0.01$ into it.

6 In the binomial expansion of $(a + 2x)^5$, the coefficient of the term in x^2 is four times the coefficient of the term in x. Find the value of the constant a.

Answer

6 $(a + b)^n = a^n + \binom{n}{1}a^{n-1}b + \binom{n}{2}a^{n-2}b^2 + \ldots$

Here $a = a$, $b = 2x$ and $n = 5$.

Putting these values into the formula gives:

$$(a + 2x)^5 = a^5 + \binom{5}{1}a^4(2x) + \binom{5}{2}a^3(2x)^2 + \ldots$$

Now $\binom{5}{1} = \frac{5!}{1!(5-1)!} = \frac{5!}{1!4!} = 5$ and $\binom{5}{2} = \frac{5!}{2!(5-2)!} = \frac{5!}{2!3!} = 10$

Both combinations have been found using the nCr button on a calculator.

Hence:

$$(a + 2x)^5 = a^5 + (5)a^4(2x) + (10)a^3(2x)^2 + \ldots$$
$$= a^5 + 10a^4x + 40a^3x^2 + \ldots$$

Coefficient of x^2 is four times the coefficient of x, so

$$40a^3 = 4 \times 10a^4$$

$$40a^3 = 40a^4$$

Dividing both sides by $40a^3$ gives $a = 1$. $(a \neq 0)$

---

7 Expand $(a + b)^4$. Hence expand $\left(2x + \frac{1}{2x}\right)^4$, simplifying each term of the expansion.

Answer

7 $(a + b)^n = a^n + \binom{n}{1}a^{n-1}b + \binom{n}{2}a^{n-2}b^2 + \binom{n}{3}a^{n-3}b^3 + \ldots$

$$(a + b)^4 = a^4 + \binom{4}{1}a^3b + \binom{4}{2}a^2b^2 + \binom{4}{3}ab^3 + \binom{4}{4}b^4$$

Finding $\binom{4}{1}, \binom{4}{2}, \binom{4}{3}, \binom{4}{4}$ by using the formula or by using Pascal's triangle and substituting them in to the above formula gives:

$$(a + b)^4 = a^4 + 4a^3b + 6a^2b^2 + 4a\,b^3 + b^4$$

$$\left(2x + \frac{1}{2x}\right)^4 = (2x)^4 + 4(2x)^3\left(\frac{1}{2x}\right) + 6(2x)^2\left(\frac{1}{2x}\right)^2 + 4(2x)\left(\frac{1}{2x}\right)^3 + \left(\frac{1}{2x}\right)^4$$
$$= 16x^4 + 16x^2 + 6 + \frac{1}{x^2} + \frac{1}{16x^4}$$

Progress check

4. Use the binomial theorem to expand $(3 + 2x)^3$, simplifying each term of your expansion.
5. Find the term in x^2 in the binomial expansion of $\left(x + \frac{3}{x}\right)^6$.
6. Expand fully $\left(x + \frac{2}{x}\right)^5$ and simplify each term of the expansion.
7. (a) Expand $(1 + x)^6$ simplifying each term of the expansion.

   (b) Use your expansion from part (a) to calculate the value of $(1.02)^6$ giving your answer to four decimal places.

5.2 Probability situations giving rise to the binomial distribution

Simple probability

In your GCSE work you will have come across simple probability. There are two important laws that need to be remembered when working out probabilities. They are the addition law and the multiplication law. The addition law is sometimes called the OR law and the multiplication law is sometimes called the AND law.

The addition law for mutually exclusive events

If events A and B are mutually exclusive, it means that event A can happen or event B can happen but they cannot both happen.

If you want the probability of A or B happening, you simply add the probability of A occurring to the probability of B occurring. This can be written as follows:

$$P(A \text{ OR } B) = P(A) + P(B)$$

This formula only applies to mutually exclusive events and needs to be remembered.

Multiplication law for independent events

When an event has no effect on another event, they are said to be independent events. For example, if event A occurs then it will have no effect on event B happening and vice versa.

The multiplication law for independent events is as follows:

$$P(A \text{ AND } B) = P(A) \times P(B)$$

This formula is not included on the examination paper and will need to be remembered. Note also that this formula only applies to independent events. Note that P(A AND B) represents the probability of events A and B both occurring. Students are often confused between independent events and mutually exclusive events. Note the difference.

Discrete probability distributions

The score on a die is an example of a random variable because there is no way of predicting what the score will be. As well as being a random variable, the score is also a discrete variable as only isolated values (i.e. scores 1, 2 , 3, 4, 5, 6) are possible. This topic deals with discrete probability distributions where there is a set of isolated values each having a certain probability of occurring.

Here is a probability distribution of a random variable X. The x-values show particular values of X and the probability of each occurring is denoted by $P(X = x)$. For example, $P(X = 1)$ is the probability that x takes the value 1. All the possible values x can take are shown in the table.

x	1	2	3	4
$P(X = x)$	0.2	0.4	0.3	0.1

The sum of the probabilities for the distribution shown in the table is 1, as all the values x can take are shown.

Hence $P(X = 1) + P(X = 2) + P(X = 3) + P(X = 4) = 0.2 + 0.4 + 0.3 + 0.1 = 1$

To save time the above can be written in the following way:

$P(1) + P(2) + P(3) + P(4) = 1$

Example

8 (a) The probability distribution of the discrete random variable X is given in the following table.

x	1	2	3
$P(X = x)$	0.45	0.35	a

Find the value of a.

(b) Find the probability that x is more than 1.

The table shows the all the possible values of x. The associated probabilities will add up to 1.

An alternative method is simply to add the probability that x is 2 to the probability that x is 3.

Answer

8 (a) $0.45 + 0.35 + a = 1$

Hence, $a = 0.2$

(b) The probability is either 1 or more than 1.

Hence, probability of more than 1 $= 1 -$ probability that x is 1.

$= 1 - 0.45$

$= 0.55$

Situations where the binomial distribution can be used

Suppose we toss a fair die 6 times and we want to find the probability that it lands on the number six 3 times. This is a problem that can be solved using the binomial distribution because there are two possible events we are interested in. The die can land on a six or not land on a six (i.e. there are only two things that can happen, success and failure). There is also a fixed probability of obtaining a six which is $\frac{1}{6}$. We also know the number of trials, which is 6 and the number of successes to be calculated, which is 3. Hence, this problem and similar problems can be solved using the binomial distribution.

There are a number of conditions that must be met to be able to use the binomial distribution.

- Independent trials (i.e where the probability of one event does not depend on another)
- Trials where there is a constant probability of success
- A fixed number of trials
- Where there is only success or failure

5.3 Calculating probabilities using the binomial distribution

When a probability problem has only two outcomes, success or failure, then if the probability of success is p, then the probability of failure is $1 - p$. This is because the probabilities of success and failure must add to give 1. As there are two possible outcomes, the distribution of probabilities is binomial.

The binomial distribution

A binomial experiment consists of a fixed number of trials, n, each with a probability p of occurring and it counts the number of successes, r. The binomial distribution is a probability distribution where the probability of a particular number of successes, r, occurring is given by the following formula:

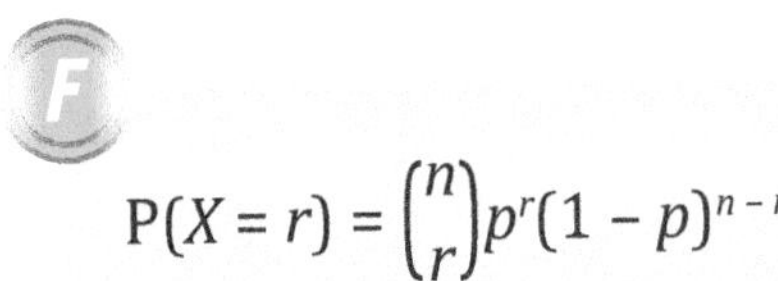

$$P(X = r) = \binom{n}{r} p^r (1 - p)^{n-r}$$

TIP

Print out a copy of the formula sheet and keep using it. This way you will remember which formulae are on the sheet and which you will need to remember.

Note that $\binom{n}{r}$ can also be written as ${}^nC_r$ so when there are numerical values for n and r, these can be substituted into your calculator for n and r to obtain a value for $\binom{n}{r}$.

Examples

9 A salesperson makes 60 calls to potential customers during a particular week. The probability of making a sale at each call is independent of other calls and is 0.3.

Find the probability that during a particular week, he makes:

(a) Exactly 10 sales.

(b) Exactly 19 or 20 sales.

Answers

9 (a) Using $P(X = r) = \binom{n}{r} p^r (1 - p)^{n-r}$,

with $r = 10$, $n = 60$ and $p = 0.3$ we obtain

$$P(X = 10) = \binom{60}{10} 0.3^{10} (1 - 0.3)^{60-10}$$

$$= \binom{60}{10} 0.3^{10} (0.7)^{50}$$

$$= 0.008 \text{ (3 d.p.)}$$

Use the formula for the Binomial distribution $P(X = r) = \binom{n}{r}p^r(1 - p)^{n-r}$

(b) Using $P(X = r) = \binom{n}{r}p^r(1 - p)^{n-r}$,

with $r = 19$, $n = 60$ and $p = 0.3$ we obtain

$$P(X = 19) = \binom{60}{19}0.3^{19}(1 - 0.3)^{60-19}$$
$$= \binom{60}{19}0.3^{19}(0.7)^{41}$$
$$= 0.1059 \text{ (4 d.p.)}$$

Using $P(X = r) = \binom{n}{r}p^r(1 - p)^{n-r}$,

with $r = 20$, $n = 60$ and $p = 0.3$ we obtain

$$P(X = 20) = \binom{60}{20}0.3^{20}(1 - 0.3)^{60-20}$$
$$= \binom{60}{20}0.3^{20}(0.7)^{40}$$
$$= 0.0931 \text{ (4 d.p.)}$$

The probability of obtaining 19 or 20 is found by adding the two probabilities together.

Now, $P(X = 19 \text{ or } 20) = P(X = 19) + P(X = 20)$

$$= 0.1059 + 0.0931$$
$$= 0.199 \text{ (3 d.p.)}$$

10 The probability that a machine part fails in its first year is 0.05 independently of all other parts. In a batch of 20 randomly selected parts, find the probability, giving your answers to four significant figures, that in the first year:

(a) Exactly 1 part fails.

(b) More than 2 parts fail.

Answer

10 (a) Using $P(X = r) = \binom{n}{r}p^r(1 - p)^{n-r}$,

with $r = 1$, $n = 20$ and $p = 0.05$ we obtain

$$P(X = 1) = \binom{20}{1}0.05^1(1 - 0.05)^{20-1}$$
$$= \binom{20}{1}0.05^1(0.95)^{19}$$
$$= 0.377\,353$$
$$= 0.3774 \text{ (4 s.f.)}$$

(b) P(>2 parts fail) = 1 – (P[0 parts fail] + P[1 part fails] + P[2 parts fail])

$$P(X = 0) = \binom{20}{0}0.05^0(1 - 0.05)^{20-0}$$
$$= \binom{20}{0}0.05^0(0.95)^{20}$$
$$= 0.358486$$
$$= 0.3585 \text{ (4 s.f.)}$$

$$P(X = 2) = \binom{20}{2}0.05^2(1 - 0.05)^{20-2}$$
$$= \binom{20}{2}0.05^2(0.95)^{18}$$
$$= 0.188677$$
$$= 0.1887 \text{ (4 s.f.)}$$

P(>2 parts fail) = 1 – (P(0 parts fail) + P(1 part fails) + P(2 parts fail))

$$= 1 - (0.358486 + 0.377353 + 0.188677)$$
$$= 0.075484$$
$$= 0.07548 \text{ (4 s.f.)}$$

Always use the accurate answers in your calculations and then give the answer to a certain number of significant figures or decimal places in your final answer.

Progress check

8 On a turtle farm, turtles are bred and hatched from eggs under controlled conditions.

The probability of producing a female turtle from an egg is 0.4 under the controlled conditions. The probability of producing a particular female from an egg is independent of other eggs hatching to produce female turtles. When 10 eggs are kept under the controlled conditions, find the probability that:

(i) Exactly 5 female turtles are produced.

(ii) Less than 2 female turtles are produced.

9 John throws 3 fair dice.

(a) Calculate the probability of John throwing 3 sixes.

(b) Calculate the probability of John throwing 0 sixes.

(c) Calculate the probability that John throws at least 2 sixes.

Exam practice

1. A die has 6 faces numbered one to six. The die is biased so that when it is thrown the probability of obtaining a six is $\frac{1}{5}$.

   The die is thrown 5 times.

   Find the probability of obtaining:

   (i) At least 1 six. [2]

   (ii) Exactly 3 sixes. [4]

(OCR FSMQ May 2012 q2)

Answer

It would take time to calculate the above so instead we find the probability of no sixes and then subtract the answer from 1.

1. (i) At least 1 six means 1, 2, 3, 4, 5 or 6 sixes.

   Probability of at least 1 six = 1 − probability of no sixes

   $$= 1 - \left(\frac{4}{5}\right)^5$$

   $$= 0.672 \text{ (3 s.f.)}$$

   There is also the following alternative method making use of the binomial formula

   Using $P(X = r) = \binom{n}{r}p^r(1-p)^{n-r}$,

   with $r = 0$, $n = 5$ and $p = 0.2$ we obtain

   $$P(X = 0) = \binom{5}{0}0.2^0(1-0.2)^{5-0}$$

   $$= \binom{5}{0}(1)(0.8)^5$$

   $$= 0.328 \text{ (3 s.f.)}$$

   Hence, probability of at least 1 six = 1 − 0.328

   $$= 0.672$$

   (ii) Using $P(X = r) = \binom{n}{r}p^r(1-p)^{n-r}$,

   with $r = 3$, $n = 5$ and $p = 0.2$ we obtain

   $$P(X = 3) = \binom{5}{3}0.2^3(1-0.2)^{5-3}$$

   $$= \binom{5}{3}(0.2)^3(0.8)^2$$

   $$= 0.0512 \text{ (3 s.f.)}$$

2 Eggs are delivered to a supermarket in boxes of 6.

For each egg, the probability that it is cracked is 0.05 independently of other eggs.

Find the probability that:

(i) In one box there are no cracked eggs. [2]

(ii) In one box there is exactly 1 cracked egg. [4]

The manager checks the eggs as follows.

- He takes a box at random from the delivery.
- He accepts the whole delivery if this box contains no cracked eggs.
- He rejects the whole delivery if the box contains 2 or more cracked eggs.
- If the box contains 1 cracked egg then he chooses another box at random.
- He accepts the delivery only if this second box contains no cracked eggs.

(iii) Find the probability that the delivery is rejected. [6]

(OCR FSMQ June 2011 q11)

Answer

2 (i) Probability of no cracked eggs in a box of 6 = $(0.95)^6$

$= 0.7351$

$= 0.735$ (3 s.f.)

If the probability of obtaining a cracked egg is 0.05, then the probability of obtaining an egg that is not cracked is $1 - 0.05 = 0.95$.

(ii) For the probability of one cracked egg we use the binomial formula.

Using $P(X = r) = \binom{n}{r}p^r(1-p)^{n-r}$,

with $r = 1$, $n = 6$ and $p = 0.05$ we obtain

$$P(X = 1) = \binom{6}{1}0.05^1(1-0.05)^{6-1}$$

$$= \binom{6}{1}(0.05)^1(0.95)^5$$

$$= 0.2321$$

$$= 0.232 \text{ (3 s.f.)}$$

(iii) P(2 or more cracked eggs in 1st box)

= 1 − (P[no cracked eggs] + P[1 cracked egg])

= 1 − (0.7351 + 0.2321)

= 0.0328

P(any cracked eggs in 2nd box) = 1 – P(no cracked eggs in 2nd box)
= 1 – 0.7351
= 0.2649

Probability consignment is rejected = 0.0328 + 0.2649 × 0.2321
= 0.0943 (3 s.f.)

---

3 The work-force of a large company is made up of males and females in the ratio 9 : 11. One-third of the male employees work part-time and one half of the female employees work part-time.

Eight employees are chosen at random.

Find the probability that

(i) all are males, [2]

(ii) exactly 5 are females, [4]

(iii) at least 2 work part-time. [6]

(OCR FSMQ June 2007 q12)

Answer

3 Probability of choosing a male $= \frac{9}{20} = 0.45$

Probability of choosing a female $= \frac{11}{20} = 0.55$

Probability of a male part-time employee $= \frac{3}{20} = 0.15$

Probability of a female part-time employee $= \frac{5.5}{20} = 0.275$

It is easier to work with decimals rather than fractions when you use a calculator to do the calculations.

(i) Probability of 8 males being chosen $= (0.45)^8 = 0.00168$ (3 s.f.)

(ii) Probability of exactly 5 females $= \binom{8}{5}(0.45)^3(0.55)^5 = 0.257$ (3 s.f.)

(iii) Probability of a part-time employee
= prob of male PT + prob of female PT
= 0.15 + 0.275
= 0.425

Probability of a full-time employee = 1 – probability of a PT employee
= 1 – 0.425
= 0.575

Probability of at least 2 part-time employees out of 8 is the probability of 2, 3, 4, 5, 6, 7 and 8 part-time employees added together. This would involve lots of calculations so we need to think of a better way to calculate this.

Probability of at least 2 PT employees
= 1 – (prob of no PT employees + prob of 1 PT employee)

For probability of no part-time employees

Using $P(X = r) = \binom{n}{r}p^r(1-p)^{n-r}$,

with $r = 0$, $n = 8$ and $p = 0.425$ we obtain

$$P(X = 0) = \binom{8}{0}0.425^0(1-0.425)^{8-0}$$
$$= \binom{8}{0}(0.425)^0(0.575)^8$$
$$= 0.0119 \text{ (3 s.f.)}$$

Using $P(X = r) = \binom{n}{r}p^r(1-p)^{n-r}$,

with $r = 1$, $n = 8$ and $p = 0.425$ we obtain

$$P(X = 1) = \binom{8}{1}0.425^1(1-0.425)^{8-1}$$
$$= \binom{8}{1}(0.425)^1(0.575)^7$$
$$= 0.0707 \text{ (3 s.f.)}$$

Substituting these two probabilities into the equation

Probability of at least 2 PT employees
= 1 – (prob of no PT employees + prob of 1 PT employee)

we obtain Probability of at least 2 PT = (1 – (0.0119 + 0.0707))
= 0.9174
= 0.917 (3 s.f.)

---

4 Glass marbles are produced in two colours, red and green, in the proportion 7 : 3 respectively. From a large stock of the marbles, 5 are taken at random.

Find the probability that

(i) all 5 are red, [6]

(ii) exactly 3 are red. [3]

(OCR FSMQ June 2008 q4)

> Here you need to understand ratios. Look back at your GCSE work or a GCSE book if you are unsure about ratios.

Answer

4 (i) Probability of a red marble = $\frac{7}{10} = 0.7$

Probability 5 out of 5 are red = $(0.7)^5$
= 0.168 (3 s.f.)

(ii) Using $P(X = r) = \binom{n}{r}p^r(1-p)^{n-r}$,

with $r = 3$, $n = 5$ and $p = 0.7$ we obtain

$$P(X = 3) = \binom{5}{3}0.7^3(1-0.7)^{5-3}$$
$$= \binom{5}{3}(0.7)^3(0.3)^2$$
$$= 0.309 \text{ (3 s.f.)}$$

---

5 Amanda throws 3 fair dice. What is the probability that

(i) exactly 2 sixes are thrown, [3]

(ii) at least 1 six is thrown? [3]

(OCR FSMQ June 2013 q6)

Answer

5 (i) $P(X = r) = \binom{n}{r}p^r(1-p)^{n-r}$

$p = \frac{1}{6}$, $n = 3$ and $r = 2$.

$$P(X = 2) = \binom{3}{2}\left(\frac{1}{6}\right)^2\left(1-\frac{1}{6}\right)^{3-2}$$
$$= \binom{3}{2}\left(\frac{1}{6}\right)^2\left(\frac{5}{6}\right)$$
$$= 0.0694 \text{ (3 s.f.)}$$

(ii) Probability at least 1 six = 1 – Probability of no sixes

$$P(X = 0) = \binom{3}{0}\left(\frac{1}{6}\right)^0\left(1-\frac{1}{6}\right)^{3-0}$$
$$= \left(\frac{5}{6}\right)^3$$

Hence, Probability at least 1 six $= 1 - \left(\frac{5}{6}\right)^3$

$$= 0.421 \text{ (3 s.f.)}$$

Note that any number or letter to the power zero is always one. Hence $\left(\frac{1}{6}\right)^0 = 1$

---

6 (i) Expand $\left(x - \frac{1}{x}\right)^4$ using the binomial expansion.

Show all your working. [4]

(ii) Explain why the substitution $x = 1$ will help you to justify your answer. [1]

(OCR FSMQ June 2005 q6)

Answer

6 (i) $(a+b)^4 = a^n + \binom{n}{1}a^{n-1}b + \binom{n}{2}a^{n-2}b^2 + \binom{n}{3}a^{n-3}b^3 + \ldots$

$(a+b)^4 = a^4 + \binom{4}{1}a^3b + \binom{4}{2}a^2b^2 + \binom{4}{3}ab^3 + \binom{4}{4}b^4$

Finding $\binom{4}{1}, \binom{4}{2}, \binom{4}{3}, \binom{4}{4}$ by using the formula or by using Pascal's triangle and substituting them into the above formula gives:

$(a+b)^n = a^4 + 4a^3b + 6a^2b^2 + 4a\,b^3 + b^4$

$\left(x - \frac{1}{x}\right)^4 = (x)^4 + 4(x)^3\left(-\frac{1}{x}\right) + 6(x)^2\left(-\frac{1}{x}\right)^2 + 4(x)\left(-\frac{1}{x}\right)^3 + \left(-\frac{1}{x}\right)^4$

$= x^4 - 4x^2 + 6 - \frac{4}{x^2} + \frac{1}{x^4}$

(ii) If $x = 1$ is substituted into $\left(x - \frac{1}{x}\right)^4$ we obtain $\left(1 - \frac{1}{1}\right)^4 = 0$.

If $x = 1$ is substituted into the expansion $x^4 - 4x^2 + 6 - \frac{4}{x^2} + \frac{1}{x^4}$ we should obtain 0.

Hence $x^4 - 4x^2 + 6 - \frac{4}{x^2} + \frac{1}{x^4} = 1 - 4 + 6 - 4 + 1 = 0$

The two answers are the same so the expansion is likely to be correct.

TIP

Substitution of a simple number into the original expression and the expansion is a useful check. If you do not obtain the same number then you can re-check.

Test yourself

1. In the binomial expansion of $(2 + 3x)^5$, find the coefficient of the term in x^2.
2. Write down and simplify the first four terms in the binomial expansion of $(1 + 3x)^6$.
3. It is known that 25% of the bulbs in a box produce yellow flowers. A customer buys 20 of these bulbs. Find the probability that exactly 4 bulbs produce yellow flowers.
4. When a bulb is planted in the autumn, the probability of the bulb flowering the following spring is 0·8. The probability of the bulb flowering is independent of other bulbs flowering.
   In the autumn 20 of these bulbs are planted. Find the probability that exactly 15 of these bulbs flower the following spring.
5. Each time a dart player throws a dart at the bulls-eye they hit the bulls-eye with probability 0.12. The dart player throws 10 darts at the bulls-eye. Find the probability that she hits the bulls-eye once. Give your answer to four significant figures.

Topic summary

The binomial expansion of $(a + b)^n$ for positive integer n

$$(a + b)^n = a^n + \binom{n}{1} a^{n-1}b + \binom{n}{2} a^{n-2}b^2 + \ldots + \binom{n}{r} a^{n-r}b^r + \ldots + b^n$$

$$\binom{n}{r} = {}^nC_r = \frac{n!}{r!(n-r)!}$$

The binomial expansion of $(1 + x)^n$ for positive integer n

$$(1 + x)^n = 1 + nx + \frac{n(n-1)}{2!}x^2 + \frac{n(n-1)(n-2)}{3!}x^3 + \ldots$$

Discrete probability distribution

A discrete probability distribution for a random variable X, is a set of isolated values each having a certain probability of occurring. Probabilities must add up to 1.

The binomial distribution

For a fixed number of trials, n, each with a probability p of occurring, the probability of a number x of successes is given by the formula:

$$P(X = r) = \binom{n}{r}p^r(1-p)^{n-r}$$

Conditions for using the binomial distribution

The conditions for using the binomial distribution are:

- Independent trials (i.e where the probability of one event does not depend on another)
- Trials where there is a constant probability of success
- A fixed number of trials
- Where there is only success or failure

Coordinate geometry of straight lines

This topic is concerned with coordinates (x, y) and lines connecting these coordinates.

This topic covers the following:

6.1 The gradient of a line

6.2 Calculating the distance between two points

6.3 Proving two lines are the same length using vectors

6.4 Finding the mid-point of a straight line joining two points

6.5 The equation of a straight line graph

6.6 Finding the gradient and the intercept on the y-axis from the equation of a straight line

6.7 Equations of vertical and horizontal lines

6.8 Finding the equation of a straight line

6.9 Condition for two straight lines to be parallel to each other

6.10 Condition for two straight lines to be perpendicular to each other

6.11 Determining the equation of a line that is parallel to another line

6.12 A quicker way to determine the equation of a line through a point that is parallel to another line

6.13 Proving that a point (x, y) lies on a line

6.14 Finding the coordinates of the point of intersection of two straight lines

6.1 The gradient of a line

The gradient is the steepness or slope of a line. A steep line has higher gradient than a less steep line. Gradients can be positive, negative, zero or infinite. A line with a positive gradient slopes upwards from left to right, so its y-value increases as its x-value increases. A line with a negative gradient slopes downwards from left to right, so its y-value decreases as its x-value increases. A line with a zero gradient does not slope at all and is parallel to the x-axis. A line with an infinite gradient is a line which is parallel to the y-axis.

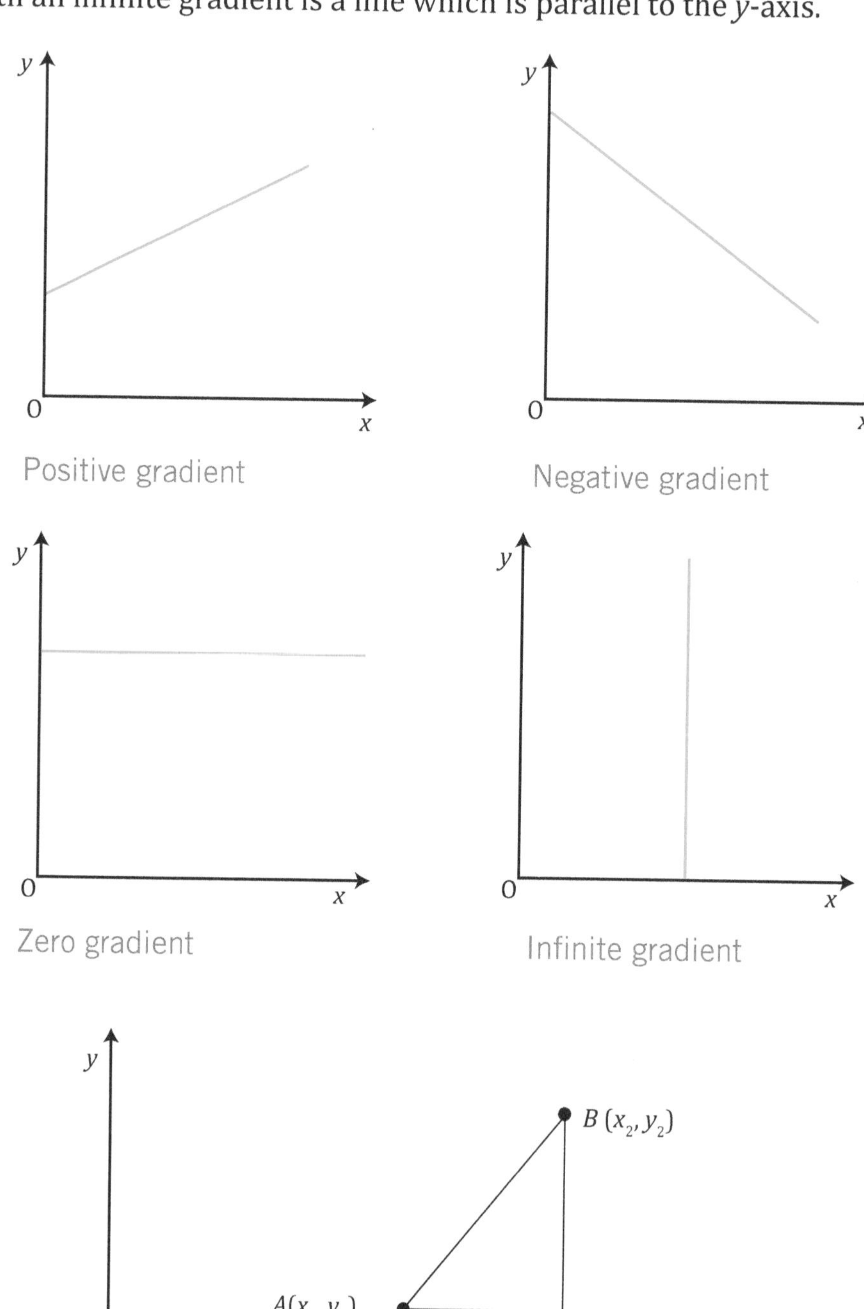

As this line segment slopes upward from left to right, it has a positive gradient.

From the graph on page 118, length $AC = x_2 - x_1$ and length $BC = y_2 - y_1$

Gradient of line $AB = \frac{BC}{AC} = \frac{y_2 - y_1}{x_2 - x_1}$

The gradient of the line joining points (x_1, y_1) and (x_2, y_2) is given by:

$$\text{Gradient} = \frac{y_2 - y_1}{x_2 - x_1}$$

Note that this formula can be expressed in words as 'the gradient is the difference in the y-coordinates divided by the difference in the x-coordinates.

TIP

Be systematic about the way you use this formula. It is a good idea to take the coordinates of the first point in the question to be (x_1, y_1) and the second point to be (x_2, y_2). This will make checking your work easier.

For example, the gradient of the straight line AB joining the points A (−3, 2) and B (1, 6) is

$$\frac{6 - 2}{1 - (-3)} = \frac{4}{4} = 1$$

Do not worry about which point to call (x_1, y_1) or (x_2, y_2). It does not matter, as you will get the same answer whichever you choose.

6.2 Calculating the distance between two points

Suppose you are given the coordinates of two points and are asked to find the distance between them, then it always best to do a quick sketch graph showing their positions. You can then make a right-angled triangle and use the line joining the two points as the hypotenuse of the triangle.

There is a formula for working out the distance between two points and the derivation of this formula is shown here.

Now $AC = x_2 - x_1$ and length $BC = y_2 - y_1$

By Pythagoras' theorem
$AB^2 = AC^2 + BC^2$

So $AB^2 = (x_2 - x_1)^2 + (y_2 - y_1)^2$

$AB = \sqrt{(x_2 - x_1)^2 + (y_2 - y_1)^2}$

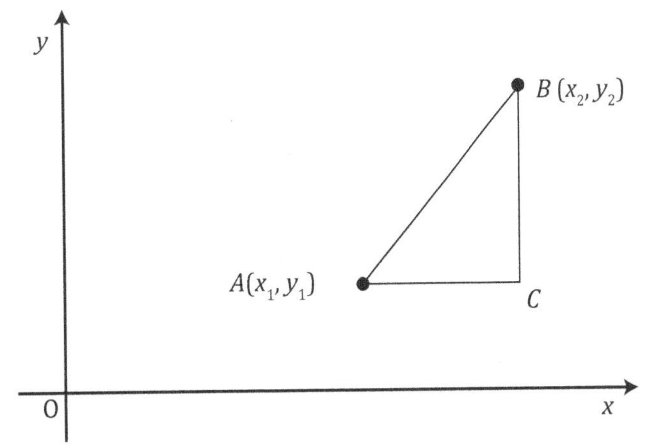

TIP

This is a difficult formula to remember. If you forget it, draw a sketch graph showing the line joining the points and form a triangle and work out the lengths and then use Pythagoras' theorem to work out the length of hypotenuse.

The length of a straight line joining the two points (x_1, y_1) and (x_2, y_2) is given by:

TIP

This formula is just an application of Pythagoras' theorem.

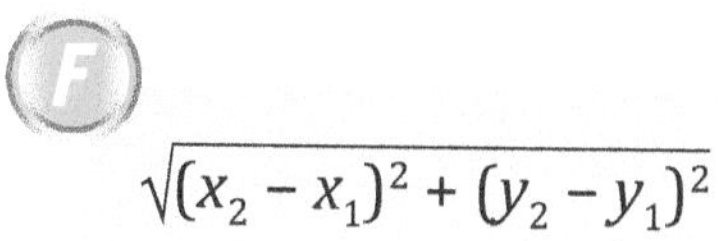

$$\sqrt{(x_2 - x_1)^2 + (y_2 - y_1)^2}$$

For example, the length of the straight line joining the points A (−3, −1) and B (1, 2) is

$$\sqrt{(1 - (-3))^2 + (2 - (-1))^2} = \sqrt{16 + 9} = \sqrt{25} = 5 \text{ units}$$

TAKE NOTE!

Be careful putting negative numbers into this formula. It is best to add brackets to emphasise the negative numbers. Always remember that when a minus number is squared, the result is always positive.

Example

1 Find the length of the line joining the two points (−1, −2) and (4, 10).

Answer

1 Using the formula for the distance between two points

The length of a straight line joining the two points (x_1, y_1) and (x_2, y_2) is given by:

$\sqrt{(x_2 - x_1)^2 + (y_2 - y_1)^2}$

Putting the coordinates (−1, −2) and (4, 10) into this gives

Length $= \sqrt{(4 - (-1))^2 + (10 - (-2))^2} = \sqrt{25 + 144} = \sqrt{169} = 13$

6.3 Proving two lines are the same length using vectors

Suppose we want to express A to B as a vector where A is (1, 2) and B is (5, 4). If you look at the following graph you can see that to go from A to B you go 4 units in the positive x-direction and 2 units up in the positive y-direction.

This can be written in vector form (i.e. $\begin{pmatrix} x \\ y \end{pmatrix}$) as $\begin{pmatrix} 4 \\ 2 \end{pmatrix}$.

You can spot this vector without drawing a graph by looking at the increases in the x-coordinates and y-coordinates when you go from A to B. The x-coordinate goes from 1 to 5 (i.e. an increase of 4) and the y-coordinate goes from 2 to 4 (i.e. an increase in 2).

The vector can thus be written as $\begin{pmatrix} 4 \\ 2 \end{pmatrix}$.

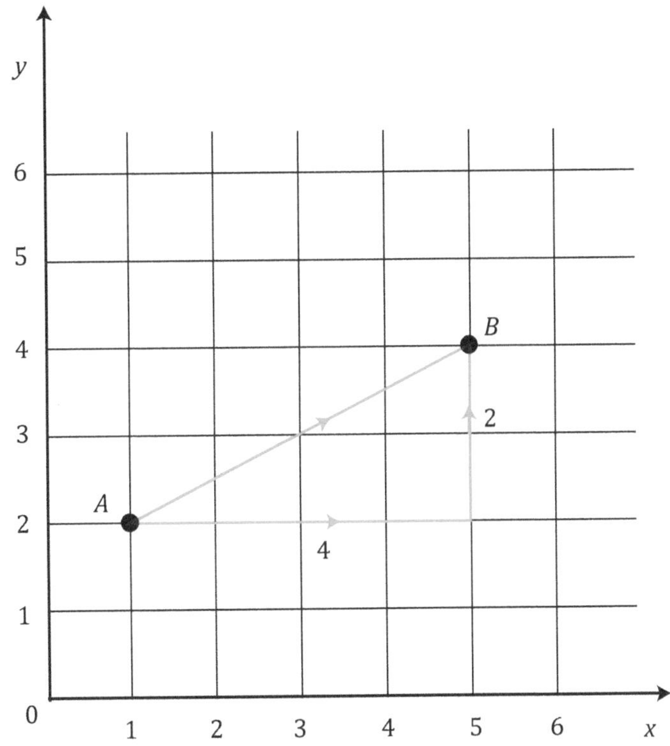

To prove that two lines are the same length it is only necessary to show that the two vectors representing the lines are the same. It does not matter if the x and the y are swapped around nor does it matter about the signs.

What you are doing here is showing that the two sides that are either side of the right angle are the same size for both triangles formed. The length of the hypotenuse of each triangle will be equal. It is not necessary to find the length of the hypotenuse if you only have to prove that two lines are equal length.

The following vectors are equal in length.

$\begin{pmatrix}3\\2\end{pmatrix}$ and $\begin{pmatrix}2\\3\end{pmatrix}$

$\begin{pmatrix}-1\\4\end{pmatrix}$ and $\begin{pmatrix}1\\-4\end{pmatrix}$

$\begin{pmatrix}-3\\2\end{pmatrix}$ and $\begin{pmatrix}-2\\3\end{pmatrix}$

Example

2 Using vectors, show that the following pairs of lines are the same length.

AB where A and B are the points (0, 5) and (2, 2) respectively.

CD where C and D are the points (3, 1) and (6, 3) respectively.

Answer

2 Here we have drawn the lines AB and CD on a grid.

The vector to go from A to B is $\begin{pmatrix}2\\-3\end{pmatrix}$ because you go two squares to the right and three down.

The vector to go from C to D is $\begin{pmatrix}3\\2\end{pmatrix}$ because you go three squares to the right and two up.

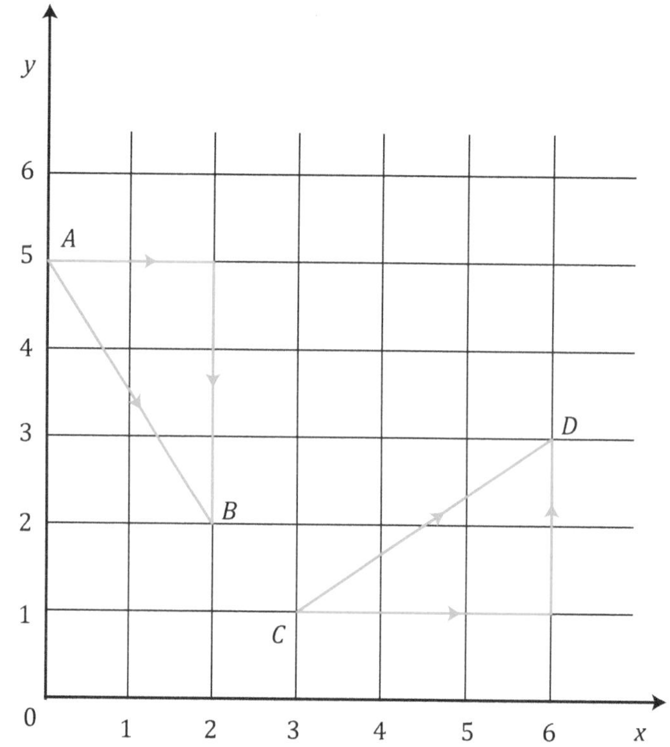

Vectors $\begin{pmatrix} 2 \\ -3 \end{pmatrix}$ and $\begin{pmatrix} 3 \\ 2 \end{pmatrix}$ have the same length, so *AB* and *CD* are the same length.

6.4 Finding the mid-point of a straight line joining two points

The mid-point of a line joining the points (x_1, y_1) and (x_2, y_2) is given by:

$$\left(\frac{x_1 + x_2}{2}, \frac{y_1 + y_2}{2}\right)$$

Note that sometimes the word 'line' is used. A line is always a straight line.

The mid-point of the line joining the two points with coordinates (2, 6) and (8, 4) is

$$\left(\frac{2+8}{2}, \frac{6+4}{2}\right) = (5, 5)$$

Example

3 Find the mid-point and the gradient of the line joining the two points *A* (−2, 0) and *B* (6, 10).

Answer

3 The mid-point of the line joining the two points with coordinates (−2, 0) and (6, 10) is

$$\left(\frac{-2+6}{2}, \frac{0+10}{2}\right) = (2, 5)$$

TIP

You may see examination questions referring to a line segment. A line segment is part of a line. Usually you will be given the coordinates of the point where the line segment starts and the coordinates where it finishes. Using these coordinates you can find the mid-point of the line segment or the length of the line segment.

$$\text{Gradient} = \frac{y_2 - y_1}{x_2 - x_1} = \frac{10 - 0}{6 - (-2)} = \frac{10}{8} = \frac{5}{4}$$

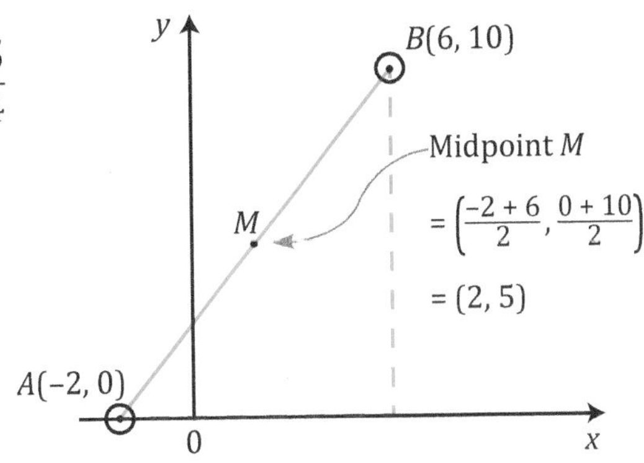

6.5 The equation of a straight line graph

Straight line graphs are also called linear graphs and have an equation of the form

$y = mx + c$

Notice there is one y on the left-hand side of the equation.

m is the gradient (i.e. the steepness of the line) and c is the intercept on the y-axis.

It is important that in this equation there is only an x term, so there are no terms containing x^2, x^3, $\sqrt{x}$, $\frac{1}{x}$, etc.

The following equation is an equation of a straight line:

$y = 2x - 3$

Comparing this equation with $y = mx + c$ you can see that the gradient, m is 2 and intercept on the y-axis, c is −3.

Suppose you are asked to draw the line with equation $y = 2x - 3$.

The quickest way to do this is to find where the line cuts the x- and y-axes.

To find where the line cuts the y-axis, we substitute $x = 0$ (which is the equation of the y-axis) into the equation of the line. Hence, $y = 2(0) - 3$, giving $y = -3$.

To find where the line cuts the x-axis, we substitute $y = 0$ (which is the equation of the x-axis) into the equation of the line. Hence, $0 = 2x - 3$, giving $2x = 3$, so $x = \frac{3}{2}$.

These two points $(0, -3)$ and $(\frac{3}{2}, 0)$ are plotted on a set of axes and the line is drawn passing through each of them. Remember to label the axes and add the equation to the line.

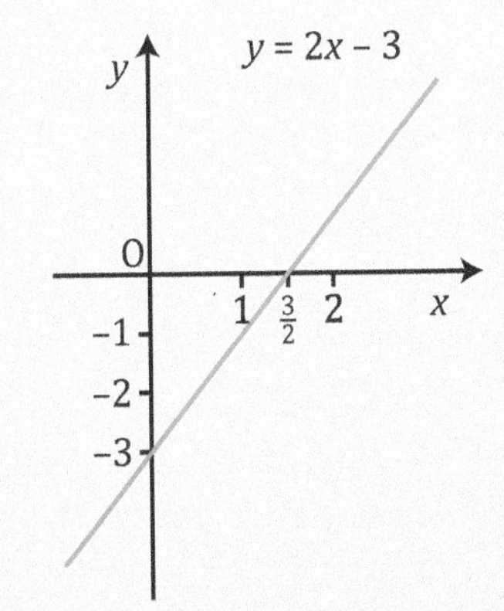

Examples

4 Which of each of the following equations are equations of straight lines?

(a) $y = 1.4x + 7$ (b) $y = 4x^2 + 1$ (c) $y = \frac{2}{x}$ (d) $y = -4x$ (e) $y = \sqrt{x}$ (f) $2y = 8x + 6$ (g) $5x + 2y = 3$ (h) $y = \frac{4}{3}x - 2$

Answers

4 (a) Yes, $y = 1.4x + 7$ is in the form $y = mx + c$

(b) No, $y = 4x^2 + 1$ is not in the form $y = mx + c$ as it contains a term in x^2.

(c) No, $y = \frac{2}{x}$ is not in the form $y = mx + c$

(d) Yes, $y = -4x$ is in the form $y = mx + c$ with $c = 0$.

(e) No, $y = \sqrt{x}$ is not in the form $y = mx + c$

(f) Yes, $2y = 8x + 6$ can be divided by 2 to give

$y = 4x + 3$ which is in the form $y = mx + c$

(g) Yes, $5x + 2y = 3$ can be rearranged to give

$2y = -5x + 3$ and this can be divided by 2 to give $y = -\frac{5}{2}x + \frac{3}{2}$ which is in the form $y = mx + c$

(h) Yes, $y = \frac{4}{3}x - 2$ is in the form $y = mx + c$

5 The line AB has coordinates of A $(-5, 0)$. If the mid-point of AB has coordinates $(0, -2)$, find the coordinates of B.

Answer

5 Let the coordinates of B be (x, y).

The x-coordinate of the mid-point $= \frac{x + (-5)}{2}$

The x-coordinate is 0, so $0 = \frac{x - 5}{2}$

Solving gives $x = 5$

The y-coordinate of the mid-point $= \frac{y + 0}{2}$

The y-coordinate is -2, so $-2 = \frac{y + 0}{2}$

Solving gives $y = -4$

Hence, coordinates of B are $(5, -4)$

6.6 Finding the gradient and the intercept on the *y*-axis from the equation of a straight line

To find the gradient and intercept on the y-axis, we first need to check that the equation for the straight line is in the form $y = mx + c$. If the equation isn't in this format, it needs to be rearranged to put it into this format.

You need to remember that the general equation for a straight line is $y = mx + c$. This is GCSE material so you may need to look back.

Example

6 Find the gradient and intercept on the y-axis for the following straight line graphs.

(a) $y = 4x + 7$

Comparing this with $y = mx + c$, the gradient m is 4 and the intercept on the y-axis, c is 7.

(b) $y = 6 - 2x$

Rearranging this slightly so it is in the form $y = mx + c$, we obtain

$y = -2x + 6$.

Hence, gradient is −2 and the intercept on the y-axis is 6.

(c) $3y = 6x - 5$

Dividing through by 3 gives $y = 2x - \frac{5}{3}$

Hence, gradient is 2 and the intercept on the y-axis is $-\frac{5}{3}$.

(d) $4y + 3x - 6 = 0$

Rearranging gives $4y = -3x + 6$

Dividing through by 4 gives

$y = -\frac{3}{4}x + \frac{3}{2}$

Hence, gradient is $-\frac{3}{4}$ and the intercept on the y-axis is $\frac{3}{2}$.

Progress check

1 For each of the following lines, say whether the gradient is positive, negative, zero or infinite:

(a)

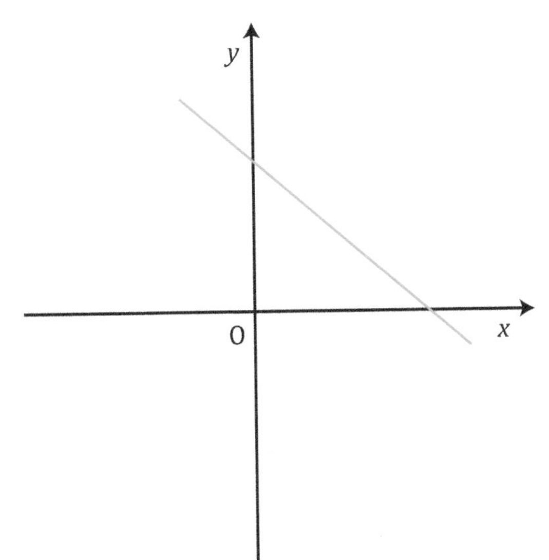

(b)

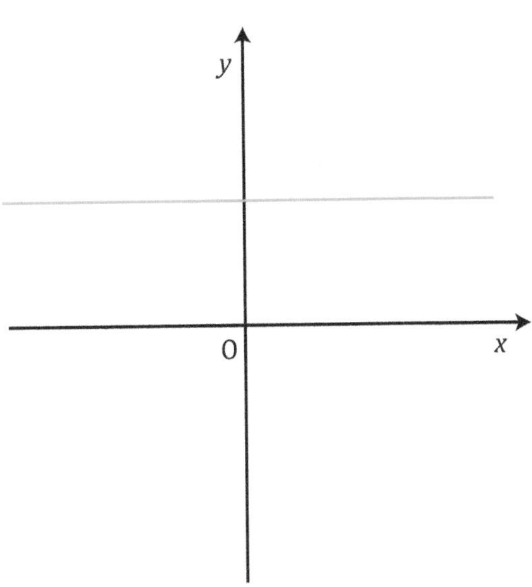

(c)

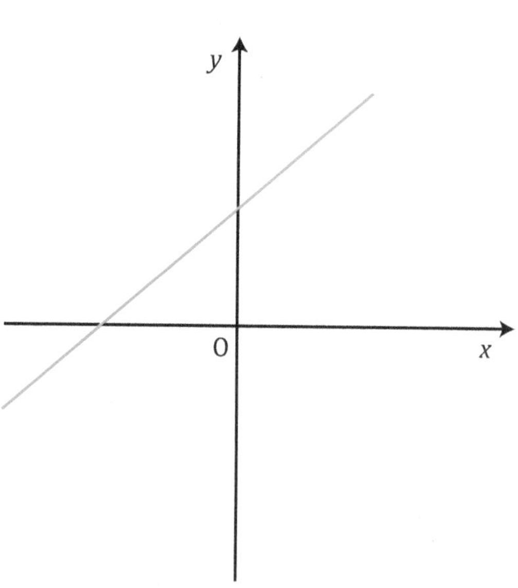

(d)

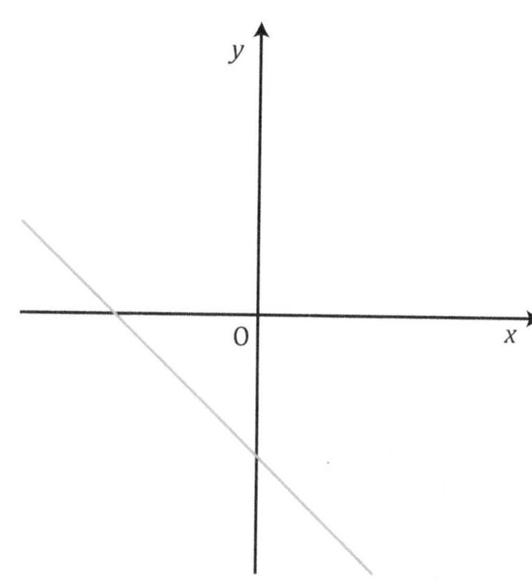

(e)

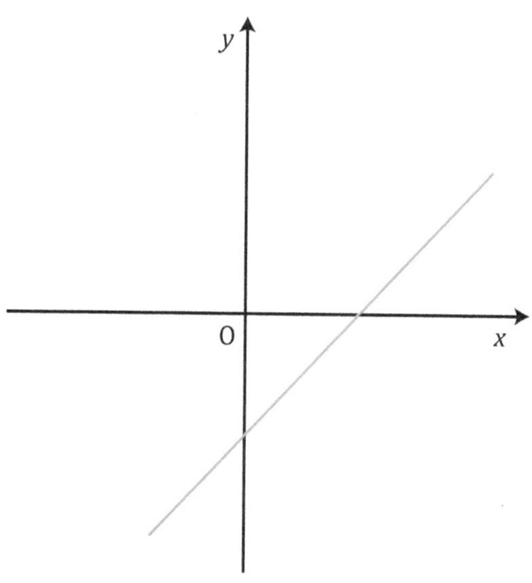

(f)

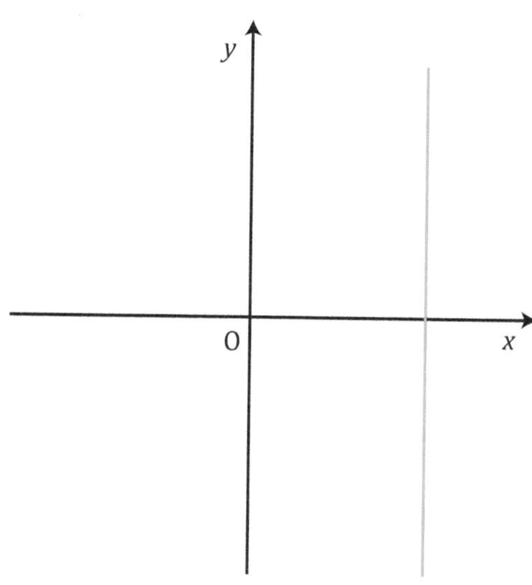

(g)

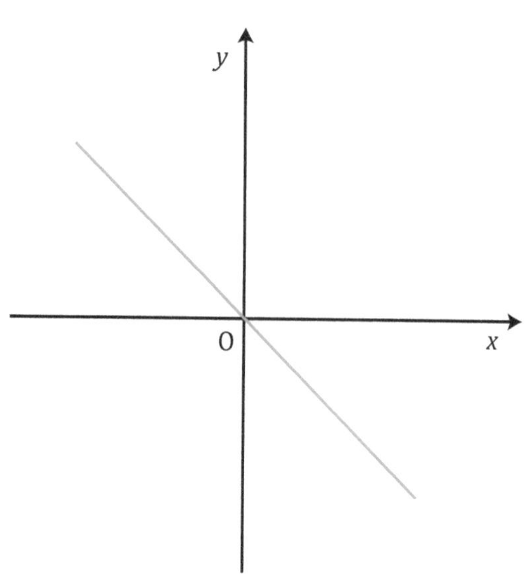

(h)

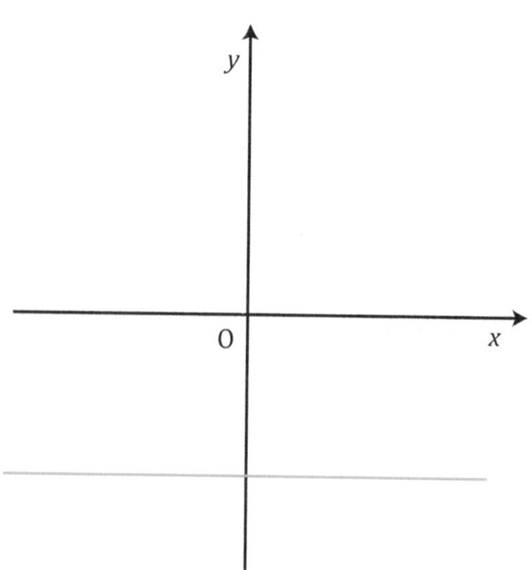

2 Find the gradients of the lines joining each of the following pairs of points:

(a) (2, 3) and (4, 9)

(b) (1, 0) and (9, 12)

(c) (−2, 3) and (−5, 0)

(d) (−1, 10) and (−5, 1)

(e) (0, −3) and (1, 6)

(f) (1, −2) and (4, 2)

(g) (10, −4) and (−1, −5)

3 Find the coordinates of the mid-point of the lines joining the following points:

(a) (1, 2) and (3, 8)

(b) (0, 2) and (4, 1)

(c) (−2, 5) and (0,−5)

(d) (−8, 4) and (−2, −6)

(e) (10, 12) and (−3, 0)

(f) (−3, −4) and (−4, 6)

(g) (8, −1) and (−5, 7)

4 Find the lengths of the lines joining the following points, giving each answer to three significant figures:

(a) (1, 5) and (5, 9)

(b) (3, 4) and (6, 9)

(c) (1, 0) and (6, 12)

(d) (−3, 2) and (2, 6)

(e) (−5, 0) and (0, 4)

(f) (−12, 5) and (0, 10)

(g) (−6, −3) and (−7, 2)

5 Using vectors, show that the following pairs of lines are the same length:

(a) *AB* where *A* and *B* are the points (0, 5) and (3, 4) respectively.

CD where *C* and *D* are the points (5, 6) and (8, 5) respectively.

(b) *AB* where *A* and *B* are the points (0, 1) and (5, 2) respectively.

CD where *C* and *D* are the points (0, −1) and (5, 0) respectively.

(c) *AB* where *A* and *B* are the points (−2, −3) and (4, −4) respectively.

CD where *C* and *D* are the points (−6, −5) and (0, −6) respectively.

(d) *AB* where *A* and *B* are the points (0, 10) and (6, 9) respectively.

CD where *C* and *D* are the points (2, 7) and (8, 8) respectively.

(e) *AB* where *A* and *B* are the points (8, 0) and (6, 4) respectively.

CD where *C* and *D* are the points (9, −1) and (5, −3) respectively.

(f) *AB* where *A* and *B* are the points (0, −7) and (6, −6) respectively.

CD where *C* and *D* are the points (−3, 1) and (−2, 7) respectively.

(g) *AB* where *A* and *B* are the points (−1, 0) and (0, 2) respectively.

CD where *C* and *D* are the points (2, 2) and (4, 3) respectively.

6 Using the distance formula $\sqrt{(x_2 - x_1)^2 + (y_2 - y_1)^2}$ for the distance between two points, calculate the lengths of the following lines, giving your answers to three significant figures:

(a) *AB* where *A* is (1, 4) and *B* is (6, 7).

(b) *CD* where *C* is (0, 5) and *D* is (5, 17).

(c) *EF* where *E* is (−1, −5) and *F* is (−3, 0).

(d) *GH* where *G* is (4, −1) and *H* is (2, 4).

7. Find the gradient and the intercept on the y-axis for each of the following straight lines:

   (a) $y = 3x + 2$

   (b) $2y = 4x + 6$

   (c) $3y = 2x + 3$

   (d) $4x + 3y = 9$

   (e) $5x - 10y - 15 = 0$

   (f) $6y - 3x + 8 = 0$

8. Find the mid-point of the line joining the points A $(-5, 12)$ and B $(1, 4)$.

9. The diameter of a circle is PQ, where P and Q are the points $(-4, 3)$ and $(4, 5)$ respectively.

   (a) The centre of the circle is the mid-point M of the diameter PQ. Find the coordinates of M.

   (b) Show that the diameter of the circle PQ is $2\sqrt{17}$.

10. Find the lengths of the lines joining each of the following pairs of points:

   (a) $(1, -2)$ and $(6, 1)$

   (b) $(-4, 0)$ and $(0, -3)$

   (c) $(0, 8)$ and $(4, 7)$

11. Points A and B are joined by a straight line. If the coordinates of A are $(2, 3)$ and the mid-point of the line is at $(4, 4)$, find the coordinates of point B.

12. The points A and B have coordinates $(0, 2)$ and $(5, k)$ respectively. If the gradient of the line joining points A and B is $\frac{4}{5}$, find the value of k.

13. Find the gradients of each of the following lines:

   (a) $y = 4x - 1$

   (b) $2y = 3x + 6$

   (c) $4y - x = 6$

   (d) $3y - 2x - 9 = 0$

14. The equation of line AB is $5x - 2y = 2$.

   A is the point $(4, 9)$ and B is the point $(2, k)$.

   (a) Show that $k = 4$.

   (b) Find the coordinates of the mid-point of AB.

6.7 Equations of vertical and horizontal lines

Horizontal lines (i.e. lines parallel to the x-axis and including the x-axis) have an equation of the form $y = a$, so, for example, $y = 2$, $y = -3$, $y = 0$ are all examples of horizontal lines.

Vertical lines (i.e. lines parallel to the y-axis and including the y-axis) have an equation of the form $x = a$, so, for example, $x = 1$, $x = -4$, $x = 0$ are all equations of vertical lines.

Here are some examples of lines parallel to the x- or y-axes and their equations.

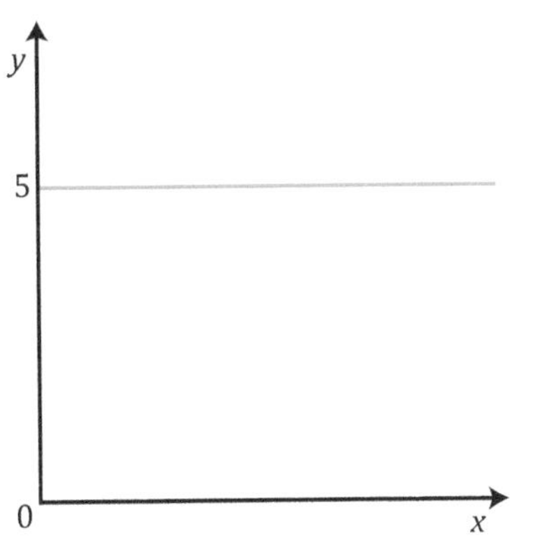

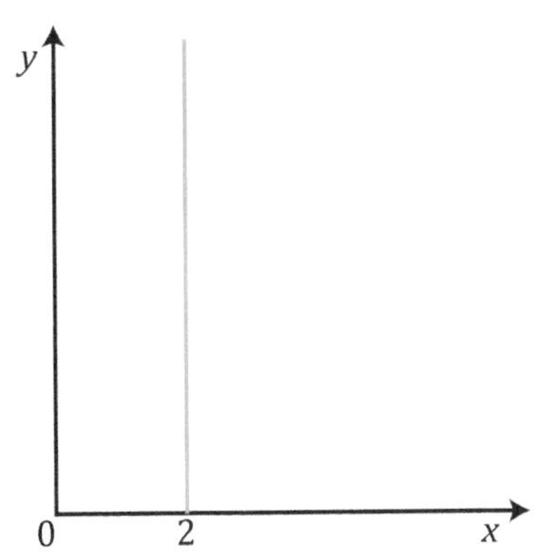

Equation is $x = 2$

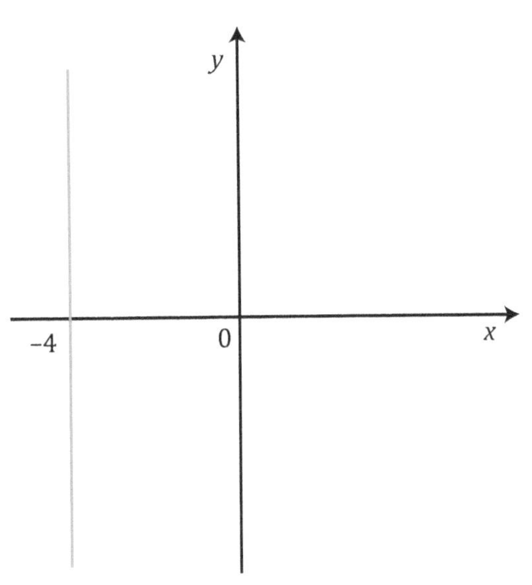

Equation is $x = -4$

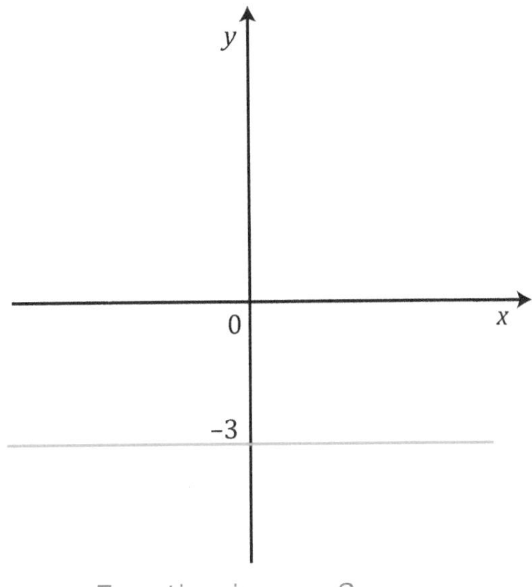

Equation is $y = -3$

A line parallel to the x-axis will always have the equation y = a number and a line parallel to the y-axis will always have the equation x = a number.

6.8 Finding the equation of a straight line

To find the equation of a straight line you need to know the gradient of the line (m) and the coordinates of a point (x_1, y_1) that lies on the line.

The equation of a straight line with gradient m and which passes through a point (x_1, y_1) is given by:

F

$$y - y_1 = m(x - x_1)$$

For example, the equation of the straight line with a gradient of 2 and passing through the point (2, 5) is

$y - 5 = 2(x - 2)$

$y - 5 = 2x - 4$

So $y = 2x + 1$ or $2x - y + 1 = 0$

Note that here $x_1 = 2, y_1 = 5$ and $m = 2$ in the equation $y - y_1 = m(x - x_1)$

Notice that the first equation is in the form $y = mx + c$, so you can immediately see that the gradient $m = 2$ and the intercept on the y-axis c is $+1$.

The second form gives the equation as $ax + by + c = 0$.

Which form you use depends on whether you are asked for a particular form in the question. You can give the equation of a straight line in either form if a form is not specified in the question.

TIP

Write down the general equation for a straight line and then substitute values into it for m, x_1 and y_1.

Examples

7 Find the equation of the line L, having gradient 3 and passing through the point (2, 3).

Answer

7 $y - y_1 = m(x - x_1)$ where $m = 3$ and $(x_1, y_1) = (2, 3)$.

$y - 3 = 3(x - 2)$

$y - 3 = 3x - 6$

$y = 3x - 3$

This equation is in the form $y = mx + c$, where m is the gradient and c is the intercept on the y-axis.

8 Find the equation of the line in the form $ax + by + c = 0$ that has a gradient of 2 and passes through the point $(-1, 0)$.

Answer

8 $y - y_1 = m(x - x_1)$ where $m = 2$ and $(x_1, y_1) = (-1, 0)$

$y - 0 = 2(x - (-1))$

$y = 2(x + 1)$

$y = 2x + 2$

$2x - y + 2 = 0$

TAKE NOTE!

Remember to give the equation in the format asked for in the question.

6.9 Condition for two straight lines to be parallel to each other

For two lines to be parallel to each other, they must have the same gradient.

For example, the equation of the line that is parallel to the line $y = 3x - 2$ but intersects the y-axis at $y = 2$ is:

$y = 3x + 2$ as $m = 3$ and $c = 2$ (i.e. using the equation $y = mx + c$).

6.10 Condition for two straight lines to be perpendicular to each other

When two lines are perpendicular to each other (i.e. they make an angle of 90°), the product of their gradients is −1.

If one line has a gradient m_1 and the other a gradient of m_2 then

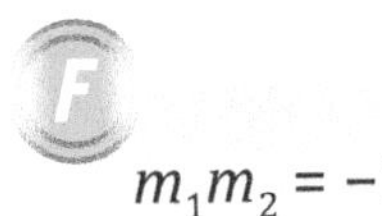

$$m_1 m_2 = -1$$

if the lines are perpendicular to each other.

For example, if a straight line has gradient $-\frac{1}{3}$ then the gradient of the line perpendicular to this is given by

$\left(-\frac{1}{3}\right)m_2 = -1$, hence gradient $m_2 = 3$

6.11 Determining the equation of a line that is parallel to another line

Parallel lines have the same gradient and you are often asked to find the equation of a line that is parallel to another line. Here you simply take the gradient of the parallel line and use it with a point on the other line to find the equation of the other line.

Examples

9 Find the equation of line L_1 which passes through the point (1, 2) and is parallel to the line L_2 which has equation $2x - y + 1 = 0$.

Answer

9 First find the equation of the line L_2 in the form $y = mx + c$

$2x - y + 1 = 0$

So $\quad y = 2x + 1$

Hence the gradient of $L_2 = 2$.

Comparing this equation with $y = mx + c$ gives the gradient, $m = 2$.

Since lines L_1 and L_2 are parallel, they both have the same gradient of 2.

TAKE NOTE !

Always check to see if a form for the equation of a straight line is given in the question. If the form is not specified, then either equation specified here is acceptable.

Finding the equation of line L_1

$y - y_1 = m(x - x_1)$ where $m = 2$ and $(x_1, y_1) = (1, 2)$.

$y - 2 = 2(x - 1)$

$y = 2x \quad (\text{or } y - 2x = 0)$

---

10 Four straight lines have the following equations:

Line 1 $\quad 3y = x + 6$

Line 2 $\quad 2y = x + 10$

Line 3 $\quad y = -3x + 7$

Line 4 $\quad 6y = 3x + 12$

(a) Rearrange the equations of each of these lines into the form $y = mx + c$ and then use the equations of the lines to determine the line numbers of the two lines which are parallel to each other.

(b) Determine the line numbers of the two lines which are perpendicular to each other.

Answer

10 (a) Writing each equation into the form $y = mx + c$ we obtain the following:

Line 1 $\quad y = \frac{1}{3}x + 2$

Line 2 $\quad y = \frac{1}{2}x + 5$

Line 3 $\quad y = -3x + 7$

Line 4 $\quad y = \frac{1}{2}x + 2$

Lines 2 and 4 have the same gradient $\left(\text{i.e. } \frac{1}{2}\right)$ and so are parallel.

(b) Lines 1 and 3 are perpendicular as the product of their gradients $\left(\text{i.e. } \frac{1}{3}(-3)\right)$ is −1.

6.12 A quicker way to determine the equation of a line through a point that is parallel to another line

Suppose you want to find the equation of the straight line passing through the point (1, 4) which is parallel to the line having equation $4x + 2y = 5$.

A line parallel to the equation $4x + 2y = 5$ will have an equation of the form

$4x + 2y = c$.

Notice the way the number on its own is replaced with c.

You now substitute the coordinates of the point through which the line passes, into this equation. Hence, we have

$4x + 2y = c$

Here $x = 1$ and $y = 4$ are substituted into the equation.

$4(1) + 2(4) = c$, giving $c = 12$.

This value is substituted back into the equation, so the equation of the line is

$4x + 2y = 12$

Examples

11 Find the equation of the line parallel to the line $2x - 5y + 4 = 0$, if the line passes through the point (3, 1).

Answer

11 Let the equation of the parallel line be $2x - 5y + c = 0$.

The number on its own is replaced by c.

Substituting the coordinates (3, 1) into this equation gives

$2(3) - 5(1) + c = 0$

$1 + c = 0$

Hence, $c = -1$.

The equation of the required line is $2x - 5y - 1 = 0$

12 P is the point (0, 6) and Q is the point $(5, p)$.

(a) (i) Find the gradient of the line with equation $2x + 5y = 40$.

(ii) Find the equation of the line through P which is parallel to the line $2x + 5y = 40$.

(b) The line through P also passes through the point $(5, p)$. Find the value of p.

To obtain the gradient, we need to rearrange this equation into the form $y = mx + c$. The gradient will be given by the value of m.

Answer

12 (a) (i) $2x + 5y = 40$

Hence $5y = -2x + 40$

$$y = -\frac{2}{5}x + 8$$

Comparing this with the equation for a straight line, $y = mx + c$

we obtain, gradient $= -\frac{2}{5}$

Parallel lines have the same gradient.

(ii) The line parallel to $2x + 5y = 40$ will have gradient $-\frac{2}{5}$.

The equation of a line with gradient $-\frac{2}{5}$ and passing through the point P (0, 6) is

$$y - y_1 = m(x - x_1)$$

$$y - 6 = -\frac{2}{5}(x - 0)$$

$$5y - 30 = -2x$$

Hence, equation of line is $2x + 5y = 30$

 **TIP**

You could use the other method here where you let the equation of the parallel line be $2x + 5y = c$, and then substitute the coordinates of the points through which the line passes into the equation to find the value of c. Once this is done, this will be the required equation.

(b) The coordinates $(5, p)$ lie on the line, so these coordinates will satisfy the equation for the line.

$x = 5$ and $y = p$ are substituted into the equation of the straight line and the resulting equation is solved to find the numerical value of p.

So, $5y + 2x = 30$

$$5p + 10 = 30$$

$$5p = 20$$

$$p = 4$$

6.13 Proving that a point (x, y) lies on a line

To prove that a point (x, y) lies on a line you substitute the coordinates of the point for x and y into the equation. If the left-hand side of the equation equals the right-hand side, the point lies on the line.

Take the following equation of a straight line as an example:

$$2y - 5x = 7$$

The point $(-1, 1)$ lies on the straight line because when the x-coordinate is substituted into the equation we obtain:

$$2y - 5(-1) = 7$$

$$2y + 5 = 7$$

$$2y = 2$$

$$y = 1$$

Now as this is the y-coordinate of the point $(-1, 1)$, we can say the point lies on the line.

Progress check

15 Find the equation of the line parallel to the line $4x - 3y = 10$ and passing through the point $(-3, 2)$.

16 The points A, B and C have coordinates $(1, 1)$, $(3, 3)$ and $(6, 0)$ respectively.

(a) Find the gradients of lines AB and BC.

(b) Prove that lines AB and BC are perpendicular to each other.

17 The points P and Q have coordinates $(0, 6)$ and $(4, 0)$ respectively.

(a) Find the equation of the line PQ.

(b) Find the equation of the line perpendicular to PQ through its mid-point.

18 Here is an equation of a straight line:

$y = 6x - 5$

Say whether each of the following points lies on the straight line:

(a) $(1, 1)$

(b) $(0, -5)$

(c) $(2, 4)$

(d) $(\frac{1}{2}, -2)$

(e) $(-1, 1)$

19 By substituting $x = 0$ into each of these equations, determine the y-coordinate of the point where the line cuts the y-axis:

(a) $y = 4x - 1$

(b) $y = 3x + 5$

(c) $4x - 2y = 0$

(d) $5y - x = 2$

(e) $2x + y - 1 = 0$

(f) $y - x - 3 = 0$

20 By substituting $y = 0$ into each of these equations, determine the x-coordinate of the point where the line cuts the x-axis:

(a) $y = 4x + 2$

(b) $y = -3x + 15$

(c) $3x + 2y = 12$

(d) $5y - x = 9$

(e) $5x - 7y = 25$

(f) $x - y + 7 = 0$

(g) $5x - 3y - 10 = 0$

6.14 Finding the coordinates of the point of intersection of two straight lines

Provided the two straight lines are not parallel, they will intersect (i.e. cut) at a single point. The coordinates of this point of intersection can be found by:

- Solving the two equations of the straight lines simultaneously, or
- Plotting the two lines and finding from the graph where they intersect.

The first method is usually quicker than the second and is the method you will need to use most often.

Examples

13 The two straight lines with equations $2y - x - 4 = 0$ and $y + x - 8 = 0$ intersect at a point P. Find the coordinates of point P.

Answer

13 Look at the two equations carefully. You are looking for a way of eliminating either x or y by adding or subtracting the two equations. Sometimes it is not that simple as it may be necessary to **multiply** one or both equations by numbers so that the coefficients (i.e. the numbers in front of the x or y) are equal.

You have to decide whether to eliminate x or y. Looking at the two equations you can see that the coefficient of x in the equation $2y - x - 4 = 0$ is -1 and that in the other equation $y + x - 8 = 0$, it is $+1$. Because the coefficients have the same number but a different sign, by adding them we can eliminate x.

$$2y - x - 4 = 0 \quad \text{.......... (1)}$$

$$y + x - 8 = 0 \quad \text{.......... (2)}$$

Adding equations (1) and (2) gives $3y - 12 = 0$

So, $3y = 12$

$y = 4$

Substituting $y = 4$ into equation (1) gives $2(4) - x - 4 = 0$

$8 - x - 4 = 0$

$x = 4$

Coordinates of point P are (4, 4)

Note you should do a quick check by substituting $x = 4$ and $y = 4$ into the equation you did not use for the substitution. So here we would use equation (2). If the right and left sides of the equation are equal then it is correct.

14 The lines $y = 2x + 2$ and $2y = 9 - x$ intersect at the point D.

Show that D has coordinates (1, 4).

Answer

14 Solving the equations of the lines simultaneously to find the point of intersection:

$$2y = -x + 9 \quad \text{......} \quad (1)$$

$$y = 2x + 2 \quad \text{......} \quad (2)$$

Multiplying equation (1) by 2.

$$4y = -2x + 18$$

$$y = 2x + 2$$

Adding these two equations gives:

$$5y = 20$$

$$y = 4$$

Substituting $y = 4$ into equation (1) gives:

$$8 = -x + 9$$

$$-1 = -x$$

$$x = 1$$

Check by putting the values of x and y into equation (2).

$$y = 2x + 2$$

$$y = 2(1) + 2$$

$$y = 4$$

Hence D is the point (1, 4)

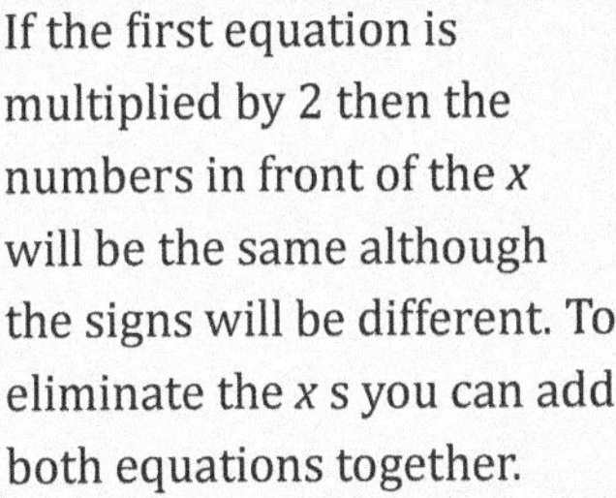

Always check the values for x and y by substituting them into the equation that you have not used already for the substitution.

Check that the value calculated on the right is the same as that in the equation on the left.

Progress check

21 Find the coordinates of the point of intersection of the following two lines:

$$7x + 2y = 19$$

$$x - y = 4$$

22 Find the coordinates of the point of intersection of the following two lines:

$$7y = 5x - 27$$

$$4y = 3x - 16$$

23 Explain why the two lines having equations $y - 3x + 4 = 0$ and $4y - 12x + 1 = 0$ do not intersect.

24 The line AB has equation $4x + y = 1$

The line with equation $3x + 2y = 7$ intersects the line AB at point A. Find the coordinates of A.

» TIP

In many questions you would be advised to take the time to plot the points given on a quick sketch graph. This is a simple question so it is not really worth the time. In questions involving more points, you should mark the points and lines on a graph.

Exam practice

1 A line passes through the points A (1, −1) and B (3, 4).

(a) Find the gradient of line AB.

(b) Find the coordinates of C, the mid-point of AB.

(c) The line L is perpendicular to line AB and passes through the point C.

Find the equation of line L.

TAKE NOTE !

We often re-write equations involving fractions into a form that does not contain fractions (i.e. they only contain whole numbers). Choose the smallest number that the denominators both go into and then multiply the whole equation by this number thus removing the fractions.

Answer

1 (a) Gradient $= \dfrac{y_2 - y_1}{x_2 - x_1} = \dfrac{4-(-1)}{3-1} = \dfrac{5}{2}$

(b) The mid-point of a line joining the points (x_1, y_1) and (x_2, y_2) is given by:

$$\left(\frac{x_1 + x_2}{2}, \frac{y_1 + y_2}{2}\right)$$

Hence mid-point of $AB = \left(\dfrac{1+3}{2}, \dfrac{-1+4}{2}\right) = \left(2, \dfrac{3}{2}\right)$

(c) The product of the gradients of perpendicular lines is −1.

Hence $m\left(\dfrac{5}{2}\right) = -1$

Giving $m = -\dfrac{2}{5}$

Equation of straight line L having gradient $-\dfrac{2}{5}$ and passing through the point $\left(2, \frac{3}{2}\right)$ is:

$$y - \frac{3}{2} = -\frac{2}{5}(x - 2)$$

Multiplying through by 10 gives

$10y - 15 = -4(x - 2)$

$10y - 15 = -4x + 8$

$4x + 10y - 23 = 0$

---

2 The points A, B, C, D have coordinates $(-4, 4), (-1, 3), (0, 1), (k, 0)$ respectively.

The straight line CD is parallel to the straight line AB.

(a) Find the gradient of AB.

(b) Find the gradient of CD and hence find the value of the constant k.

(c) Line L is perpendicular to CD and passes through point C. Find the equation of line L in the form $ax + by + c = 0$.

TIP

There are lots of points in the question so spend the time drawing the points on a set of axes. Keep the scale on the x- and y-axes the same. As you proceed through the question you can add points and lines to your graph.

Answer

2

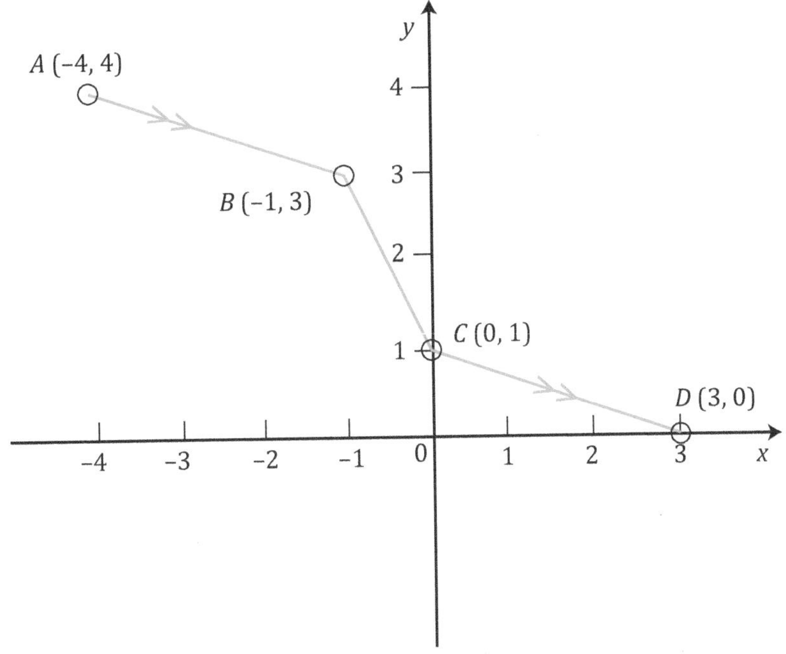

The fact that lines AB and CD are parallel can be shown by drawing double-headed arrows halfway along each line.

Gradient of $AB = \frac{y_2 - y_1}{x_2 - x_1} = \frac{3 - 4}{-1 - (-4)} = -\frac{1}{3}$

Notice how you can use the graph to check the signs of the gradients of any lines. A quick look at the graph reveals the gradients of lines AB, BC and CD are all negative.

(b) Gradient of $CD = \frac{y_2 - y_1}{x_2 - x_1} = \frac{0 - 1}{k - 0} = -\frac{1}{k}$

As line CD is parallel to AB the gradients are equal.

Hence, $-\frac{1}{3} = -\frac{1}{k}$

The gradients are equated here.

Giving $k = 3$

This means D is the point (3, 0) and this point can be added to the graph.

TAKE NOTE!

You must show all the working out here. Do not simply change the sign and invert the fraction without explaining why this is done.

TAKE NOTE!

Leaving the equation in the form $y = mx + c$ (i.e. as $y = 3x + 1$) would cost you a mark here as the question asks that the equation be given in the form

$ax + by + c = 0$.

(c) As line L is perpendicular to CD the product of their gradients is −1.

$$\left(-\frac{1}{3}\right)m_2 = -1$$

Giving gradient of $L = 3$

Equation of line L is:

$$y - 1 = 3(x - 0)$$

$$y = 3x + 1$$

Hence $3x - y + 1 = 0$

Test yourself

Answer the following questions and check your answers before moving on to the next topic.

1. The points A, B, C, D have coordinates (1, 0), (4, 1), (−1, 3), (2, 4) respectively.
   (a) Show that lines AB and CD are parallel.
   (b) Find the equation of AB in the form $ax + by + c = 0$.
2. The points A and B have coordinates (−7, 4) and (k, −1) respectively.
   (a) If the gradient of AB is $-\frac{1}{2}$, find the value of the constant k.
   (b) The line BC is perpendicular to AB. Find the equation of line BC.
3. The points A, B, C have coordinates (−3, 2), (1, 6), (6, 1).
   (a) Show that AB is perpendicular to BC.
   (b) Find the length of AB and the length of BC.
   (c) Find the value of $\tan A\hat{C}B$ in the form $\frac{a}{b}$.
4. A line has the equation $3x + 2y = 5$. Another line is drawn having the same gradient and passing through the point (3, 4). Find the equation of this line.

5 The points P and Q have coordinates $(-4, 0)$ and $(0, 2)$ respectively.

(a) Find the equation of the line PQ.

(b) Find the equation of the line perpendicular to PQ through its mid-point.

6 The points P, Q, R have coordinates $(1, 0)$, $(3, 5)$, $(-2, 6)$ respectively.

(a) Find the gradient of line PQ.

(b) Find the equation of line PQ and simplify your answer.

(c) S is the point such that $PQRS$ forms a parallelogram.

State the gradient of line RS and use this to find the equation of the line RS.

(d) If the equation of line SP is $5y + x = 1$, find the coordinates of point S.

7 The coordinates of the points A, B, C and D are $(2, -5)$, $(6, -7)$, $(9, -4)$ and $(5, -2)$ respectively.

(a) Find the gradient of the line joining points A and B.

(b) Prove that the lines AB and DC are parallel.

(c) Prove that the lines AB and DC are the same length.

(d) Prove that the quadrilateral $ABCD$ is a parallelogram.

8 A $(4, 2)$ and B $(1, 5)$ are two points.

(a) Find the coordinates of the mid-point, M of AB.

(b) Find the gradient of the line joining A and B.

(c) The line from point M passes through the point C $(4, 5)$.

Prove that the lines AB and MC are perpendicular.

(d) Find the equation of the line MC.

9 The line PQ has equation $2x + 3y = 5$. The point R has coordinates $(3, 3)$.

(a) Find the gradient of line PQ.

(b) A line is drawn which passes through R and is parallel to PQ.
If this line crosses the y-axis at point S, find the coordinates of S.

10 The line AB has equation $4x + 5y = 10$.

(a) Find the gradient of AB.

(b) Prove that the point C $(-5, 6)$ lies on AB.

(c) Find the equation of the line through C which is at right angles to AB.

Topic summary

There are many formulae to remember in this topic and the best way to do this is by usage. This means that you should try to remember them as you are attempting any questions.

If you forget a formula you may be able to work out the answer by drawing a diagram.

Many coordinate geometry questions in the examination are similar and you usually require use of most of the material summarised here to answer a single question. It is also important to note that this is a very important topic because as well as being asked to answer whole questions on coordinate geometry, the content of this topic can crop up in parts of questions on other topics.

The gradient of the line joining two points

The gradient of the line joining points (x_1, y_1) and (x_2, y_2) is given by:

$$\text{Gradient} = \frac{y_2 - y_1}{x_2 - x_1}$$

The length of a line joining two points

The length of a straight line joining the two points (x_1, y_1) and (x_2, y_2) is given by:

$$\sqrt{(x_2 - x_1)^2 + (y_2 - y_1)^2}$$

The mid-point of the line joining two points

The mid-point of a line joining the points (x_1, y_1) and (x_2, y_2) is given by:

$$\left(\frac{x_1 + x_2}{2}, \frac{y_1 + y_2}{2}\right)$$

The equation of a straight line

The equation of a straight line with gradient m and which passes through a point (x_1, y_1) is given by:

$$y - y_1 = m(x - x_1)$$

Condition for two straight lines to be parallel to each other

The lines must both have the same gradient.

Condition for two straight lines to be perpendicular to each other

If one line has a gradient m_1 and the other a gradient of m_2 then

$$m_1 m_2 = -1$$

if the lines are perpendicular to each other.

Coordinate geometry of the circle

In this topic you will be expanding your knowledge of coordinate geometry learnt in the last topic to include the coordinate geometry of circles. You will need to be proficient at completing the square and coordinate geometry before starting this topic.

This topic covers the following:

7.1 The equation of a circle
7.2 Finding the equation of a tangent to a circle
7.3 Finding where a circle and straight line intersect or touch

7.1 The equation of a circle

The equation of a circle can be written in the form:

$$(x-a)^2+(y-b)^2=r^2$$

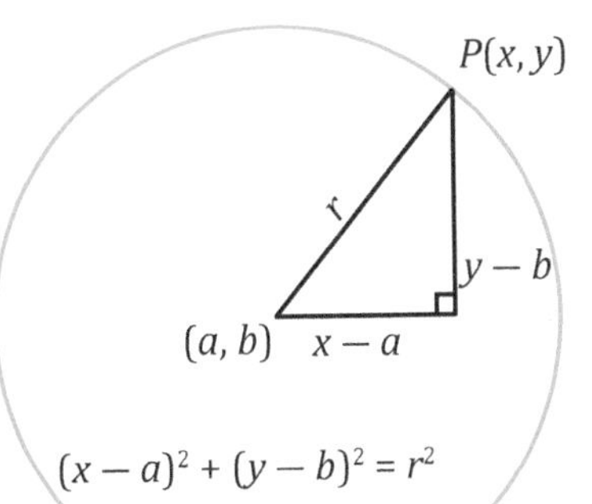

A circle having the above equation will have centre (a, b) and radius r.

For example, if you had a circle with the equation $(x-2)^2+(y+4)^2=16$, this circle would have a centre of $(2, -4)$ and a radius of 4 (i.e. $\sqrt{16}$).

Note that for a circle centred on the origin (0, 0) the values of a and b will be 0 so the above equation for the circle becomes:

$$x^2+y^2=r^2$$

So a circle having equation $x^2+y^2=4$, would have centre (0, 0) and radius 2.

There is the following alternative form for the equation of a circle:

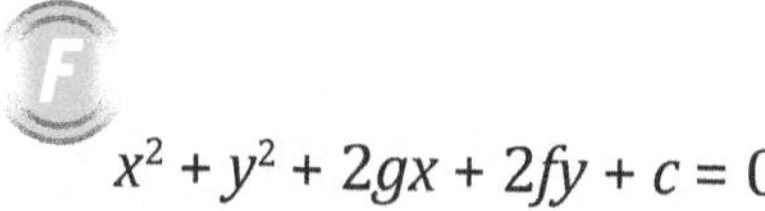

$$x^2 + y^2 + 2gx + 2fy + c = 0$$

TIP

If you are able to remember these two formulae, you will have a quick way of finding the centre and radius of a circle but they are not the easiest formulae to remember.

A circle having the above equation will have centre $(-g, -f)$ and radius given by

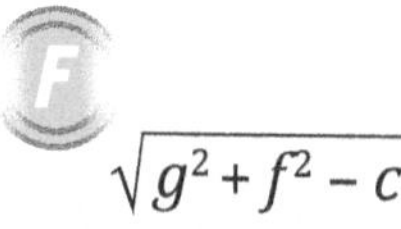

$$\sqrt{g^2 + f^2 - c}$$

If you are given the following equation of a circle

$x^2 + y^2 - 8x + 6y + 9 = 0$

we can compare this equation with $x^2 + y^2 + 2gx + 2fy + c = 0$ and you can see that $2g = -8$ giving $g = -4$ and $2f = 6$ giving $f = 3$.

Hence the centre of the circle will be $(4, -3)$ (i.e. $[-g, -f]$) and the radius is 4 (using $\sqrt{g^2 + f^2 - c}$ with $g = -4, f = 3$ and $c = 9$).

There is another way of finding the centre and radius of this circle and this involves completing the square.

We start with the equation of the circle

$x^2 + y^2 - 8x + 6y + 9 = 0$

Completing the square means $x^2 - 8x = (x - 4)^2 - 16$

Similarly $y^2 + 6y = (y + 3)^2 - 9$

Hence, equation of the circle can be written as

$(x - 4)^2 - 16 + (y + 3)^2 - 9 + 9 = 0$

Rearranging this equation gives $(x - 4)^2 + (y + 3)^2 = 16$

Comparing this with the equation for a circle in the form $(x - a)^2 + (y - b)^2 = r^2$ you can see that the centre is at $(4, -3)$ and the radius is 4.

Examples

1 Write down the coordinates of the centre and the radius of the circle having the equation:

$(x - 7)^2 + (x + 3)^2 = 36$

Answer

1 Comparing the equation $(x - 7)^2 + (x + 3)^2 = 36$ with the equation for the circle

$(x - a)^2 + (y - b)^2 = r^2$

This gives $a = 7$ and $b = -3$ so coordinates of the centre are $(7, -3)$.

$r^2 = 36$, giving radius $r = \sqrt{36} = 6$.

2 The circle C has centre A and equation $x^2 + y^2 - 2x + 6y - 6 = 0$

Find the coordinates of A and find the radius of C.

Answer

2 Comparing the equation $x^2 + y^2 - 2x + 6y - 6 = 0$ with the equation

$x^2 + y^2 + 2gx + 2fy + c = 0$ we can see $2g = -2$ giving $g = -1$, $2f = 6$ giving $f = 3$ and $c = -6$.

Centre A has coordinates $(-g, -f) = (1, -3)$

Radius $= \sqrt{g^2 + f^2 - c} = \sqrt{(-1)^2 + (3)^2 + 6} = \sqrt{16} = 4$

Alternative method involving completing the square.

The equation for the circle is

$x^2 + y^2 - 2x + 6y - 6 = 0$

Completing the square means $x^2 - 2x = (x - 1)^2 - 1$

Similarly $y^2 + 6y = (y + 3)^2 - 9$

Hence, equation of the circle can be written as

$(x - 1)^2 - 1 + (y + 3)^2 - 9 - 6 = 0$

$$(x - 1)^2 + (y + 3)^2 - 16 = 0$$

$$(x - 1)^2 + (y + 3)^2 = 16$$

Comparing this with the equation of the circle $(x - a)^2 + (y - b)^2 = r^2$

Gives the coordinates of centre of the circle as $(1, -3)$ and radius = 4.

TAKE NOTE !

You are usually free to use whichever method you like to find the centre and radius.

3 The circle C has centre A and equation $x^2 + y^2 - 4x + 2y - 11 = 0$

Find the coordinates of A and the radius of C.

Answer

3 The equation for C can be written as

$x^2 - 4x + y^2 + 2y - 11 = 0$

Completing the square means $x^2 - 4x = (x - 2)^2 - 4$

Similarly $y^2 + 2y = (y + 1)^2 - 1$

Hence, equation of C can be written as

$(x - 2)^2 - 4 + (y + 1)^2 - 1 - 11 = 0$

$(x - 2)^2 + (y + 1)^2 - 4 - 1 - 11 = 0$

$(x - 2)^2 + (y + 1)^2 = 16$

Comparing this with the equation of the circle $(x - a)^2 + (y - b)^2 = r^2$

Gives the coordinates of centre C as $(2, -1)$ and radius = 4.

Circle properties

There are a number of circle properties you need to know about:

1 The angle in a semicircle is always a right angle.

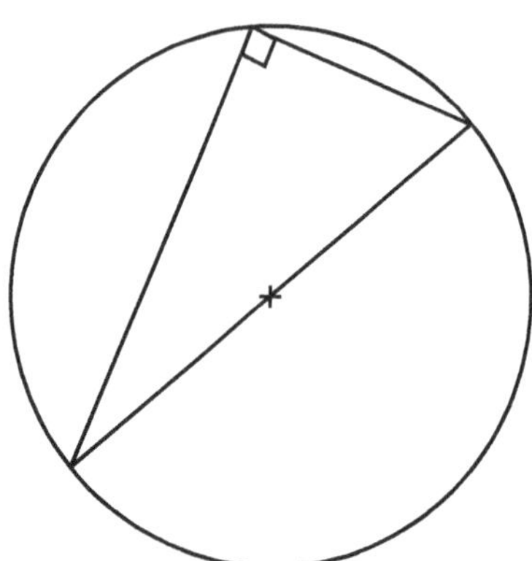

Circle properties will need to be memorised.

2 The perpendicular from the centre of the circle to a chord bisects the cord.

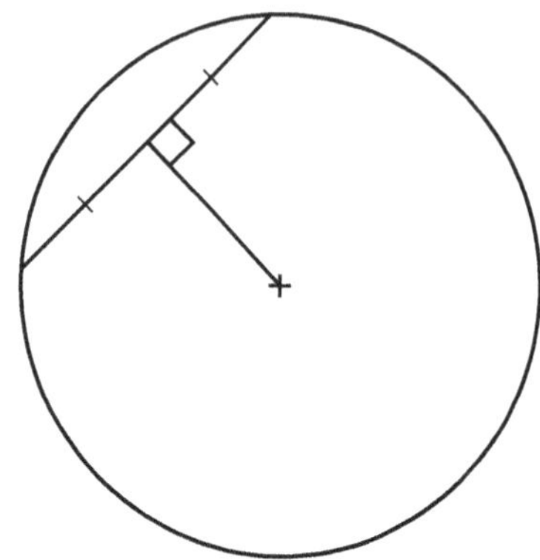

3 The tangent to a circle at a point makes a right angle to the radius of the circle at the same point.

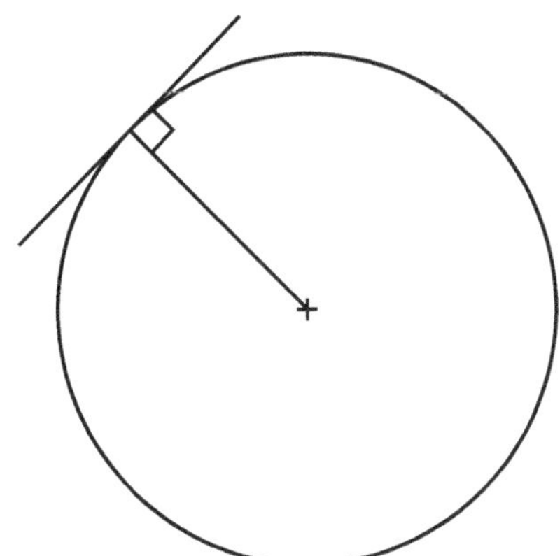

Progress check

1 All the following circles have their centre as the origin (0, 0). Find the radius of each of the following circles:

(a) $x^2 + y^2 = 1$

(b) $x^2 + y^2 = 9$

(c) $x^2 + y^2 = 25$

(d) $x^2 + y^2 - 4 = 0$

(e) $x^2 + y^2 - 49 = 0$

(f) $4x^2 + 4y^2 = 16$

(g) $8x^2 + 8y^2 = 72$

(h) $3(x^2 + y^2) - 27 = 0$

(i) $y^2 = 16 - x^2$

(j) $x^2 + y^2 - 5 = 0$

(k) $x^2 + y^2 - 50 = 0$

2 Write down the equations of the circles with centre (0, 0) and each of the following radii, r:

(a) $r = 3$

(b) $r = 4$

(c) $r = 9$

(d) $r = \sqrt{6}$

(e) $r = 2\sqrt{3}$

(f) $r = 3\sqrt{5}$

(g) $r = 3\sqrt{2}$

3 Multiply out the brackets for these equations of circles and simplify and give your answer in the form:

$$x^2 + y^2 + ax + by + c = 0 .$$

(a) $(x - 3)^2 + (y + 1)^2 = 9$

(b) $(x - 2)^2 + (y + 4)^2 = 16$

(c) $(x - 1)^2 + (y - 3)^2 = 1$

(d) $(x + 4)^2 + (y - 5)^2 = 25$

(e) $(x + 5)^2 + (y - 1)^2 = 9$

(f) $(x - 6)^2 + (y + 7)^2 = 49$

(g) $(x - 5)^2 + (y - 4)^2 = 16$

(h) $x^2 + (y - 1)^2 = 4$

7.2 Finding the equation of a tangent to a circle

If you know the coordinates of where the tangent touches the circle and the coordinates of the centre of the circle, then you can find the gradient of the line joining these two points using the formula:

$$\text{Gradient} = \frac{y_2 - y_1}{x_2 - x_1}$$

You would then use this gradient to work out the gradient of the tangent as these two lines are perpendicular to each other. If one line has a gradient m_1 and the other a gradient of m_2 then as the lines are perpendicular

$$m_1 m_2 = -1$$

You would then use the coordinates of the point where the tangent touched the circle and the gradient of the tangent and substitute them into the following formula to give the equation of the tangent

$$y - y_1 = m(x - x_1)$$

The following example will help explain the method.

Example

4 Circle C has centre A and equation $x^2 + y^2 - 4x + 2y - 20 = 0$.

(a) Find the coordinates of the centre A and the radius of C.

(b) The point P has coordinates (5, 3) and lies on circle C. Find the equation of the tangent to C at P.

Answer

4 (a) We will use the method of completing the square here to work out the coordinates of the centre A and the radius of the circle C.

$x^2 + y^2 - 4x + 2y - 20 = 0$

$(x - 2)^2 + (y + 1)^2 - 4 - 1 - 20 = 0$

$(x - 2)^2 + (y + 1)^2 = 25$

$(x - 2)^2 + (y + 1)^2 = 5^2$

Hence coordinates of the centre A are (2, −1) and radius is 5.

Completing the square is used here but you could of course use the alternative method involving the formula.

(b) Gradient of the line joining the centre of the circle A (2, −1) to point P (5, 3) is given by:

$$\text{Gradient} = \frac{y_2 - y_1}{x_2 - x_1} = \frac{3 - (-1)}{5 - 2} = \frac{4}{3}$$

Line AP is a radius of the circle. The tangent at point P will be perpendicular to the radius AP.

For perpendicular lines, the product of the gradients = − 1

Hence $m \times \left(\frac{4}{3}\right) = -1$

Gradient of tangent $m = -\frac{3}{4}$

Equation of the tangent having gradient $m = -\frac{3}{4}$ and passing through the point P (5, 3) is

$$y - 3 = -\frac{3}{4}(x - 5)$$

$$4y - 12 = -3x + 15$$

$$3x + 4y - 27 = 0$$

> The formula for a straight line is used here. The formula for the equation of a straight line having gradient m and passing through the point (x_1, y_1) is $y - y_1 = m(x - x_1)$

7.3 Finding where a circle and straight line intersect or touch

There are two ways in which a straight line can intersect or touch a circle:

1 The line and circle can intersect in two places like this:

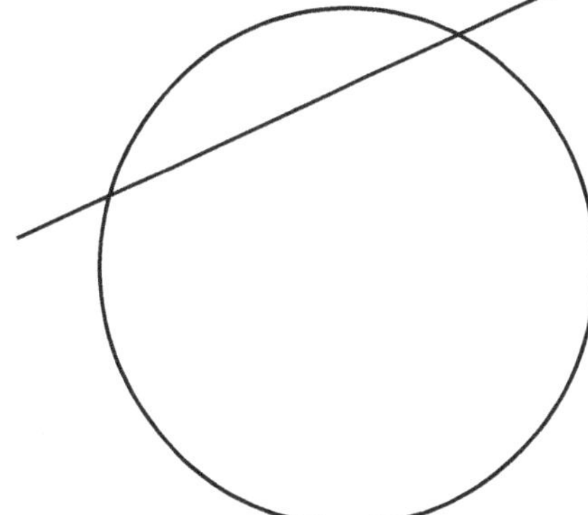

2 The line and circle can touch in one place. This means the straight line skims the surface and becomes a tangent to the circle and also makes a right angle with the radius.

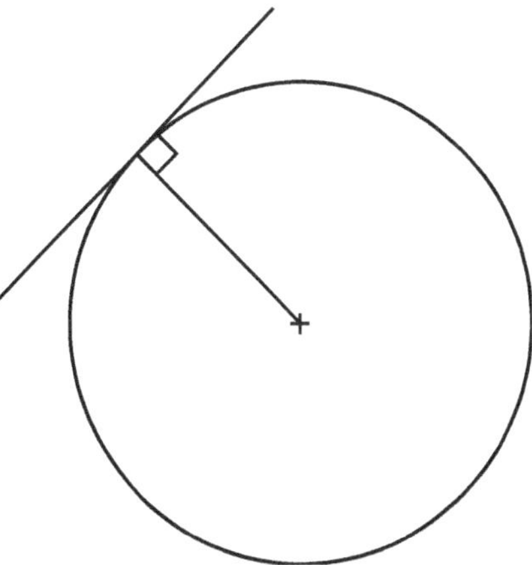

To find the coordinates of intersection or touching

To find the coordinates you need to know the equation of the circle and the equation of the straight line. These are then solved simultaneously. You can use the straight line equation to find x in terms of y or y in terms of x. You then substitute this into the equation of the circle and then solve the resulting equation. Sometimes there will be two different roots (i.e. solutions), which means the circle and line cut in two places. Sometimes there will be two equal roots which means the circle and line meet in one place, i.e. the line is a tangent to the circle.

If there are no real roots to the equation, it means the line and circle do not intersect.

Example

5 A circle C has equation $x^2 + y^2 + 2x - 12y + 12 = 0$.

The line with equation $x + y = 4$ intersects the circle at two points P and Q. Find the coordinates of P and Q.

Answer

5 To find the points of intersection we solve the two equations simultaneously.

$$x + y = 4$$

$$\text{So } y = 4 - x$$

Putting $y = 4 - x$ into the equation of the circle, gives

$$x^2 + (4 - x)^2 + 2x - 12(4 - x) + 12 = 0$$

$$x^2 + 16 - 8x + x^2 + 2x - 48 + 12x + 12 = 0$$

$$2x^2 + 6x - 20 = 0$$

Dividing by two gives $x^2 + 3x - 10 = 0$

Factorising gives $(x + 5)(x - 2) = 0$

Solving gives $x = -5$ or 2

These two x-coordinates are put into the equation of the line to find the corresponding y-coordinates.

When $x = -5$, $y = 4 - (-5) = 9$

When $x = 2$, $y = 4 - 2 = 2$

Hence coordinates of intersection are $(-5, 9)$ and $(2, 2)$.

Always check to see if a quadratic equation can be divided through by a number as it simplifies the equation and makes factorisation easier.

Identifying or showing whether a line and circle intersect and, if so, how many times

If the circle and line do not touch or intersect, the resulting quadratic equation, when the two equations are solved simultaneously, will have no real roots.

A real root is a solution such as $x = 3$. If a root is not real it will involve the square root of a negative number, so for example, $x = \sqrt{-3}$ is a non-real root as we cannot find the square root of a negative number. This is because you cannot find two numbers that are the same that multiply together to give a negative number.

When a quadratic equation is expressed in the form $ax^2 + bx + c = 0$ there is a quantity called the discriminant which is given by

Discriminant = $b^2 - 4ac$.

So if we had the quadratic equation $x^2 - 3x + 2$ we would compare this with $ax^2 + bx + c = 0$ and obtain $a = 1$, $b = -3$ and $c = 2$. The discriminant can then be found by substituting these values into $b^2 - 4ac$ thus giving $(-3)^2 - 4(1)(2) = 1$.

To prove that there are no real roots to a quadratic in the form $ax^2 + bx + c = 0$ we can show that the discriminant $b^2 - 4ac < 0$.

Note that:

If $b^2 - 4ac > 0$ there are two real and distinct roots, meaning the circle and line intersect in two places.

If $b^2 - 4ac = 0$ there are two real and equal roots (i.e. only one solution), meaning the circle and line meet in one place. The line is therefore a tangent to the circle.

If $b^2 - 4ac < 0$ there are no real roots meaning the circle and line do not intersect.

TAKE NOTE !

The sign of the disciminant is important so be careful of the signs when working it out.

Exam practice

1. The circle C has centre A and equation

$$x^2 + y^2 - 4x + 6y = 3$$

(a) Write down the coordinates of A and find the radius of C.

(b) A straight line has equation $y = 4x - 7$.
This straight line intersects the circle C at two points. Find the coordinates of these two points.

Answer

1 (a) Comparing the equation $x^2 + y^2 - 4x + 6y = 3$ with the equation $x^2 + y^2 + 2gx + 2fy + c = 0$ we can see $g = -2, f = 3$ and $c = -3$.

Centre A has coordinates $(-g, -f) = (2, -3)$

Radius $= \sqrt{g^2 + f^2 - c} = \sqrt{(2)^2 + (-3)^2 + 3} = \sqrt{16} = 4$

(b) Substituting $y = 4x - 7$ for y into the equation for the circle gives:

$$x^2 + (4x - 7)^2 - 4x + 6(4x - 7) = 3$$

$$x^2 + 16x^2 - 56x + 49 - 4x + 24x - 42 = 3$$

$$17x^2 - 36x + 4 = 0$$

$$(17x - 2)(x - 2) = 0$$

$$x = \frac{2}{17} \text{ or } x = 2$$

The x-coordinates are put into the equation of the straight line to find the y-coordinates of the points of intersection.

When $x = \frac{2}{17}, y = 4\left(\frac{2}{17}\right) - 7 = -6\frac{9}{17}$

When $x = 2, y = 4(2) - 7 = 1$

Hence the curve intersects the straight line at the points $\left(\frac{2}{17}, -6\frac{9}{17}\right)$ and $(2, 1)$

---

2 Circle C has centre A and radius r. The points $P\ (0, 5)$ and $Q\ (8, -1)$ are at either end of a diameter of C.

(a) (i) Find the coordinates of A.

(ii) Show that $r = 5$.

(iii) Write down the equation of C.

(b) Verify that the point $R\ (7, 6)$ lies on C.

(c) Find the equation of the tangent at point R.

Answer

2 (a) (i) A is the mid-point of PQ.

The formula for the mid-point $\left(\frac{x_1 + x_2}{2}, \frac{y_1 + y_2}{2}\right)$ is used here.

Hence coordinates of A are

$$\left(\frac{0 + 8}{2}, \frac{5 + (-1)}{2}\right) = (4, 2)$$

(ii) The length of a straight line joining the two points $A(4, 2)$ and $(0, 5)$ is given by:

$$\text{Distance } AP = r = \sqrt{(x_2 - x_1)^2 + (y_2 - y_1)^2}$$
$$= \sqrt{(0-4)^2 + (5-2)^2}$$
$$= \sqrt{16 + 9}$$
$$= \sqrt{25}$$
$$= 5$$

(iii) Equation of the circle is

$$(x - 4)^2 + (y - 2)^2 = 25$$

The equation of a circle having centre (a, b) and radius r is given by $(x - a)^2 + (y - b)^2 = r^2$

(b) If R (7, 6) lies on the circle, the coordinates will satisfy the equation of the circle.

$$(x - 4)^2 + (y - 2)^2 = (7 - 4)^2 + (6 - 2)^2$$
$$= 9 + 16$$
$$= 25$$
$$= 5^2$$
$$= \text{RHS}$$

So the coordinates satisfy the equation of the circle.

Here you prove that the left-hand side of the equation with the coordinates of the point entered for x and y equals the right-hand side of the equation.

(c) Gradient of line $AR = \dfrac{6-2}{7-4} = \dfrac{4}{3}$

AR is a radius so it is perpendicular to the tangent at R.

Gradient of tangent $= -\dfrac{3}{4}$

Equation of tangent is

$$y - 6 = -\frac{3}{4}(x - 7)$$
$$4y - 24 = -3x + 21$$
$$4y + 3x - 45 = 0$$

The gradient of the tangent and a point through which it passes is substituted into the equation for a straight line.

---

3 A (1, 10) , B (8, 9) and C (7, 2) are three points.

(i) Find the coordinates of the midpoint, M, of AC. [1]

(ii) Find the equation of the circle with AC as diameter. [4]

(iii) Show that B lies on this circle. [1]

(iv) Prove that AM and BM are perpendicular. [3]

(v) BD is a diameter of this circle. Find the coordinates of D. [3]

(OCR FSMQ June 2012 q10)

The mid-point formula is used here.

Answer

3 (i) The mid-point, M of the line AC joining the two points with coordinates (1, 10) and (7, 2) is

$$\left(\frac{1+7}{2}, \frac{10+2}{2}\right) = (4, 6)$$

(ii) Distance MC $= \sqrt{(x_2 - x_1)^2 + (y_2 - y_1)^2}$

$$= \sqrt{(7-4)^2 + (2-6)^2} = \sqrt{9+16} = \sqrt{25} = 5$$

The equation of a circle having centre (a, b) and radius r is given by

$(x - a)^2 + (y - b)^2 = r^2$

For this circle, centre is (4, 6) and radius is 5.

$(x - 4)^2 + (y - 6)^2 = 25$

(iii) If point B lies on the circle, then its coordinates (i.e. (8, 9)) will satisfy the equation of the circle.

$$(x - 4)^2 + (y - 6)^2 = (8 - 4)^2 + (9 - 6)^2$$
$$= 16 + 9$$
$$= 25$$

This is equal to the right-hand side of the equation so the coordinates lie on the circle.

There is an alternative way of finding the coordinates of D. You could first use the gradient of BM which has already been found and the coordinates of B to find the equation of the line BM. Then you can solve the equation of the line with the equation of the circle to find the points of intersection. One of these points will be B, which is known, and the other will be point D.

(iv) Gradient of AM $= \frac{y_2 - y_1}{x_2 - x_1} = \frac{6-10}{4-1} = \frac{-4}{3} = -\frac{4}{3}$

Gradient of BM $= = \frac{y_2 - y_1}{x_2 - x_1} = \frac{6-9}{4-8} = \frac{-3}{-4} = \frac{3}{4}$

Product of gradients $= \left(-\frac{4}{3}\right)\left(\frac{3}{4}\right) = -1$. Since the product is −1, the lines are perpendicular to each other.

(v) Vector from B to M is $\binom{-4}{-3}$

Hence, vector from M to D is the same $\left[\text{i.e. } \binom{-4}{-3}\right]$.

As M is (4, 6) we subtract 4 from the x-coordinate and 3 from the y-coordinate to give the coordinates of D which are (0, 3)

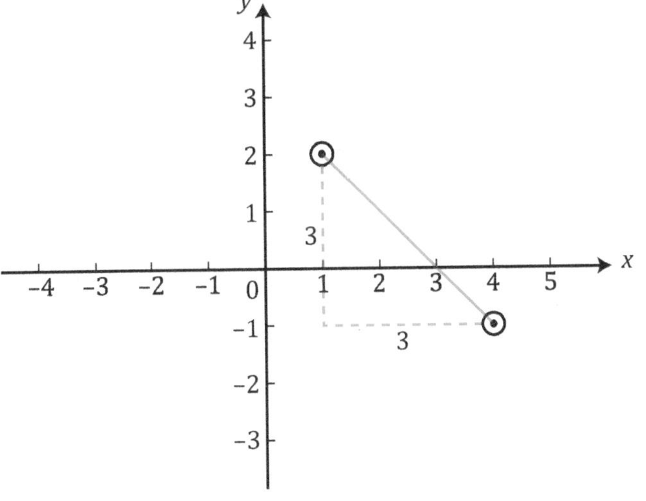

4 Find the equation of the circle having centre (1, 2) and passing through the point (4, −1).

Answer

4 First find the radius of the circle. You can either use the distance between two points formula or sketch the points on a set of axes and use Pythagoras' theorem.

Here we will use Pythagoras' theorem.

By Pythagoras' theorem, length of line $= \sqrt{3^2 + 3^2} = \sqrt{18}$.

Equation of circle having centre (1, 2) and passing through the point (4, −1) is

$$(x - 1)^2 + (y - 2)^2 = 18$$

5 A circle has the equation $x^2 + y^2 = 21$. Determine whether the point (4, 3) lies inside or outside this circle.

Answer

5 Radius of the circle $= \sqrt{21} = 4.58$

The length of a straight line joining the two points (x_1, y_1) and (x_2, y_2) is given by:

$$\sqrt{(x_2 - x_1)^2 + (y_2 - y_1)^2}$$

Distance of the point (4, 3) from the centre of the circle (0, 0)

$$= \sqrt{(x_2 - x_1)^2 + (y_2 - y_1)^2}$$

$$= \sqrt{(4 - 0)^2 + (3 - 0)^2} = \sqrt{16 + 9} = \sqrt{25} = 5$$

This distance is greater than the radius of the circle, so the point lies outside the circle.

Test yourself

Answer the following questions and check your answers before moving onto the next topic.

1 The circle C has equation $x^2 + y^2 - 8x - 6y = 0$.

Find the coordinates of the centre of circle C and its radius.

2 A circle has the equation $x^2 + y^2 - 4x + 6y = 3$.

(a) Find the coordinates of the centre of the circle and its radius.

(b) Show that the point P (2, 1) lies on the circle.

3 Circle C has centre A (2, 3) and radius 5.

(a) Find the equation of circle C in the form

$$x^2 + y^2 + ax + by + c = 0$$

where a, b and c are constants to be determined.

(b) Find the equation of the tangent to the circle at the point P (5, 7).

4 (a) Find the coordinates of the centre of the circle with equation

$$x^2 + y^2 - 4x + 8y + 4 = 0.$$

(b) Prove that the point P (6, −4) lies on the circle.

5 The diameter of a circle is AB, where A and B are the points (1, −4) and (9, 10) respectively.

(a) Find the centre of the circle.

(b) Show that the radius of the circle is $\sqrt{65}$.

(c) Using your answers to parts (a) and (b), find the equation of the circle in the form

$$x^2 + y^2 + ax + by + c = 0.$$

6 A circle has the equation $x^2 + y^2 = 40$. Determine whether the point (4, 3) lies inside or outside this circle.

7 A circle has diameter AB where A and B are the points (0, −3) and (4, 1) respectively.

(a) Find the coordinates of the centre of the circle.

(b) Show that the radius of the circle is $2\sqrt{2}$.

Topic summary

The two forms for the equation of a circle

A circle having an equation in the form $(x - a)^2 + (y - b)^2 = r^2$ has centre (a, b) and radius r.

A circle having an equation in the form $x^2 + y^2 + 2gx + 2fy + c = 0$ has a centre $(-g, -f)$ and radius $\sqrt{g^2 + f^2 - c}$.

Circle properties

The angle in a semicircle is a right angle.

The perpendicular from the centre to a chord bisects the chord.

The radius to a point on the circle and the tangent through the same point are perpendicular to each other.

Finding the equation of a tangent to a circle at a point on the circle

If the coordinates of the centre of the circle and the point where the tangent touches the circle are known you can use these to find the gradient of the line joining these two points.

You can then use the equation of perpendicular lines $m_1m_2 = -1$ to work out the gradient of the tangent.

Then use the coordinates of the point where the tangent touches the circle and the gradient of the tangent and put these into the equation $y - y_1 = m(x - x_1)$ to find the equation of the tangent.

Inequalities and linear programming

In this topic you will be expanding on the material covered in Topic 4 to look at how graphs can be used to represent linear inequalities in two variables rather than just one. You will show the information containing the two variables graphically and use linear graphs to solve two-dimensional maximisation and minimisation problems.

This topic covers the following:

8.1 Drawing lines and regions representing inequalities

Here is some advice about drawing straight line graphs before you start:

- Choose a scale that will make your graph as large as possible.
- Label both set of axes.
- Ensure that you label the origin.
- Write the equation (NB not the inequality) of the line next to the line to which it refers.

Suppose we want to show the region represented by the following inequalities:

$$x \geq 0$$

$$y \geq 0$$

$$3x + 2y \geq 12$$

We first need to draw the boundary lines which are the lines given by the following equations:

$x = 0$

$y = 0$

$3x + 2y = 12$

If an inequality contains an equals component (e.g. $x + y \geq 1$) then it is possible to have values of x and y which lie on the line itself. When this happens we show that values are allowed on the line by drawing the line as a solid line. For lines not containing an equals component (e.g. $x + y > 1$) values are not allowed on the line so the line is shown as a broken line (dotted or dashed). In both cases the lines themselves are often called boundary lines.

The lines $x = 0$ and $y = 0$ are the y-axis and x-axis respectively. The $3x + 2y = 12$ line can be drawn by finding two points which lie on the line. If we substitute $x = 0$ and then $y = 0$ into the equation we can obtain the corresponding y- and x-values.

When $x = 0$ is substituted into the equation of the line we obtain $3(0) + 2y = 12$ which gives the y-coordinate, $y = 6$. Hence, the point is $(0, 6)$.

When $y = 0$ is substituted into the equation of the line we obtain $3x + 2(0) = 12$, which gives the x-coordinate $x = 4$. Hence, the point is $(4, 0)$.

The line can now be added to a graph.

 **TIP**

You must write the equation next to the line and not the inequality.

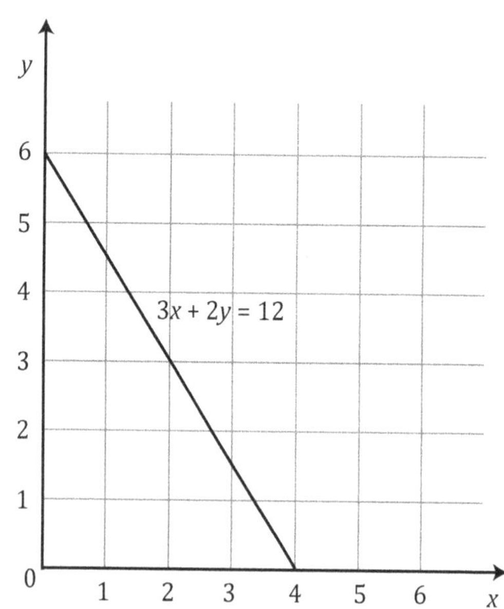

Remember that we already have the lines $x = 0$ and $y = 0$ as they are the y-axis and x-axis respectively.

We have to show the region represented by the inequality $3x + 2y \geq 12$. As there is a greater than or equals in the inequality, the allowable (sometimes called the feasible) region is on or above this line. We always shade the region not required, which is below this line.

For the other two inequalities which represent the axes, we want the region above the x-axis and to the right of the y-axis, so we shade underneath the x-axis and to the left of the y-axis.

Note that we just add the shading to near the lines for the moment as the complete shading can be added once the allowable region has been established.

Adding the shading, we obtain the following.

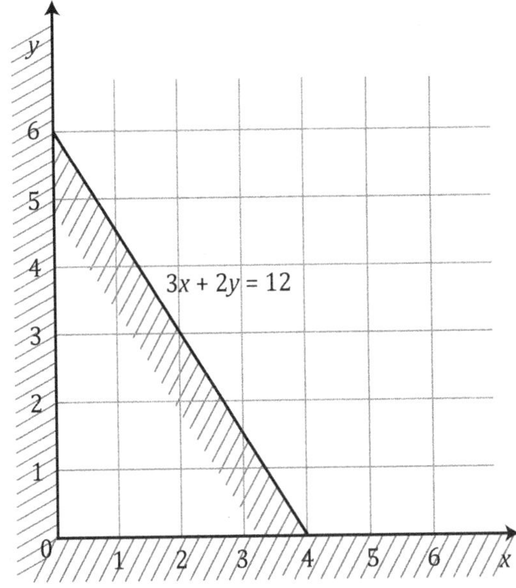

The allowable region is above the sloped line and above the x-axis from $x = 4$ onwards and the region to the right of the y-axis from $y = 6$. We now complete the shading to show all the regions covered by the graph that are not allowed. Doing this we obtain the following.

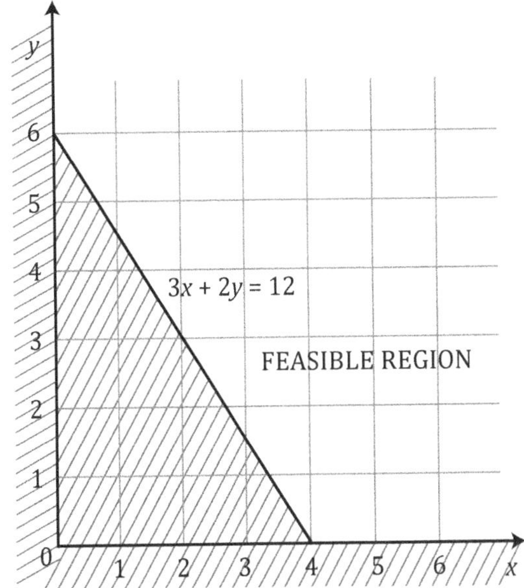

Do not assume that the feasible region is a set shape. You have to go by the shading to determine the feasible region. In the above it is not the triangular region that is feasible. You can also see that the feasible region is not a closed shape. You will find that in a lot of the examination questions the feasible region is open-ended (i.e. not a closed shape).

Examples

1 Draw lines representing the following three inequalities on the one graph:

$$y \geq 2x + 1$$

$$x + y \geq 1$$

$$y \leq -3$$

Indicate on your graph the region for which the above inequalities hold. You should shade the region which is **not** required.

Answer

1 In order to draw a graph it is necessary to find the points of intersection of the lines with the x- and y-axes.

For $y = 2x + 1$ when $x = 0, y = 1$ and when $y = 0, x = -\frac{1}{2}$.

For $x + y = 1$ when $x = 0, y = 1$ and when $y = 0, x = 1$.

For $y = 3$ we have a line parallel to the x-axis.

It is important to note that all the inequalities in the question have an equals part (i.e. $\geq$ or $\leq$) and this means that all the lines can be drawn as solid lines.

The graph showing the straight lines can now be drawn.

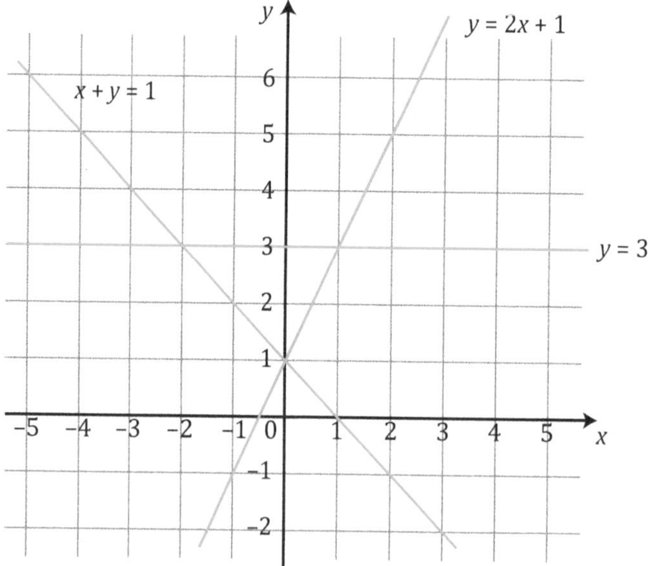

Now we add the shading to each line in turn.

Starting with $y = 2x + 1$, as we are showing $y \geq 2x + 1$, the feasible region is on and above this line. We shade the unwanted region, which is below the line.

TIP

You should always write the equations rather than the inequalities next to the lines.

The shading is added like this:

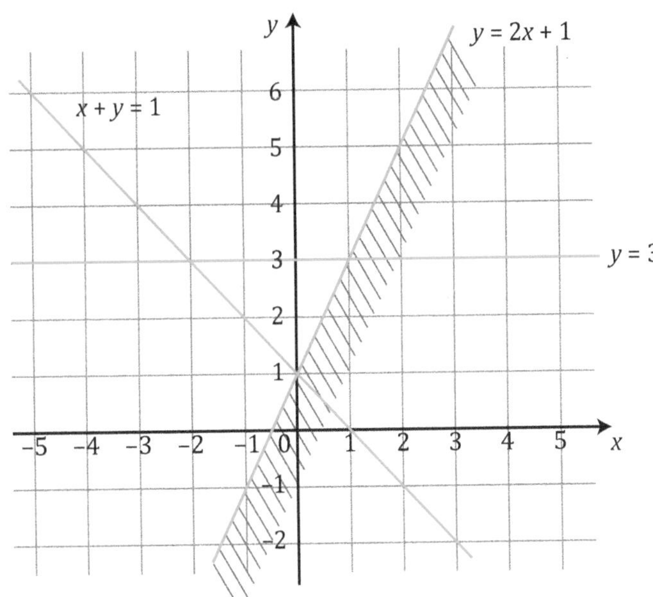

For the inequality $x + y \geq 1$ the feasible region is above the line so we need to shade the region not required which is under the line. For the line $y \leq -3$ the feasible region is below the line so we need to shade above the line.

The graph is now as follows:

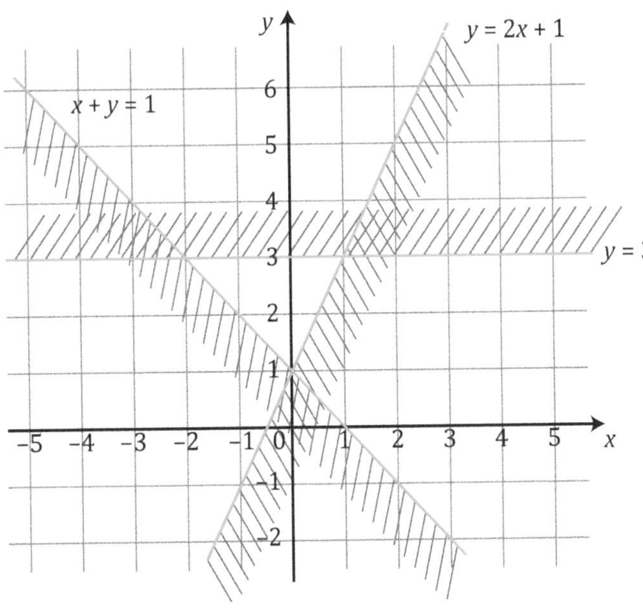

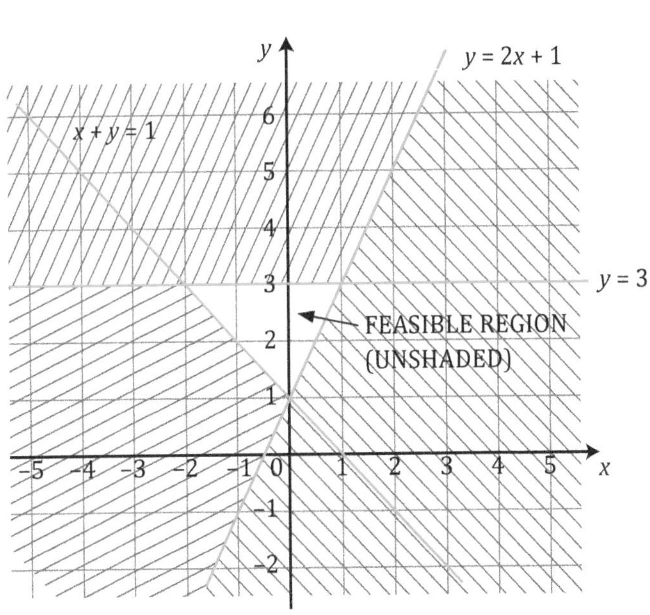

The feasible region (i.e. the area where all the inequalities are true) is the area that is bounded by shaded lines on all its sides. To make it clear where this is, we need to shade all the parts of the graph except this region.

2 Here are some inequalities. You have to decide which region of the graph (1 to 6) is covered by each of the following lists of inequalities.

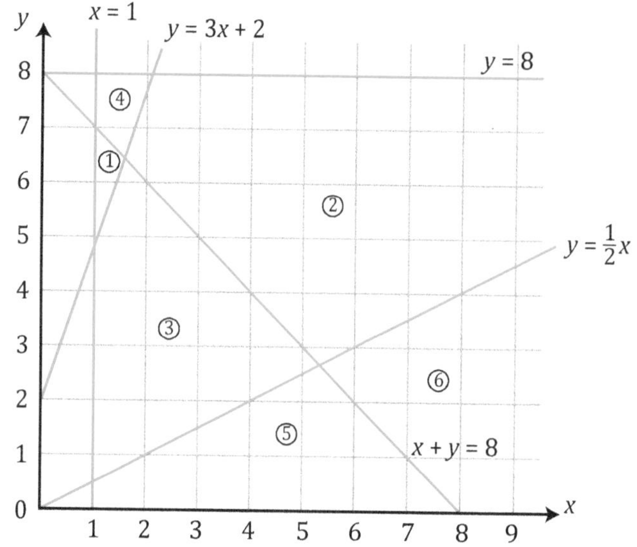

(a) $x \geq 1, y \geq \frac{1}{2}x, y \leq 3x + 2, x + y \leq 8.$

(b) $x \geq 1, y \leq 8, y \geq 3x + 2, x + y \geq 8.$

(c) $y \geq 0, x \geq 1, x + y \leq 8, y \leq \frac{1}{2}x.$

(d) $x + y \geq 8, y \geq \frac{1}{2}x, y \leq 8, y \leq 3x + 2.$

(e) $x \geq 1, x + y \leq 8, y \geq 3x + 2.$

(f) $y \leq \frac{1}{2}x, x + y \geq 8, y \geq 0.$

Answer

2 (a) Region = 3

(b) Region = 4

(c) Region = 5

(d) Region = 2

(e) Region = 1

(f) Region = 6

Progress check

1. For each of the following graphs use the equation of the line and the shading to write an inequality representing the unshaded part of the graph:

(a)

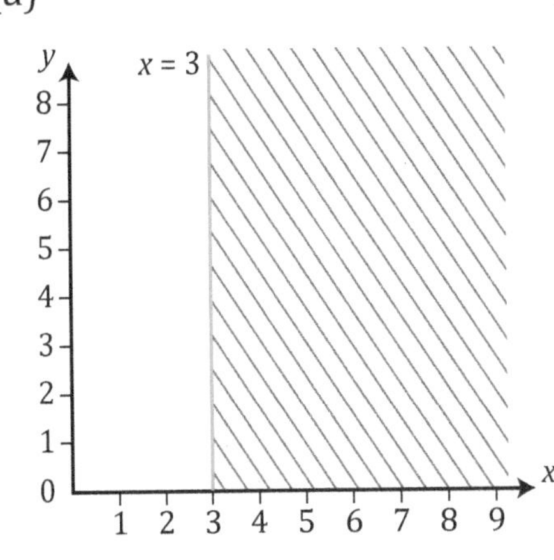

(b)

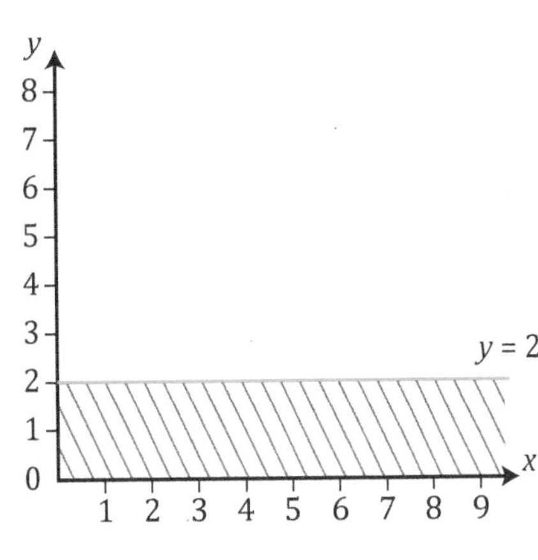

(c)

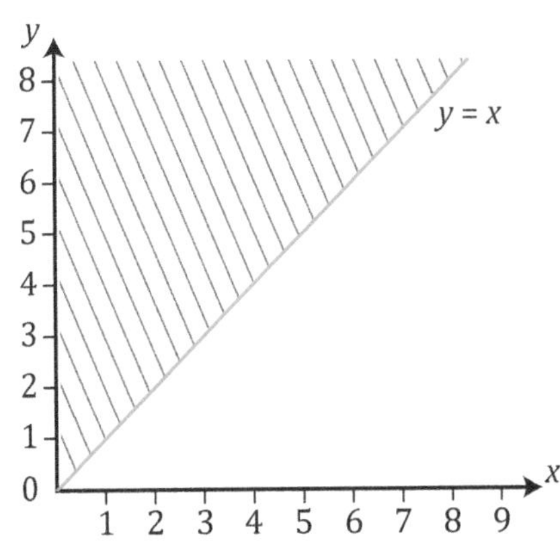

(d)

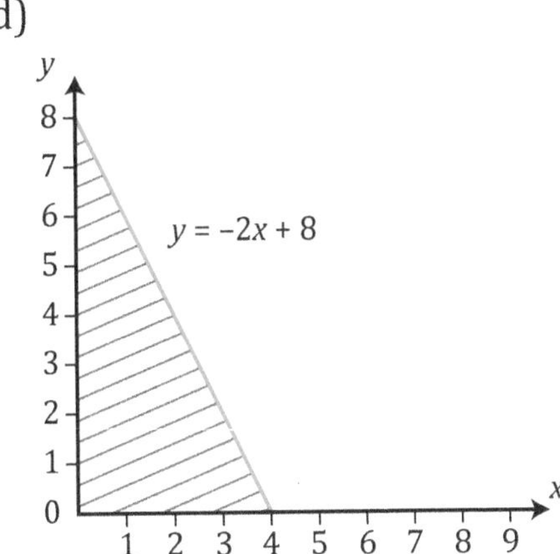

(e)

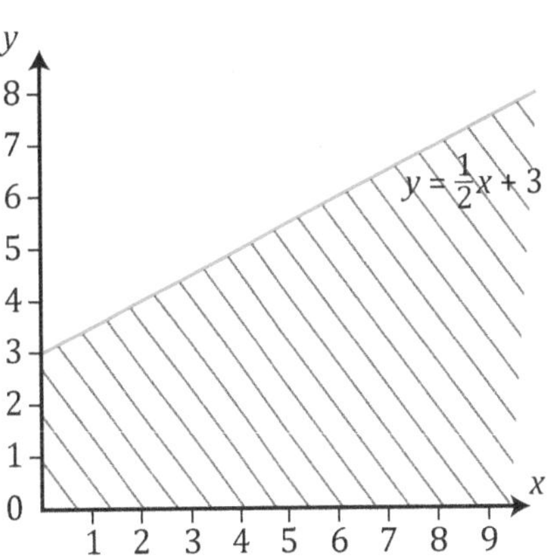

2. Here are some inequalities. You have to decide which region of the graph (1 to 5) is covered by each of the following lists of inequalities:

(a) $x \geq 0, 3x + 4y \leq 24, 7x - 12y \geq 0$

(b) $x \geq 6, 3x + 4y \leq 24, y \geq 0$

(c) $x \geq 0, y \leq 7, 3x + 4y \geq 24, x \leq 6$

(d) $x \leq 6, y \geq 0, 7x - 12y \leq 0, 3x + 4y \leq 24$

(e) $x \leq 6, 7x - 12y \leq 0, 3x + 4y \geq 24$

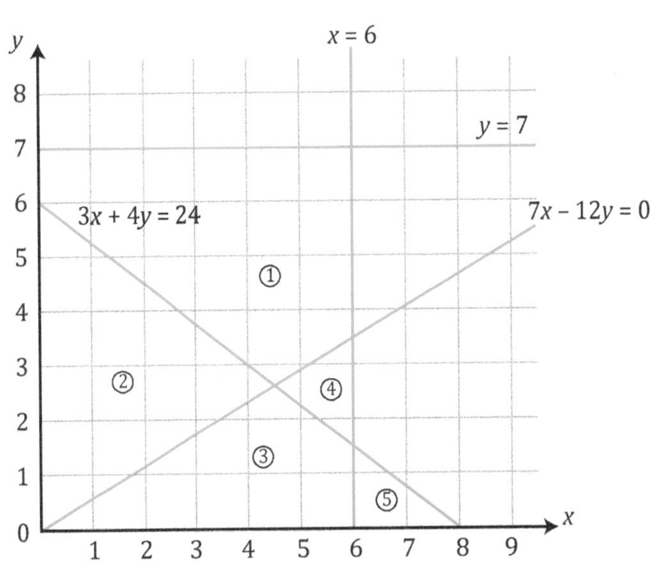

3 Draw axes from 0 to 12 on graph paper and draw lines for each of the following inequalities. Show the feasible (allowable) region by shading all the parts of graph that are **not** in the feasible region.

$y \geq 0$

$x \geq 2$

$y \leq \frac{1}{3}x$

$2y \leq 12 - x$

4 Copy out the graph. Indicate on your graph the region where the following inequalities hold. You should indicate the region by shading the regions where the inequalities do not hold.

$2y \geq 10 - x$

$y \leq -1.5x + 15$

$y \geq x$

$x \geq 0$

$y \geq 0$

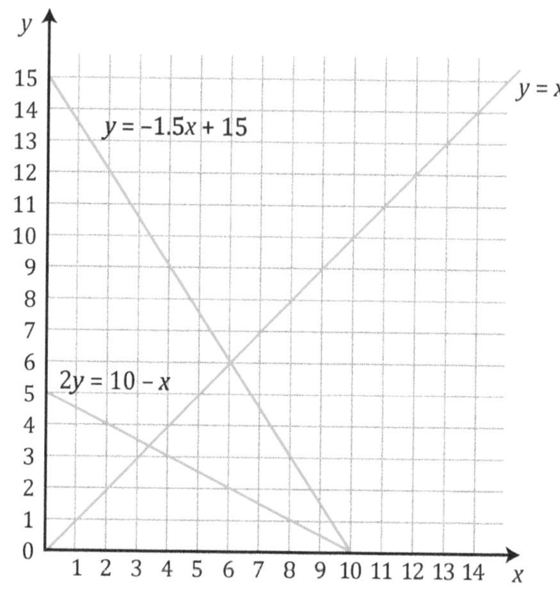

8.2 Expressing real situations as linear inequalities

Expressing real situations as linear inequalities can be hard unless you can translate the important words in a sentence into an inequality.

Here are some phrases and their translations into inequalities:

Phrase	Word inequality	Symbol inequality
At least	Greater than or equal to	$\geq$
Up to	Less than or equal to	$\leq$
More than	Greater than	$>$
No/Never more than	Less than or equal to	$\leq$
Less than	Less than	$<$

Examples

3 If the number of boys in a class is x and the number of girls in the same class is y, express each of the following statements as inequalities in terms of x, y or both.

(a) The number of girls is always less than the number of boys in the class.

(b) The total number of pupils in the class is always less than 30.

(c) The number of boys in the class is never more than double the number of girls in the class.

TAKE NOTE !

Note that 'never more than' means less than or equal to.

Answer

3 (a) $y < x$

(b) $x + y < 30$

(c) $x \leq 2y$

4 Tickets are being sold for a school play. Full price tickets cost £10 and concession tickets cost £6. There can be no more than 400 tickets sold and the money from the sale of the tickets must cover at least the cost of the production which is £1500.

If x is the number of full price tickets and y is the price of concession tickets, write four inequalities that must be obeyed.

Answer

4 The sale of the tickets must cover at least the cost of the production which is £1500 can be expressed as

$10x + 6y \geq 1500$

There can be no more than 400 tickets sold can be expressed as

$x + y \leq 400$

Although it does not say so in the question, the number of tickets of x or y cannot be negative so we have the following two inequalities.

$x \geq 0$

$y \geq 0$

8.3 Maximisation and minimisation problems

In real-life situations in applications such as business or economics we often have to find the maximum profit, the minimum cost or the minimum use of resources. These are examples of optimisation problems which can be solved using a mathematical technique called linear programming.

Linear programming

In linear programming we have a series of inequalities which are often called constraints. By showing these inequalities graphically we can find the feasible region where all the inequalities are obeyed and find possible pairs of values for the unknown quantities x and y.

A function called an objective function is found in terms of x and y and is the quantity that is to be maximised or minimised in the problem.

8.4 Use of the objective function

Once the feasible region has been found, then any of the values of x and y lying inside this region are allowable. In linear programming problems there is usually a quantity that must be minimised or maximised. For example, if you are manufacturing two products, you may want to find out about which number of each product to make in order to maximise your profit.

The objective function is the function that must be maximised or minimised taking into account the constraints.

Suppose there are two products called A and B with the number of A made called x and the number of B made called y. There are usually a number of constraints which can be put on x and y and we can only take pairs of values that lie in the feasible region of graph.

Suppose the sale of A gives a £5 profit for each item made and sold and the sale of B gives a profit of £8 for each item made and sold. So we can write the following function for the profit that we need to maximise. If P is the total profit, we can write:

$P = 5x + 8y$

A quantity (i.e. Profit in this case) expressed in terms of the quantities plotted on the x- and y-axes is called the objective function. Hence the function $5x + 8y$ is the objective function in our example.

You would now need to find the coordinates (x, y) in the feasible region that would give the largest value for $5x + 8y$. This would occur on or very near to the corners of the area that represents the feasible region. The following example shows how the objective function can be used.

Example

5 (a) By drawing suitable graphs on the same axes, indicate the region for which the following inequalities hold. You should shade the region which is **not** required.

$$2x + 3y \le 12$$

$$2x + y \le 8$$

$$y \ge 0$$

$$x \ge 0$$

(b) Find the maximum value of $x + 3y$ subject to these conditions.

Answer

5 (a) In order to draw a graph it is necessary to find the points of intersection of the lines with the x- and y-axes.

For $2x + 3y = 12$ when $x = 0, y = 4$ and when $y = 0, x = 6$.

For $2x + y = 8$ when $x = 0, y = 8$ and when $y = 0, x = 4$.

Wait till you have done this for all the lines before drawing them on the graph as you will need to determine the scale to be used for the x- and y-axes.

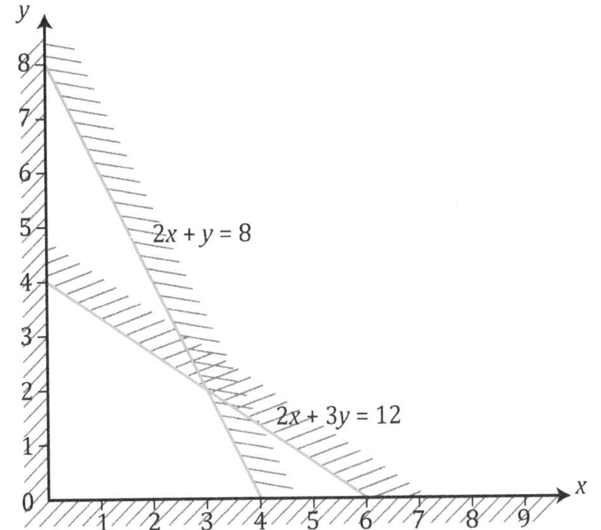

The graph can now be drawn and the two lines added. We do not need negative sections to the graph as in the question we are told $y \ge 0$ and $x \ge 0$.

Once you have worked out where the allowable (i.e. feasible) area lies, you need to complete your shading by shading all the areas shown on the graph that are outside this region.

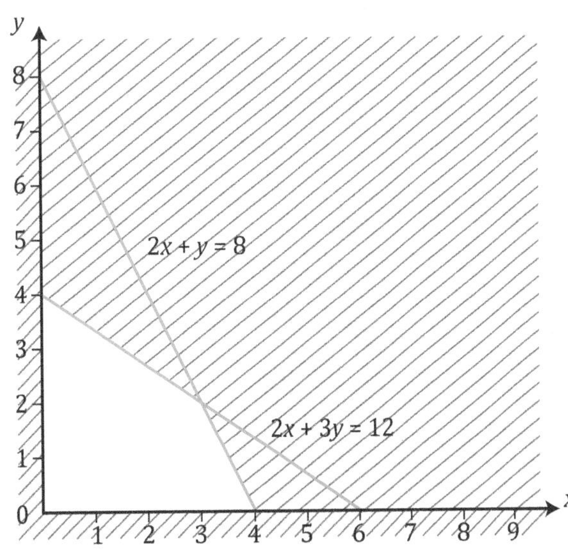

You are not asked to draw the graph on graph paper so all that is needed is to draw suitable scales which can be decided by the points of intersection of the lines on the axes. You should then add the equations to the lines and work out the parts that are not allowed so that they can be shaded. It is easy to overlook the shading for $x \ge 0$ and $y \ge 0$ which are the y-axis and x-axis respectively. Also ensure you shade the region which is **not** allowable rather than the region which is allowable.

(b) $x + 3y$ is the objective function and we need to find a point in the feasible region whose coordinates when substituted into $x + 3y$ would give the maximum value.

This will occur at or near to the vertices of the feasible region.

There are three vertices at (0, 4), (4, 0) and (3, 2).

Note that the vertices are the corners of the polygon for the feasible region.

At (0, 4), $x + 3y = 0 + 3(4) = 12$

At (4, 0), $x + 3y = 4 + 3(0) = 4$

At (3, 2), $x + 3y = 3 + 3(2) = 9$

Hence the maximum value of $x + 3y$ subject to the conditions is 12.

Progress check

5 A company manufactures two products A and B. Product A takes 3 man-hours to make and uses £20 of raw materials. Product B takes 4 man-hours to make and uses £30 of raw materials. There are up to 100 man-hours available per week and a budget of no more than £1500 for raw materials.

If x is the number of product A made and y is the number of product B made, write:

(a) An inequality showing the constraints on the number of man-hours available, and

(b) An inequality showing the constraints on the budget available for the purchase of raw materials.

(c) Marketing information means that the number of product B made should be less than three times the number of product A made. Write an inequality to represent this information.

6 A baker bakes two types of cookie, chocolate chip and oatmeal raisin. Each chocolate chip cookie sells for 80p and each oatmeal raisin cookie sells for 90p. The baker cannot make more than 800 cookies per week in total and they cannot make more than 500 cookies of each kind. The baker must make at least one-third as many chocolate chip cookies as oatmeal raisin cookies.

(a) If x is the number of chocolate chip cookies produced and y is the number of oatmeal raisin cookies produced, write down four inequalities to represent the information outlined above.

(b) Write down an equation in terms of x and y for the total amount of money in £ the sale of cookies would bring into the business in one week.

7 A new van hire firm intends to hire out two types of van: large vans and small vans. Large vans cost £20,000 to buy and small vans cost £15,000 to buy. There is a maximum of £500,000 available to buy the vans. The firm knows that larger vans are likely to be more popular so they are planning to buy at least three times more larger vans than smaller vans.

The large vans cost £50 per week to run and the smaller vans cost £40 per week to run and there is a maximum amount of £1200 per week available to cover the running costs.

If x is the number of small vans bought and y is the number of large vans bought, other than $x \geq 0$ and $y \geq 0$, write down three other inequalities described above.

Plotting a line to represent the objective function

In Example 5 we found the maximum value for the objective function by considering points on or near to the vertices of the allowable region on the graph.

There is another way the values of x and y could be found and this involves plotting the line representing the objective function.

In the example the objective function was $x + 3y$. Suppose we let $P = x + 3y$.

We now have three unknowns so it is necessary to use a numerical value for P in order to plot the line. It does not really matter what value you choose for P as long as it gives a line that can be shown on the graph you have drawn.

Suppose we choose to make $P = 3$ we can then write

$3 = x + 3y$

or $x + 3y = 3$.

To plot this line we find the intercepts on the x- and y-axes which are $x = 3$ and $y = 1$ respectively.

Plotting this line on the graph gives the following:

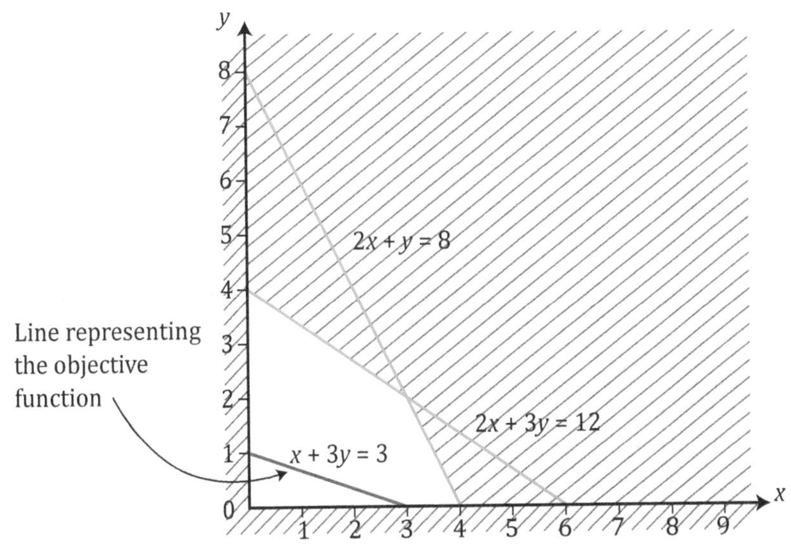

TAKE NOTE !

Ensure the axes are properly labelled and the equations for each of the lines are written next to the lines.

We can draw any line parallel to the line we have just drawn to represent the objective function. We therefore use a ruler and keeping the ruler parallel to the line we have just drawn, move the ruler until we meet the vertex furthest to the left which in this case is the point (0, 4). These are then the values of x and y that will give the maximum value for the objective function.

Exam practice

1 (i) Illustrate on one graph the following three inequalities.

$$y \geq x - 1$$

$$x \geq 2$$

$$2x + y \geq 8$$

Draw suitable boundaries and shade areas that are excluded. [4]

(ii) Write down the minimum value of y in this region. [1]

(OCR FSMQ June 2009 q10)

Answer

1 (i) For $y = x - 1$, when $x = 0$, $y = -1$ and when $y = 0$, $x = 1$.

For $2x + y = 8$, when $x = 0$, $y = 8$ and when $y = 0$, $x = 4$.

For $x = 2$, we have a line parallel to the y-axis at $x = 2$.

The graph can now be drawn and the three lines added.

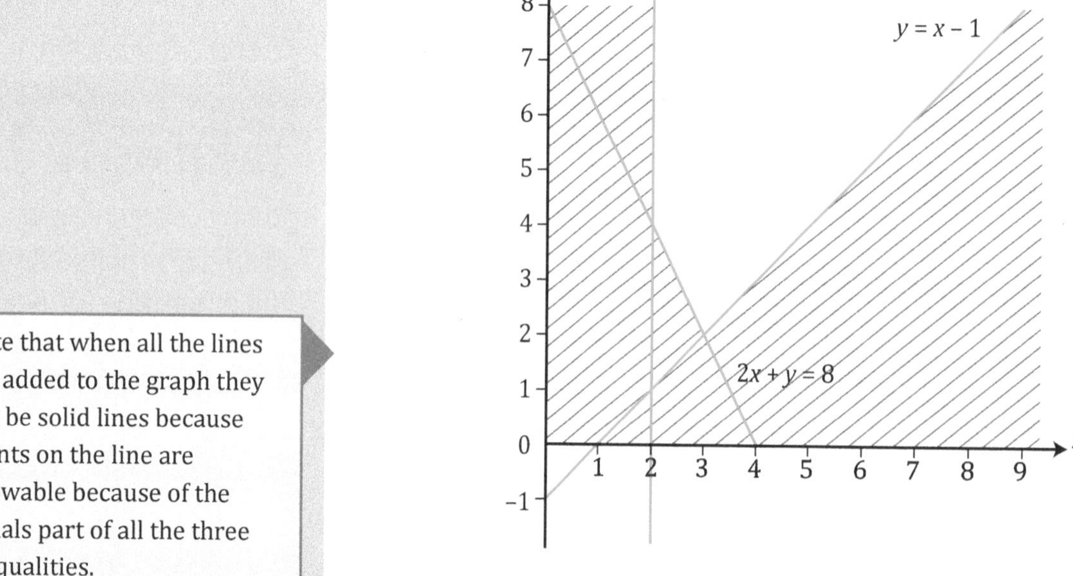

Note that when all the lines are added to the graph they can be solid lines because points on the line are allowable because of the equals part of all the three inequalities.

Once the lines are added to the graph, write the equation next to the line it represents. Now add the shading in the following way.

Because we require $x \geq 2$ the allowable area is on the line and to the right of the line. We need to shade the area that is excluded so we need to shade the area to the left of this line.

$y \geq x - 1$ means that the allowable area is above or on the line so we shade the area excluded which is below this line.

$2x + y \geq 8$ means that the allowable area is above or on the line so we shade the area excluded which is below this line.

The unshaded area shown on the above graph is the allowable area.

(ii) The smallest value of y lying in the allowable region is at $y = 2$.

You look for the lowest value of y in the allowable area.

---

2 A firm has to transport 1500 packages to a site. It has a number of large vans which will transport 200 packages each and a number of small vans which will transport 100 packages each.

Let x be the number of large vans and let y be the number of small vans used.

(i) Write down an inequality based on the number of packages transported. [2]

The firm needs to use at least as many small vans as large vans.

(ii) Write a second inequality. [1]

(iii) Plot these two inequalities on a graph, using 1 cm to represent one van on each axis. Indicate the region for which these inequalities hold. Shade the area that is **not** required. [4]

A large van costs £80 to complete the trip and a small van costs £60 to complete the trip.

(iv) Write down the objective function and hence find from your graph the number of each type of van that will minimise the cost, and work out that cost. [4]

(v) What choice of vans should be made to minimise the cost if the restriction about the large and small vans is removed? Work out the cost in this case. [2]

(OCR FSMQ June 2010 q14)

Answer

 (i) The total number of packages transported = $200x + 100y$ and this must be greater than or equal to 1500. This can be written as:

$200x + 100y \geq 1500$

To draw the lines we first find the points each line cuts the x- and y-axes.

(ii) $y \geq x$

(iii) For $200x + 100y = 1500$, when $x = 0, y = 15$ and when $y = 0, x = 7.5$

For $y = x$, when $x = 0, y = 0$. We can then put any value for x, and y will be the same.

Adding these to the graphs and shading the regions not allowed we have the following (not to scale):

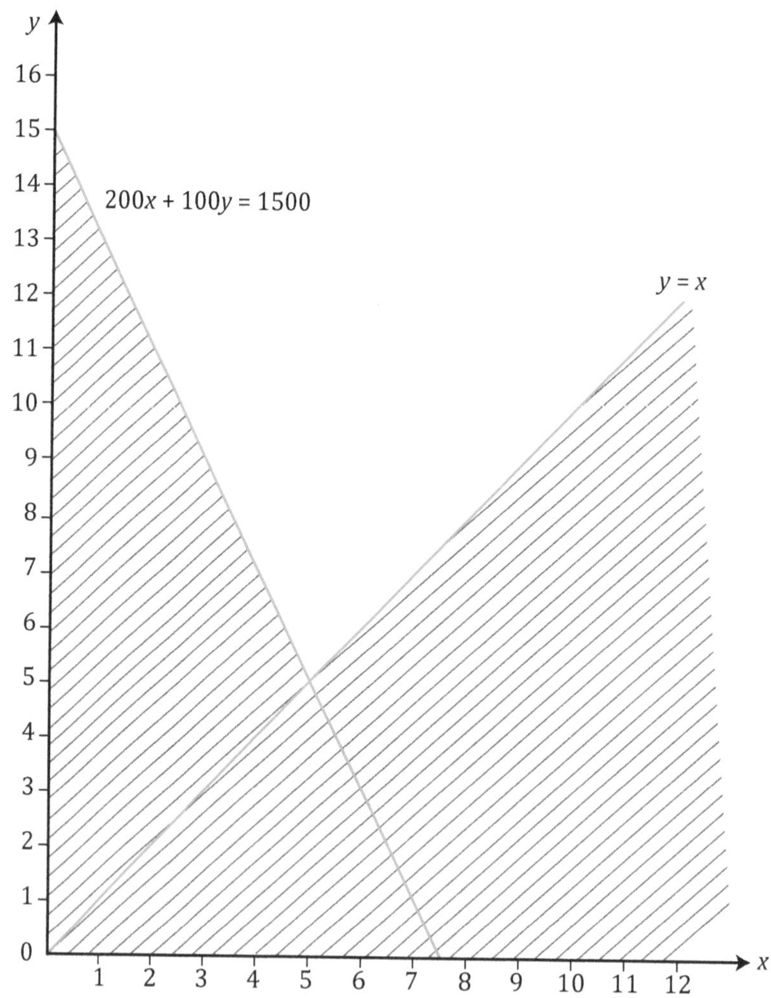

(iv) Cost $C = 80x + 60y$

The smallest value for C will occur at one of the vertices.

The smallest value will occur at (5, 5).

When $x = 5$ and $y = 5$, $C = 80(5) + 60(5) = 700$

Note that the only other possible point to consider is (0, 15) which would give a value for C of 900 which is not the smallest value.

(v) If the restriction 'use at least as many small vans as large vans' is removed then we would remove the inequality $y \geq x$ so the line $y = x$ would be removed from the graph leaving the following:

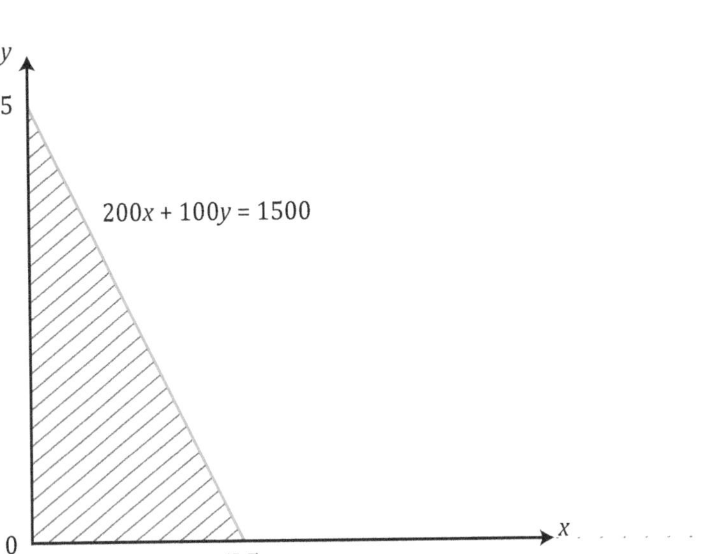

The minimum cost would be on or near the vertices.

The cost at (0,15) is C = 80(0) + 60(15) = 900

The cost at (8, 0) is C = 80(8) + 60(0) = 640

The cost at (7, 1) is C = 80(7) + 60(1) = 620

Hence the minimum cost is for 7 large vans and 1 small van giving a cost of £620.

Note that you cannot have (7.5, 0) as x has to be an integer.

Need to also investigate the points near to the vertex.

TIP

Remember to state the answer clearly at the end.

3. A small factory makes two types of components, X and Y. Each component of type X requires materials costing £18 and each component of type Y requires materials costing £11. In each week materials worth £200 are available.

Each component of type X takes 7 man-hours to finish and each component of type Y takes 6 man-hours to finish. There are 84 man-hours available each week.

Components cannot be part-finished at the end of the week. In addition, in order to satisfy customer demands, at least 2 of each type are to be made each week.

(i) The factory produces x components of type X and y components of type Y each week. Write down four inequalities for x and y. [4]

(ii) On a graph draw suitable lines and shade the region that the inequalities do not allow. (Take 1 cm = 1 component on each axis.) [5]

(iii) If all components made are sold and the profit on each component of type X is £70 and on each component of type Y is £50, find from your graph the optimal number of each that should be made and the total profit per week. [3]

(OCR FSMQ June 2005 q11)

≫ TIP

Read the question several times and try to isolate the parts of the question from which the inequalities can be written.

Answer

3. (i) Considering the cost of the components we have

$18x + 11y \leq 200$

Considering the time to make the components we have

$7x + 6y \leq 84$

Considering the customer demands we have

$x \geq 2$ and $y \geq 2$

(ii) For $18x + 11y = 200$, when $x = 0, y = 18.2$ and when $y = 0, x = 11.1$

For $7x + 6y = 84$, when $x = 0, y = 14$ and when $y = 0, x = 12$.

For $x = 2$ we have a line parallel to the y-axis.

For $y = 2$ we have a line parallel to the x-axis.

Drawing the graph and shading the areas that are unfeasible, we obtain the following:

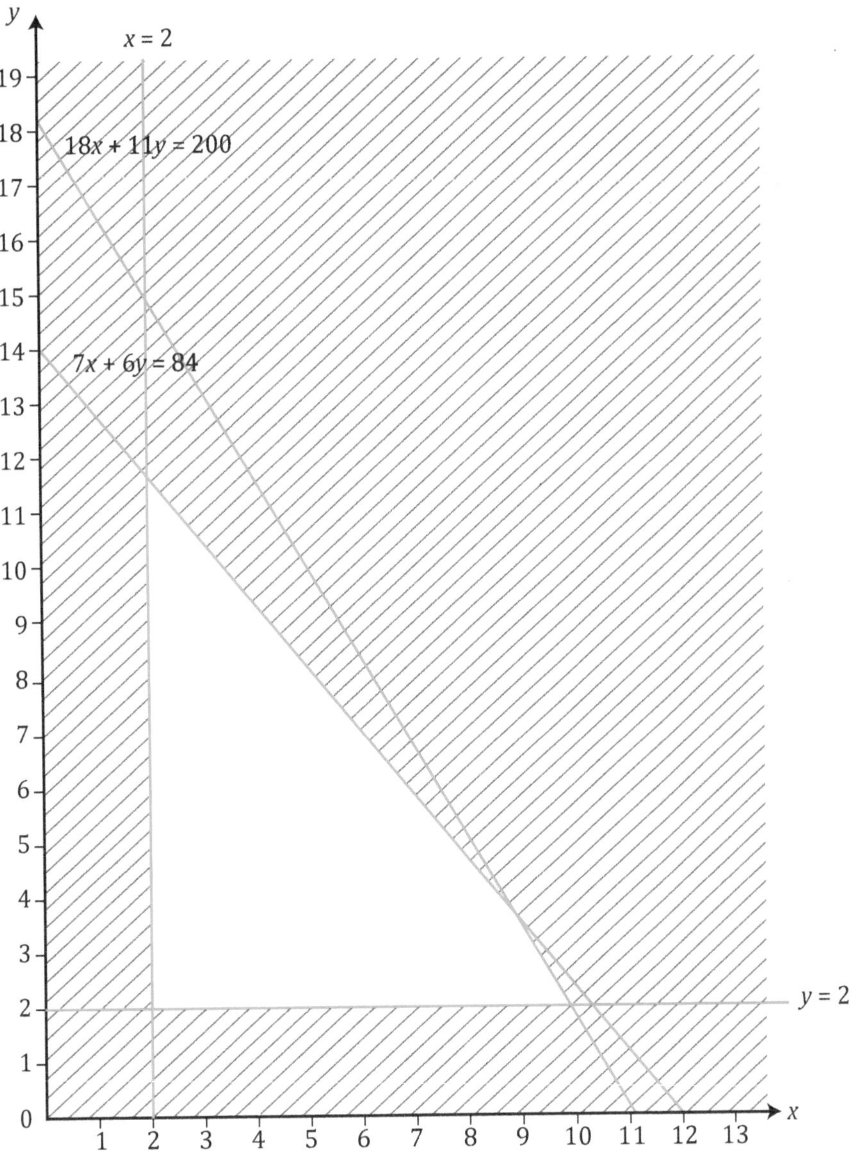

(iii) The objective function is $C = 70x + 50y$

This will have its maximum value at one of the vertices of the allowable (i.e. feasible) area.

The vertex at (9, 3) gives $C = 70(9) + 50(3) = 780$

The nearest integer point to the vertex at (2, 11.6) is (2, 11) and this gives $C = 70(2) + 50(11) = 690$.

The nearest integer point to the vertex at (9.9, 2) is (9, 2) and this gives $C = 70(9) + 50(2) = 730$.

Hence, the optimal number of each that should be made are 9 of X and 3 of Y per week and this gives a profit of £780 per week.

4 A number of students from a group of 20 boys and 30 girls are to be selected to attend a one-day conference.

The number of girls attending must be at least the same as the number of boys but no more than twice the number of boys.

(i) Let there be x boys and y girls selected.

Given that $x > 0$ and $y > 0$, write down four more inequalities to represent the information. [3]

(ii) Plot these inequalities on the grid provided. Indicate the region for which the inequalities hold. Shade the area that is *not* required. [5]

(iii) In order to attend the conference the students need to be given a special uniform.

The uniform for the boys costs £40 and the uniform for the girls costs £50. The school has £2000 to spend on the uniforms.

By plotting the appropriate line on your graph, find the maximum number of students that could go to the conference. [4]

(OCR FSMQ June 2013 q13)

Answer

4 (i) The maximum number of boys attending is 20 so this can be expressed as

$x \leq 20.$

The maximum number of girls attending is 30 so this can be expressed as

$y \leq 30.$

The number of girls attending must be at least the same as the number of boys can be expressed as $y \geq x$.

The number of girls attending must be no more than twice the number of boys can be expressed as $y \leq 2x$.

(ii) Note that the examination board supplies an answer sheet where you write your answers and for this question they include a blank graph like this so you do not have to worry about scales. If you make a mistake with your graph, then they also provide an additional blank graph you can complete.

The graphs of $y = x$ and $y = 2x$ both go through the origin. Use a suitable x-value with each such as $x = 20$ to give $y = 20$ and $y = 40$ respectively.

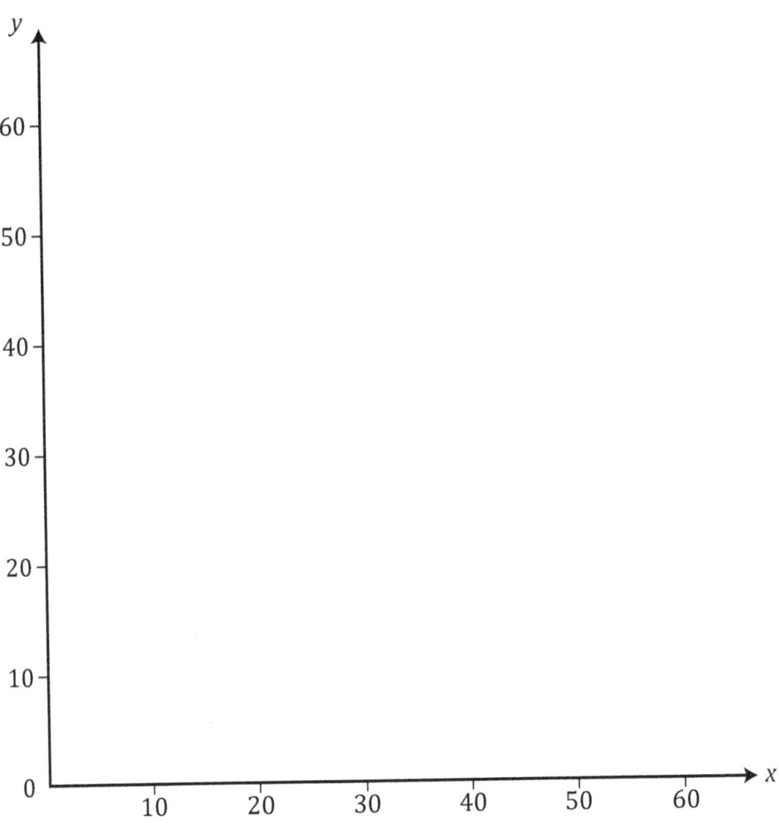

We note that all the inequalities have an equals component, which means values on the lines are allowable so all the lines are drawn as solid lines.

Adding the lines and marking on each line its equation we obtain the following:

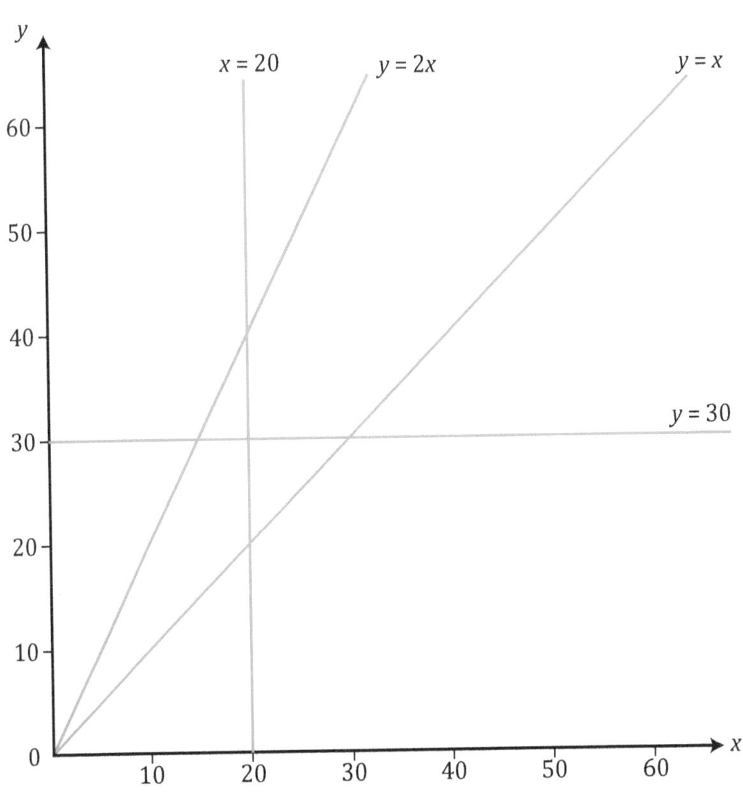

Adding the shading.

For $x \leq 20$ the allowable region lies on or to the left of the line $x = 20$, so to the right of this line is shaded.

For $y \leq 30$ the allowable region lies on and below the line $y = 30$, so above the line is shaded.

For $y \geq x$ the allowable region lies on and above the line $y = x$, so below the line is shaded.

For $y \leq 2x$ the allowable region lies on or below the line $y = 2x$ so above the line is shaded.

We add the partial shadings first so we know exactly where the allowable region is, before shading all the regions lying outside.

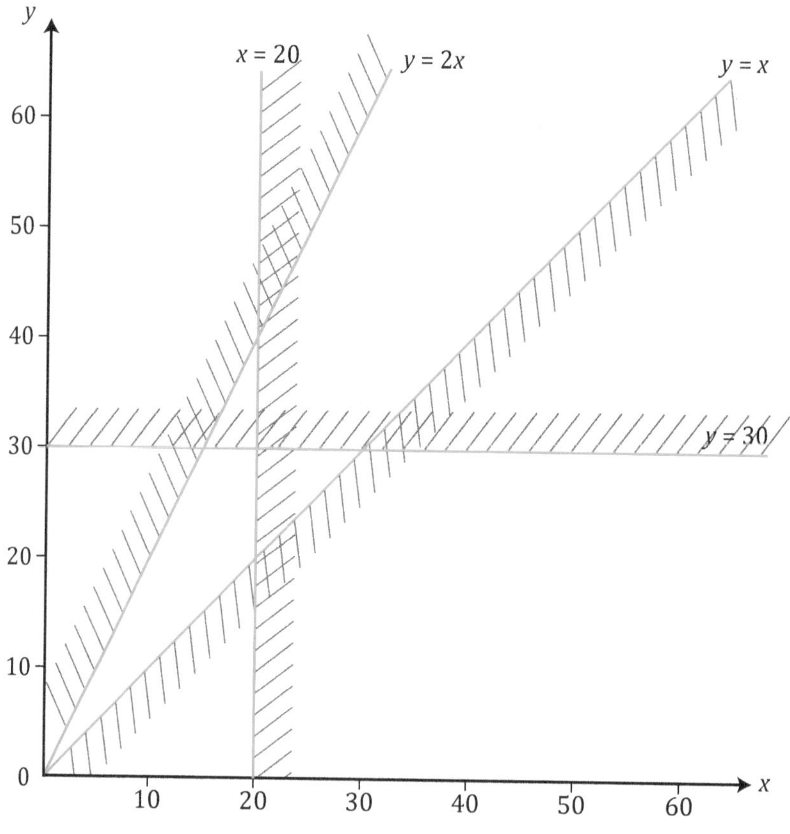

The next stage is to identify the feasible (allowable) region. This will be the region enclosed by the lines with all the shading on the opposite side of the line.

Once this is done, we can complete the shading of all the regions that are not feasible.

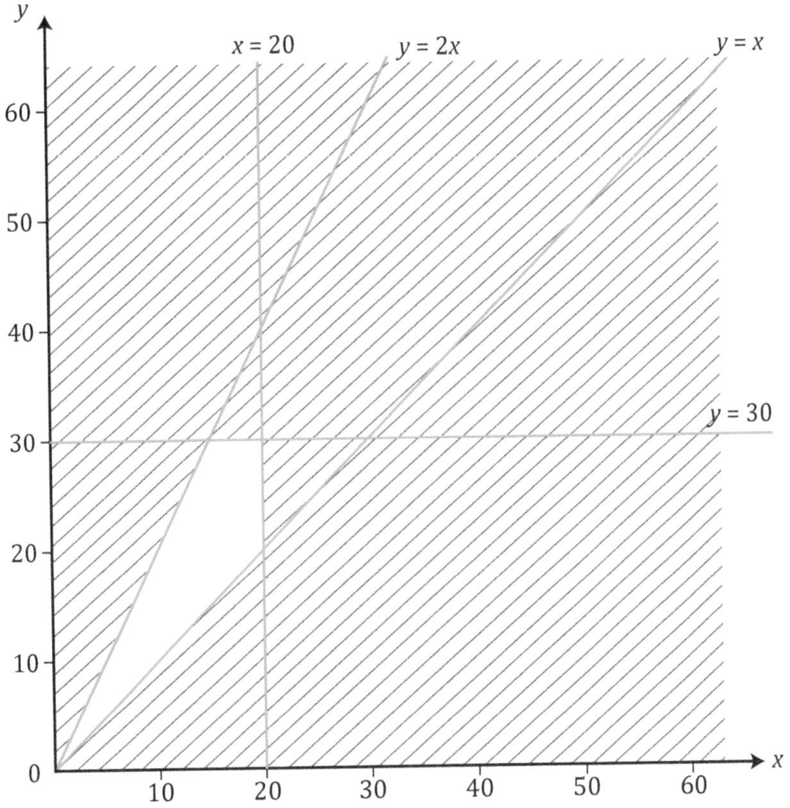

(iii) The cost for the uniforms = $40x + 50y$

Now this cost has to be less than or equal to 2000 so we can form the following inequality.

$40x + 50y \leq 2000$

The line we need to add to graph has the equation $40x + 50y = 2000$

We need to add the line to the graph, so we find the two points where the line intercepts the axes.

When $x = 0, y = 40$ and when $y = 0, x = 50$.

This line is now added to the graph and looking at the inequality we can see that above this line needs to be shaded. This small amount of shading is added and the graph is as follows:

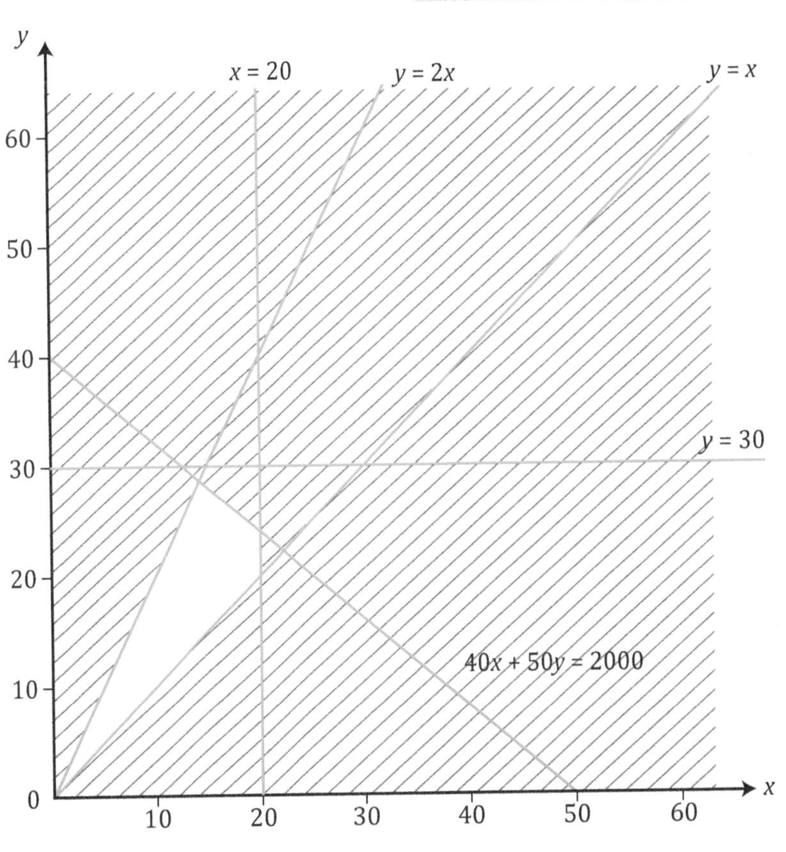

> It is important to note that this line is an additional inequality and is not the objective function.

The number of students that can attend the conference is give by $x + y$

If P is the number of persons attending, then we can write this as

$$P = x + y$$

Because we are trying to maximise the number of students attending, this is the objective function.

Now we know that $x + y$ gives the total number of students.

Just choose a value that is allowable and fairly near to the maximum which in this case is 50.

Let's say $x + y = 40$ (note that we know $x + y$ has to be 50 or less).

For the objective function, when $x = 0$, $y = 40$ and when $y = 0$, $x = 40$.

We now add the line representing the objective function to the graph.

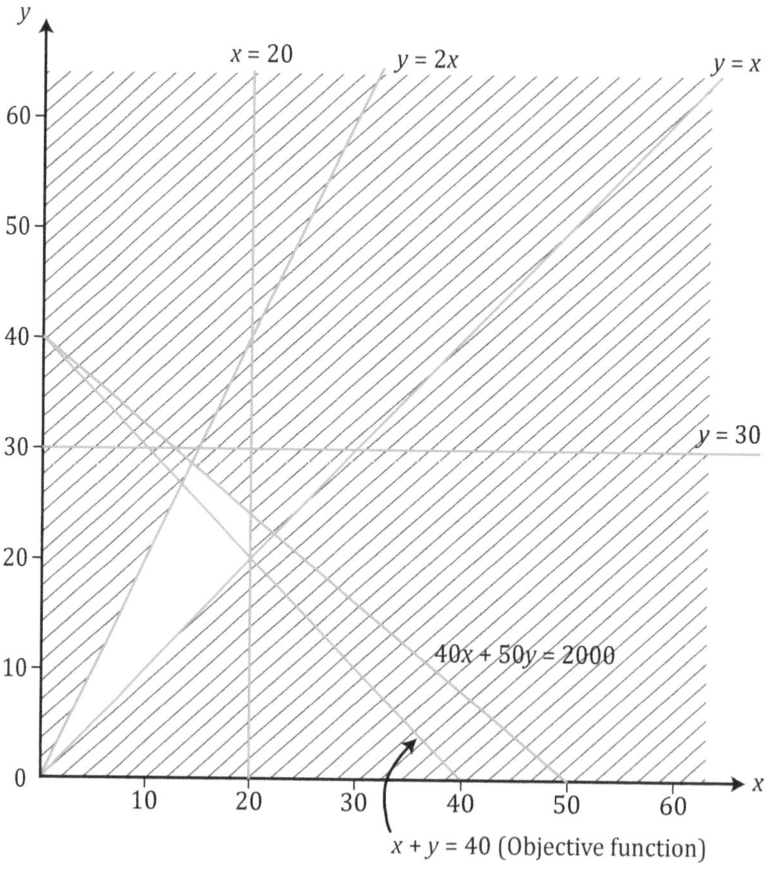

Now we could have let $x + y$ equal a whole range of values. If we plotted say $x + y = 45$ then it would be parallel to our line because it has the same gradient.

The maximum value of the objective function (i.e. $x + y$) will be given by a line which is parallel to the line we drew that passes through the allowable region that is furthest to the right.

You therefore need to add this line to the graph like this:

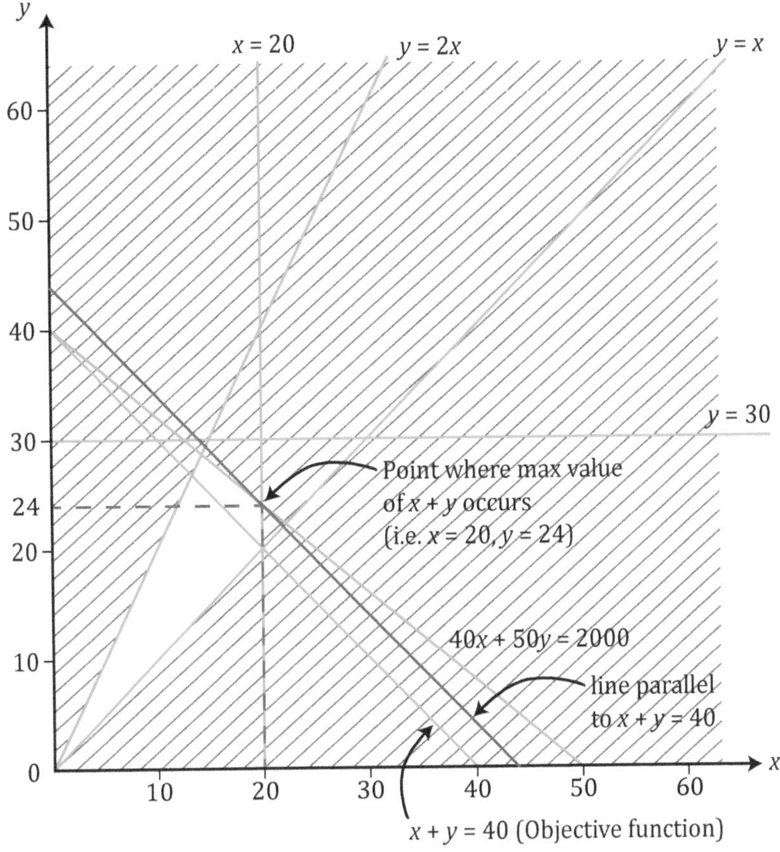

Maximum number of students that can go to the conference is 20 + 24 = 44.

Test yourself

1. A sweet manufacturer makes two types of bags of sweets: bag A with a profit of £2 and bag B with a profit of £5. A maximum of 150 of bag A and 120 of bag B can be made per week. On Monday morning enough raw materials arrive to make a total of 200 bags of sweets.

   Let x be the number of bag A and y be the number of bag B made each week.

   (a) Other than $x \geq 0$ and $y \geq 0$, write down three other inequalities that must be obeyed.

   (b) On graph paper, draw suitable boundaries for the five inequalities and shade areas that are excluded.

   (c) In order to maximise the profit, how many bags of each sweet should be made each week?

2. (a) Illustrate on one graph the following four inequalities:

   $$y \leq 10$$

   $$x \geq 2$$

   $$4x + y \leq 24$$

   $$y \geq 0$$

   Draw suitable boundaries and shade areas that are excluded.

   (b) Draw the line $2x + y = 20$ on your graph and hence use this line to find the integer values for x and y where $2x + y$ takes its minimum value.

3 72 children are going camping with their school. They are hiring tents and a large tent sleeps 8 children and costs £80 per week and a small tent sleeps 3 children and costs £20 per week.

The total number of tents cannot be more than 18. If x is the number of large tents and y is the number of small tents and at least one of each type of tent is chosen.

(a) Write an inequality to describe the constraints for the total number of tents.

(b) Write an inequality to describe the constraints for the total number of children.

(c) Plot the **four** inequalities on the same graph and indicate the region for which the inequalities hold by shading the area that is **not** required.

(d) Write down an expression for the total cost of hiring the tents.

(e) The expression for the total cost of hiring the tents is the objective function. It is a requirement that the total cost of hiring the tents is to be kept as small as possible. Find the integer values of x and y to determine the number of each tent required.

Topic summary

Many real situations have a number of constraints which can be expressed as inequalities. The values that are allowed in these situations can be shown as a region on a graph.

Graphs of inequalities

To show an inequality on a graph, follow these steps:

1 Using the equation of the boundary line find where the line cuts the x- and y-axes by substituting $y = 0$ and $x = 0$ in turn into the equation.

2 Draw a set of axes and mark the intercepts the line makes with the axes on it and join the points up with a straight line. If there is an equals part to the inequality a solid line is used and if there isn't, a dotted line is used.

3 Write the equation of the line next to the line.

4 Shade the region not required. Above the line if there is a $<$ or $\leq$ in the inequality or below the line if there is a $>$ or $\geq$ in the inequality.

Feasible regions and objective functions

The feasible region on a graph is the region where there are x- and y-values that are allowable and will obey all the inequalities. The feasible region is shown as the unshaded region on the graph.

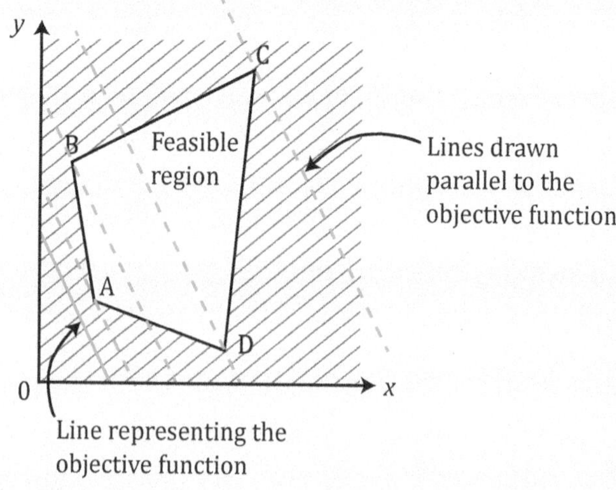

Draw a line to represent the objective function and draw a parallel line through the highest (or lowest) point in the feasible (i.e. allowable) region. The resulting values of x and y can then be substituted into the objective to find the maximum (or minimum) value.

Trigonometric ratios and the graphs of sine, cosine and tangent

This topic covers the trigonometric ratios sine, cosine and tangent and how they can be used to determine the lengths of sides and the sizes of angles. You will also learn how to draw the graphs of the trigonometric functions and how to use them. When you enter values for sin, cos or tan into a calculator you only obtain one angle, but in fact there are often several angles that need to be found. In this topic you will learn how to determine these other angles within a specified range. You will also learn about the sine and cosine rules and a new formula for finding the area of a triangle when the triangle does not contain a right angle.

This topic covers the following:

9.1 Sine, cosine and tangent functions

9.2 Finding angles using the CAST method

9.3 Finding angles using trigonometric graphs

9.4 The sine and cosine rules

9.1 Sine, cosine and tangent functions

TIP

Note that these ratios will not be given in the exam so you need to remember them.

Use the memory aid SOH CAH TOA to help remember the ratios.

The following ratios, covered in your GCSE studies, only apply to right-angled triangles:

$$\sin\theta = \frac{\textbf{opposite}}{\textbf{hypotenuse}}$$

$$\cos\theta = \frac{\textbf{adjacent}}{\textbf{hypotenuse}}$$

$$\tan\theta = \frac{\textbf{opposite}}{\textbf{adjacent}}$$

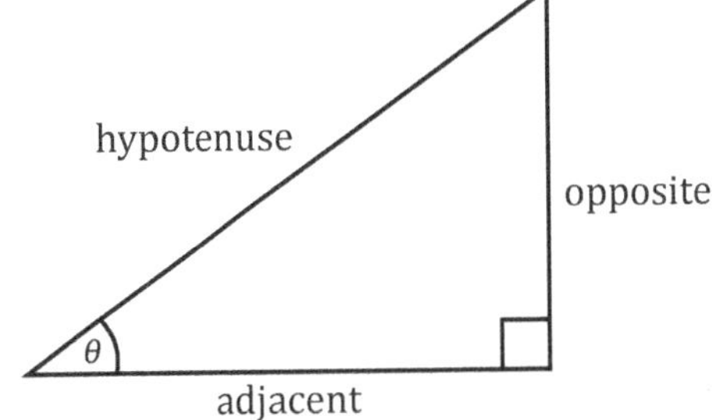

Using trigonometric ratios to find the lengths of sides

Trigonometric ratios can be used to find the unknown lengths of sides of a right-angled triangle provided one side and one angle are known. Suppose we want to find the length of the side marked x in the triangle shown.

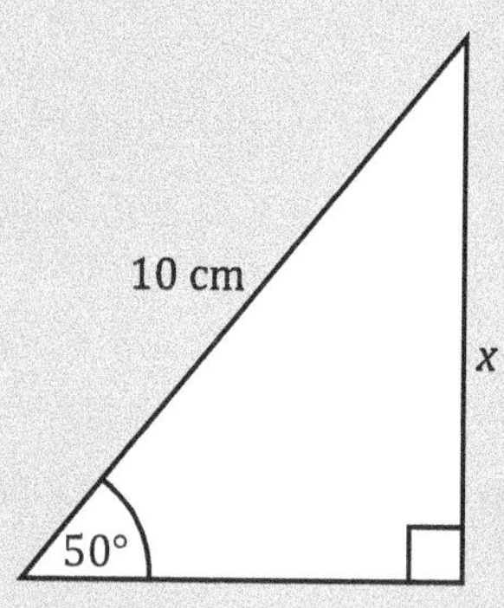

First decide which sides are known. Here 10 cm is the hypotenuse (H) and x is the opposite (O) (because it is opposite the given angle). We then pick which trigonometric ratio to use from SOH CAH TOA. Here O and H are needed so we need SOH which is short for $\text{Sin } \theta = \frac{\text{opposite}}{\text{hypotenuse}}$.

Now $\text{Sin } \theta = \frac{\text{opposite}}{\text{hypotenuse}}$

$\text{Sin } 50° = \frac{x}{10}$

Multiplying both sides by 10 we have $x = 10 \sin 50°$.

Hence $x = 7.66$ cm (3 s.f.).

Sometimes the side you need to find is on the bottom of the fraction rather than the top. The following example shows what to do in this situation.

Example

1 Find the length of the side marked x in the following triangle giving your answer to three significant figures.

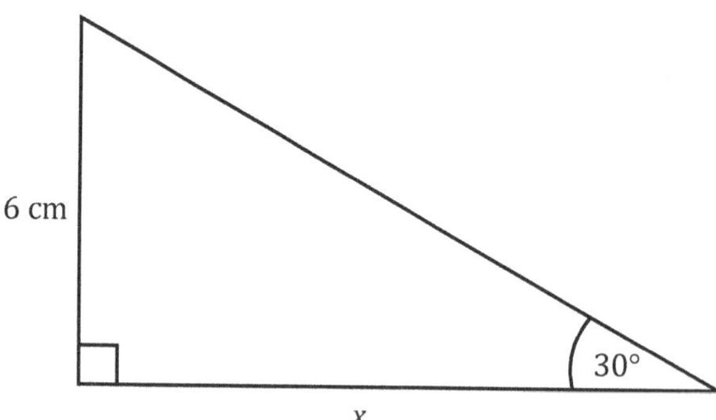

Answer

1 Here O and A are needed so we need TOA which is short for

$\text{Tan } \theta = \frac{\text{opposite}}{\text{adjacent}}$.

Now $\text{Tan } \theta = \frac{\text{opposite}}{\text{adjacent}}$

$\text{Tan } 30° = \frac{6}{x}$

Notice that x is in the denominator of the fraction.

Multiplying both sides by x we have $x \tan 30° = 6$

Dividing both sides by tan 30° we have $x = \dfrac{6}{\tan 30°}$

Hence $x = 10.4$ cm (3 s.f.).

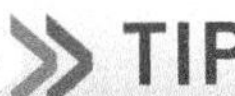

TIP

Always check with the question to see if the angle or side needs to be given to a certain number of significant figures or decimal places. You may lose marks if you do not give the answer to the required accuracy.

Using trigonometric ratios to find the size of an angle

The trigonometric ratios can be used to find the size of an angle of a right-angled triangle provided the lengths of two sides are known. The following example shows the method used.

Examples

2 Find the size of the angle θ for the following triangle giving your answer to one decimal place.

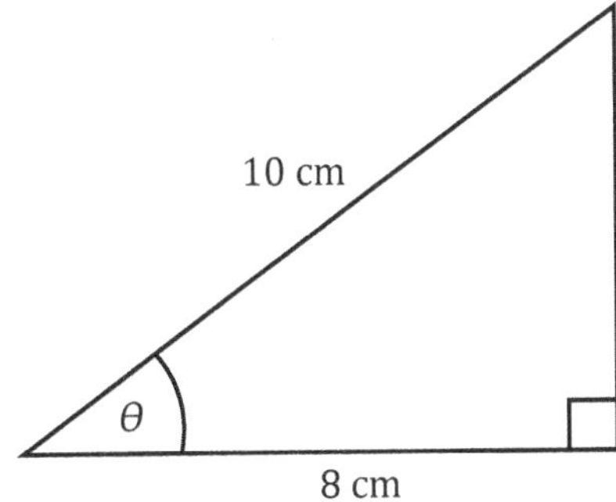

Answer

2 Here A and H are known so we need CAH which is short for

$$\text{Cos } \theta = \frac{\text{adjacent}}{\text{hypotenuse}}.$$

$$\text{Now Cos } \theta = \frac{\text{adjacent}}{\text{hypotenuse}}$$

$$= \frac{8}{10}$$

$$= 0.8$$

$$\theta = \cos^{-1}(0.8)$$

$$= 36.9° \text{ (1 d.p.)}$$

3 The diagram shows a right-angled triangle. Find the size of the angle θ giving your answer to the nearest degree.

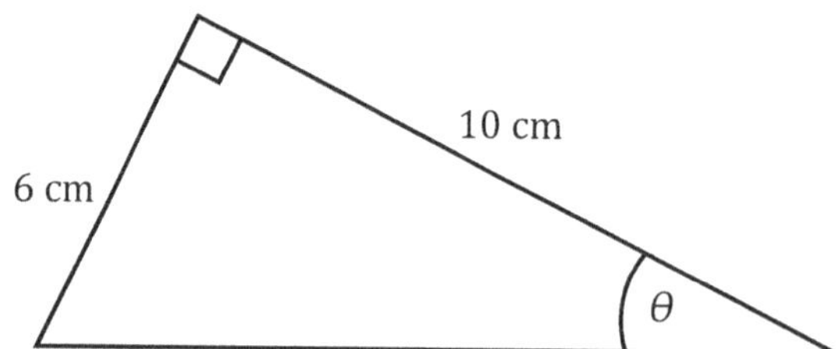

Answer

3 Here O and A are known so we need TOA which is short for

$$\text{Tan } \theta = \frac{\text{opposite}}{\text{adjacent}}.$$

$$\text{Now Tan } \theta = \frac{\text{opposite}}{\text{adjacent}}$$
$$= \frac{6}{10}$$
$$= 0.6$$
$$\theta = \tan^{-1}(0.6)$$
$$= 31° \text{ (nearest degree)}$$

4 Use the given triangle to prove that for $0° < \theta < 90°$, $\sin^2 \theta + \cos^2 \theta = 1$.

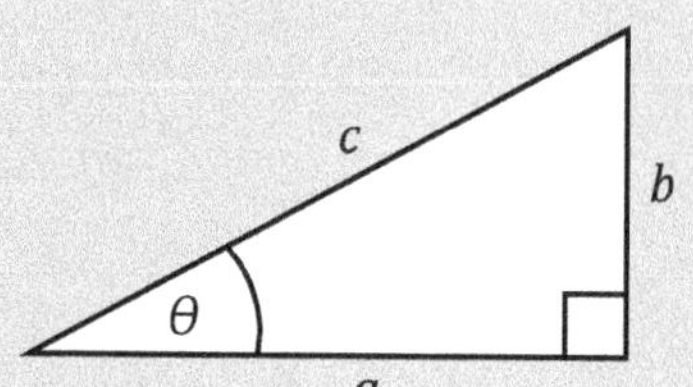

As this is a right-angled triangle, the trig ratios can be used. These ratios must be remembered as they will not be given in the exam paper.

Answer

4 $\sin \theta = \frac{b}{c} \left(\text{i.e. } \sin \theta = \frac{\text{opposite}}{\text{hypotenuse}}\right)$ and $\cos \theta = \frac{a}{c} \left(\text{i.e. } \cos \theta = \frac{\text{adjacent}}{\text{hypotenuse}}\right)$

Hence squaring both we obtain $\sin^2 \theta = \frac{b^2}{c^2}$ and $\cos^2 \theta = \frac{a^2}{c^2}$

$$\text{Now, } \sin^2 \theta + \cos^2 \theta = \frac{b^2}{c^2} + \frac{a^2}{c^2}$$
$$= \frac{a^2 + b^2}{c^2} \quad \text{......... (1)}$$

Now using Pythagoras' theorem for the triangle we have

$$c^2 = a^2 + b^2$$

Substituting this result into equation (1), we obtain

$$\sin^2 \theta + \cos^2 \theta = \frac{c^2}{c^2}$$

Note that $\frac{c^2}{c^2} = 1$.

Hence, $\sin^2 \theta + \cos^2 \theta = 1$

5 The triangle ABC shown below has an area of 25 cm^2.

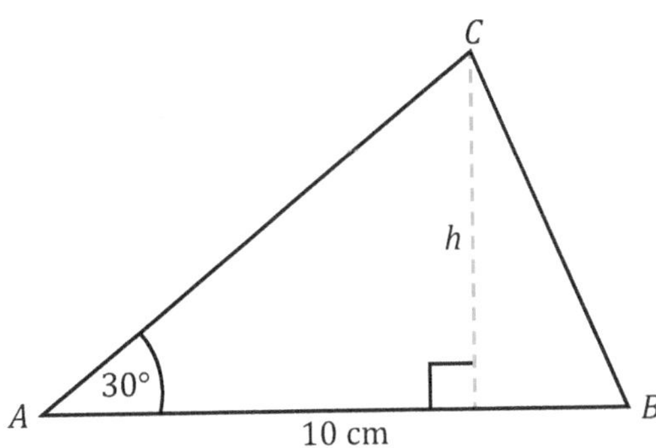

(a) Find the perpendicular height h.

(b) Calculate the length AC.

Answer

5 (a) Area $= \frac{1}{2} \times \text{base} \times \text{perpendicular height}$

$$25 = \frac{1}{2} \times 10 \times h$$

Giving $h = 5$ cm

(b) Using trigonometry, $\sin 30° = \frac{5}{AC}$

Hence, $AC = 10$ cm

Progress check

1 Find the lengths of the sides marked x in each of the following triangles. Give your lengths to two decimal places.

(a)

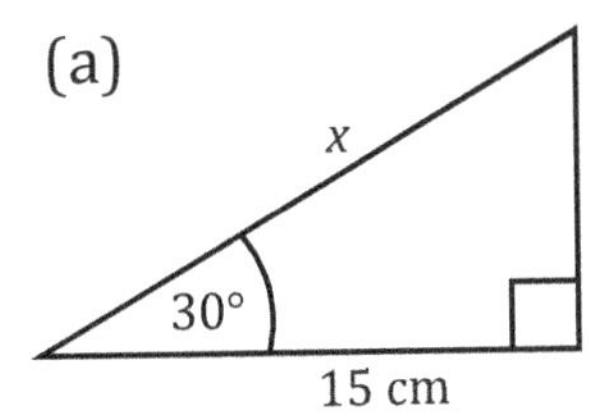

(b)

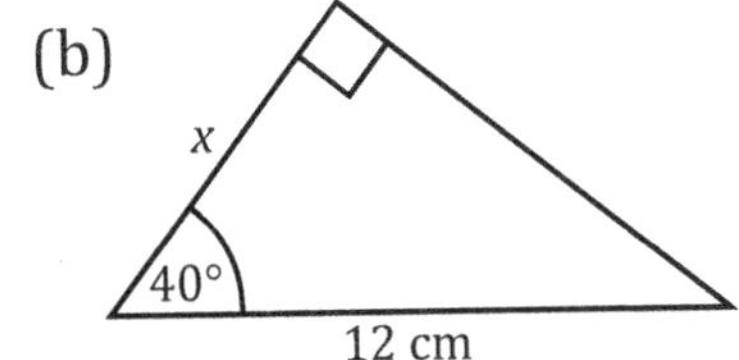

2 Determine the angle θ for each of the following triangles giving your answer to the nearest 0.1°.

(a)

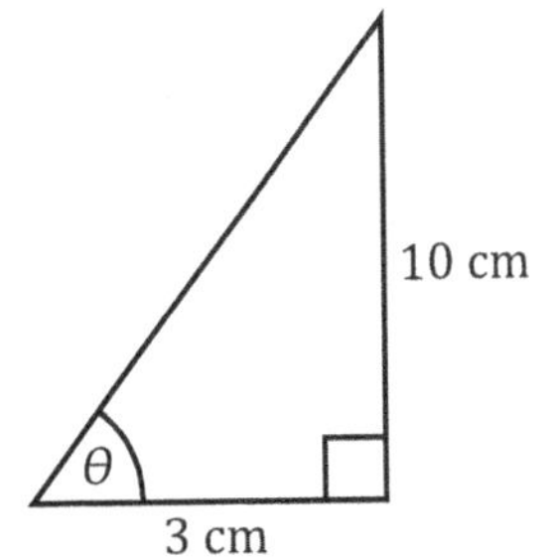

(b)

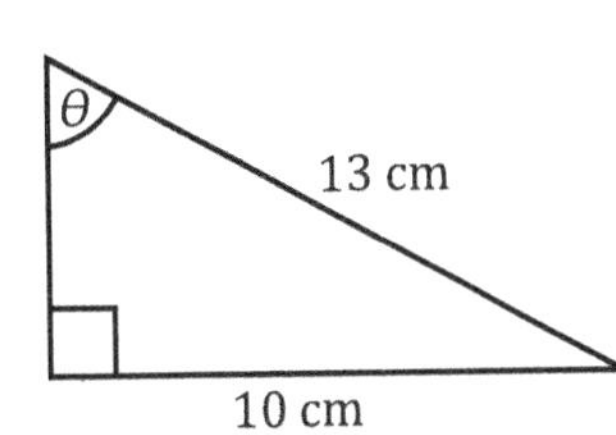

3 Using the right-angled triangle shown below, prove that for $0° < \theta < 90°$, $\frac{\sin \theta}{\cos \theta} = \tan \theta$.

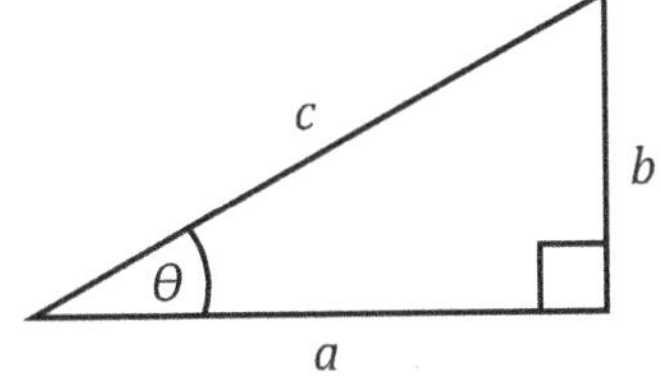

The exact values of the sine, cosine and tangent of 30°, 45° and 60°

The exact values of the above angles can be determined by drawing triangles, working out the lengths of the sides that aren't known and then using trigonometry to work out the exact values of the angles.

The exact values of the sine, cosine and tangent of 45°

The exact values can be worked out by drawing the following triangle:

The length of the hypotenuse is worked out using Pythagoras' theorem.

Hypotenuse = $\sqrt{1^2 + 1^2} = \sqrt{2}$

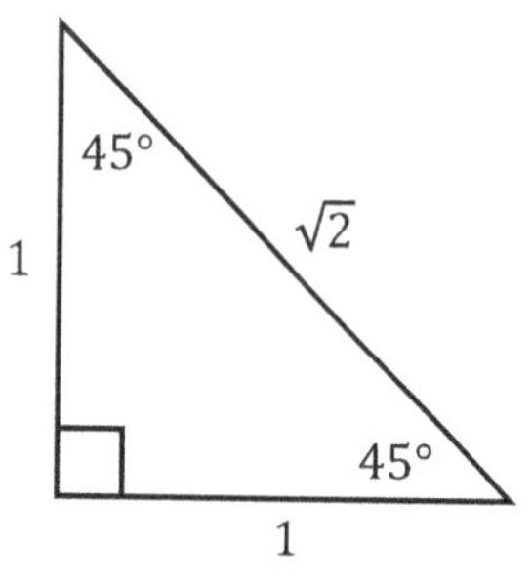

If you are asked to find the exact value you must not work out any of the sides as a decimal.

$$\sin 45° = \frac{\text{opposite}}{\text{hypotenuse}} = \frac{1}{\sqrt{2}}$$

$$\cos 45° = \frac{\text{adjacent}}{\text{hypotenuse}} = \frac{1}{\sqrt{2}}$$

$$\tan 45° = \frac{\text{opposite}}{\text{adjacent}} = \frac{1}{1} = 1$$

Note that the angles are all exact values. For example, if you enter $\frac{1}{\sqrt{2}}$ into your calculator it gives you the answer 0.707 106 781 2... which goes on forever without any repeating pattern to the decimal part. At some stage you will have to decide how many decimal places or significant figures to use so the number is no longer an exact value. By expressing numbers in terms of surds we are keeping them exact.

The exact values of the sine, cosine and tangent of 30° and 60°

The exact values can be worked out by using an equilateral triangle of lengths of sides 2 and then bisecting one of the sides and taking one of the triangles to form the following right-angled triangle:

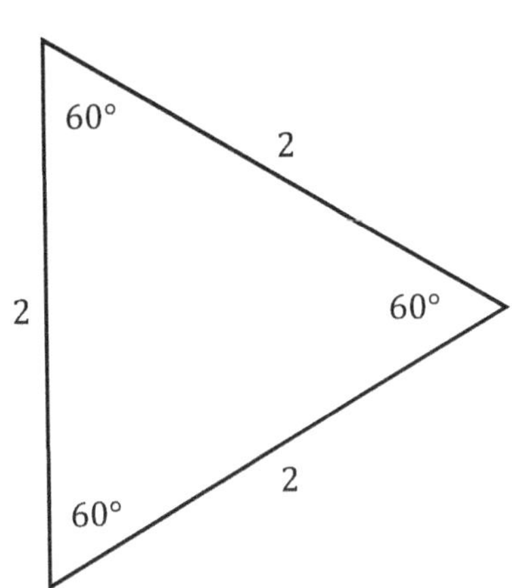

Start off with an equilateral triangle having length of side = 2. All the angles in this triangle will be 60°.

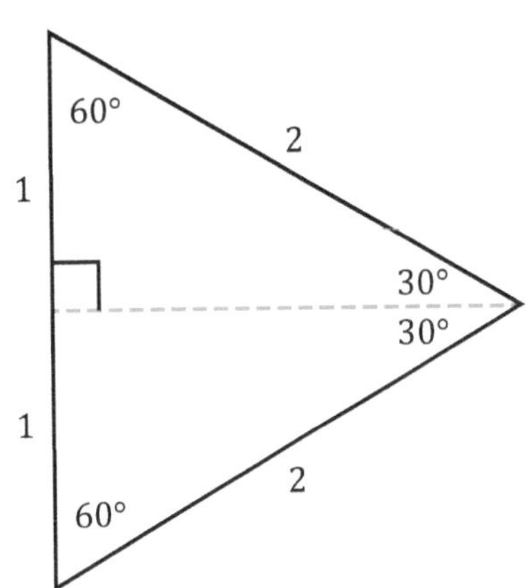

The perpendicular bisector divides the original triangle into two right-angled triangles. Notice that the angle is bisected as well as a side.

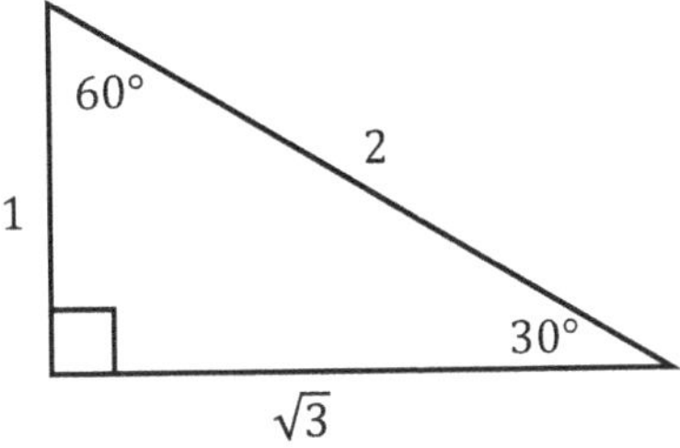

Half of the original triangle is used. The length of the base of this triangle is worked out using Pythagoras' theorem.

Base = $\sqrt{2^2 - 1^2} = \sqrt{3}$

$\sin 30° = \frac{1}{2}$

$\cos 30° = \frac{\sqrt{3}}{2}$

$\tan 30° = \frac{1}{\sqrt{3}}$

The ratio of lengths of sides is then inserted to give the sine, cosine and tangent of the various angles.

$\sin 60° = \frac{\sqrt{3}}{2}$

$\cos 60° = \frac{1}{2}$

$\tan 60° = \sqrt{3}$

9.2 Finding angles using the CAST method

One method of obtaining angles given a trigonometric ratio is called the CAST method.

The CAST method uses the diagram shown below. A indicates that all the ratios are positive in the first quadrant (for angles between 0° and 90°), S indicates that sine is positive in the second quadrant (90° to 180°), T indicates that tangent is positive in the third quadrant (180° to 270°) and C indicates that cosine is positive in the fourth quadrant (270° to 360°).

This simple diagram should be remembered if you intend to use the CAST method.

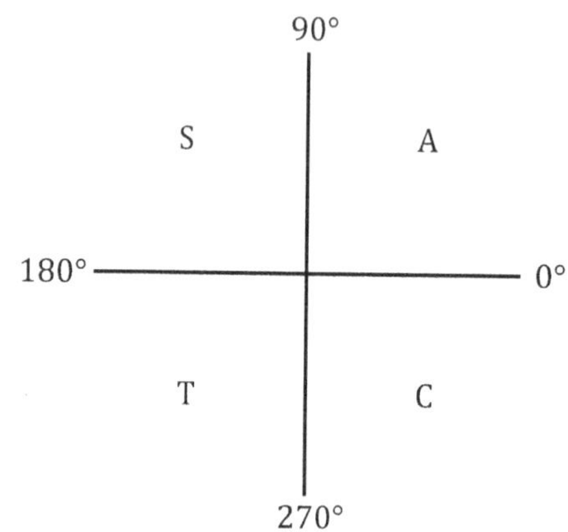

CAST stands for Cos, All, Sin, Tan and the diagram shows where these functions are positive. For example, suppose we wanted all the values of the angle θ in the range $0° \le \theta \le 360°$ where $\sin \theta = 0.6946$. Here we have a positive value for $\sin \theta$. The sine function is positive in the first and second quadrants.

Notice that the angles are measured anticlockwise from 0°.

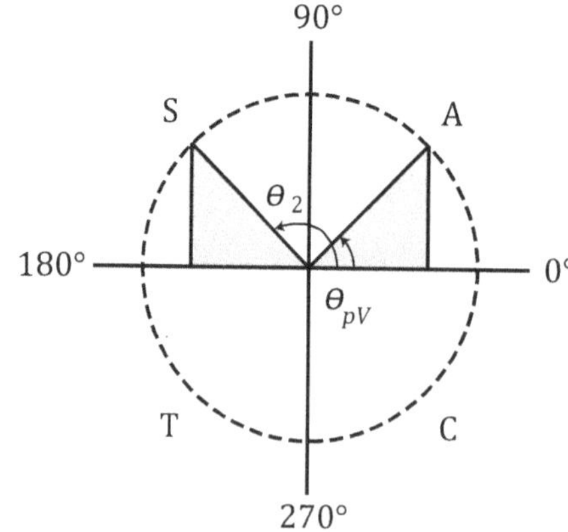

Sin is positive in the 1st and 2nd quadrants

θ_{pV} is called the principal value of the angle.

Two triangles are drawn in the regions where $\sin \theta$ is positive. You can use your calculator to find the first value θ_{pV} by working out $\sin^{-1}(0.6946)$ using a calculator. This gives $\theta_{pV} = 44°$. As both triangles are identical the value of θ_2 is found by subtracting 44° from 180°. Hence the other angle is $180° - 44° = 136°$. Therefore $\theta = 44°$ or $136°$.

Example

6 Find all the values of the angle θ in the range $0° \le \theta \le 360°$ where $\cos\theta = -\frac{1}{2}$.

Answer

6 Two triangles are drawn in the regions where $\cos\theta$ is negative. Cosine is negative in the second and third quadrants. θ_{pV} can be found by using a calculator and entering $\cos^{-1}(-0.5)$ giving a value of 120°. By symmetry, the value of θ_2 can be found by subtracting 120° from 360°. Hence the other angle is 360° – 120° = 240°. Therefore θ = 120° or 240°.

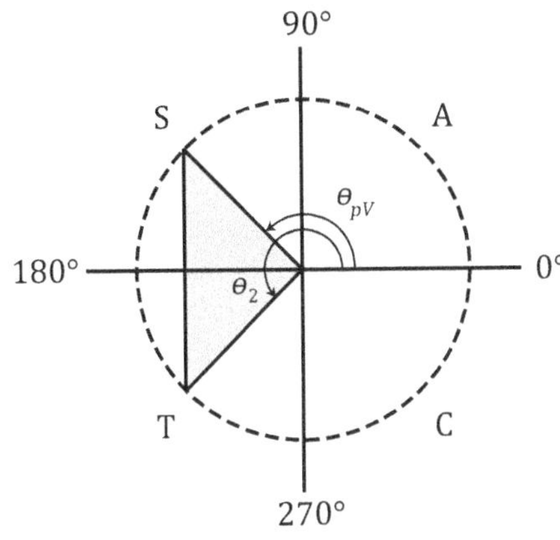

Cos is negative in the 2nd and 3rd quadrants

Using this method, the solutions are found by making the same angle from the horizontal in each of the appropriate quadrants, e.g. 180° – 60° = 120° and 180° + 60° = 240°

9.3 Finding angles using trigonometric graphs

Sine, cosine and tangent graphs

The sine graph ($y = \sin\theta$) where θ is expressed in degrees

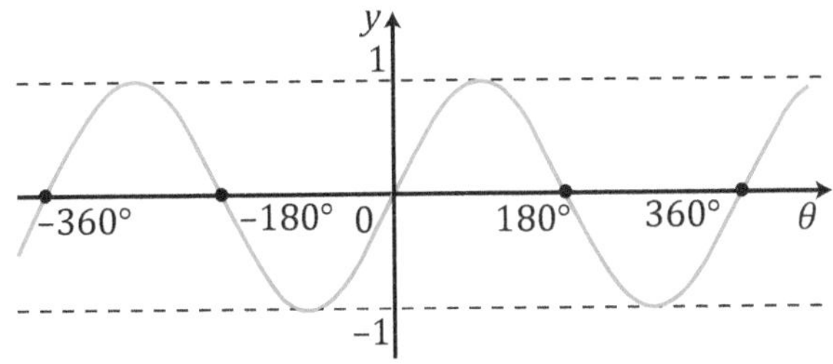

TAKE NOTE !

The sin, cos and tan graphs must be memorised.

The cosine graph ($y = \cos\theta$) where θ is expressed in degrees

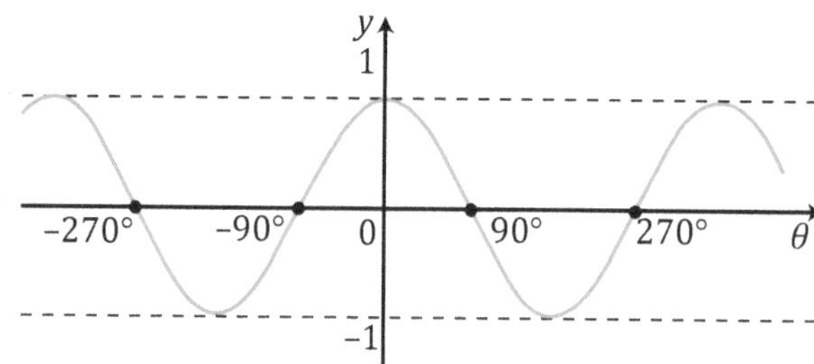

The tangent graph ($y = \tan\theta$) where θ is expressed in degrees

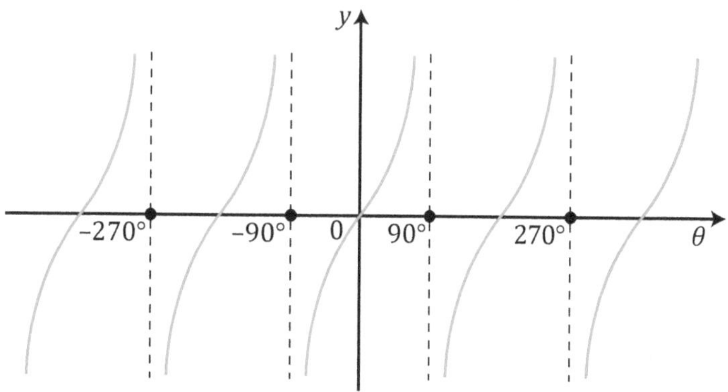

Another method involves using the trigonometric graphs to find all the angles. Here you must be able to draw the graphs of each trigonometric function (sin, cos and tan).

Examples

7 Find all the values of the angle in the range $0° \leq \theta \leq 360°$ where $\sin\theta = \frac{1}{2}$.

Answer

7 The graph of $y = \sin\theta$ is drawn in the range $0° \leq \theta \leq 360°$.

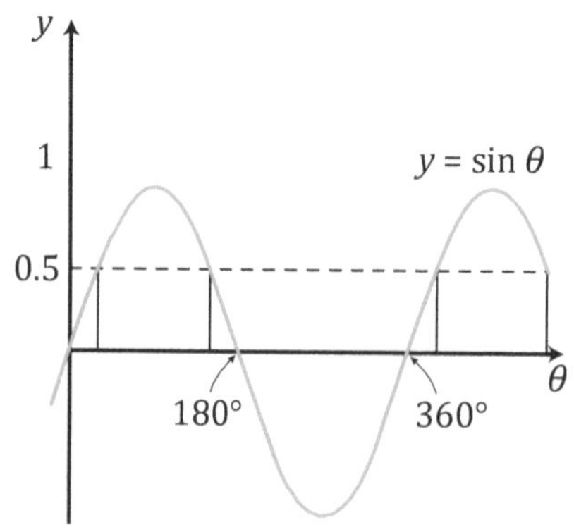

The first angle is found by performing the calculation $\sin^{-1}\left(\frac{1}{2}\right)$ or $\sin^{-1}(0.5)$ using a calculator or by recognition. The result is 30°. By the symmetry of the graph you can see that the other angle will be $180° - 30° = 150°$. Hence the two values of θ in the required range are 30° and 150°.

8 Find all the solutions in the range $0° \leq x \leq 360°$ that satisfy the equation:

(a) $\cos 2x = 1$

(b) $\sqrt{3} \tan x = 1$

Answer

8 (a) $\cos 2x = 1$

We will use the trigonometric graphs to find the solutions.

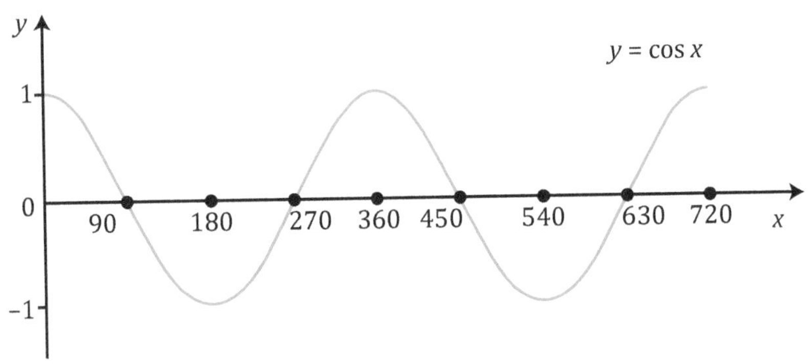

Notice that we go up to 720° with the graph so that later when the angles are divided by 2 to give the values of x, these values will lie in the required range.

So, $2x = \cos^{-1}(1)$

$= 0°, 360°, 720°$

Dividing by 2 to find the values of x, we have

$x = 0°, 180°, 360°.$

(b) You could use the method making use of the trigonometric graphs but here we will use the CAST method.

$\sqrt{3} \tan x = 1$

Dividing both sides by $\sqrt{3}$ we obtain a value for tan x.

$\text{Tan } x = \frac{1}{\sqrt{3}}$

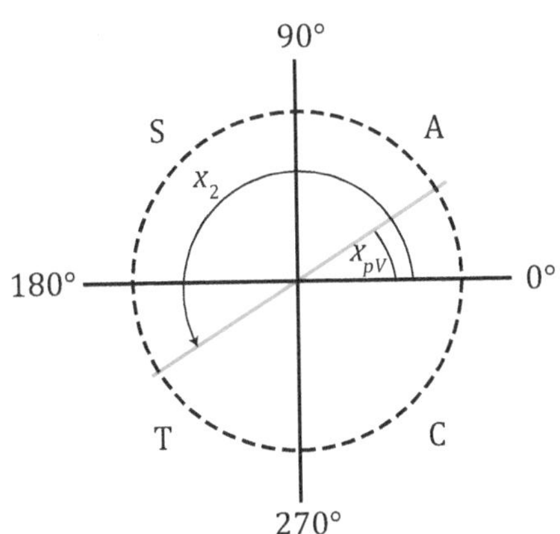

Tan x is positive in the first and third quadrants. The solution in the first quadrant is found by entering $\tan^{-1}\left(\frac{1}{\sqrt{3}}\right)$ into the calculator giving the answer $x = 30°$. By symmetry, the other value is found by adding 30° to 180° giving the other solution $x = 210°$.

Hence solutions are 30° and 210°.

Progress check

4 Using the CAST method, find all the values of the angle θ in the range $0° \leq \theta \leq 360°$ where $\cos\theta = \frac{1}{2}$.

5 Using trigonometric graphs, find all the values of the angle θ in the range $0° \leq \theta \leq 360°$ where $\sin\theta = \frac{\sqrt{3}}{2}$.

6 Find all the values of x in the range $0° \leq \theta \leq 360°$ where $\tan x = -\frac{1}{2}$.

7 Find all the values of θ in the range $0° \leq \theta \leq 360°$ satisfying $2\sin\theta = 1$

8 Find to the nearest degree all the solutions of θ in the range $0° \leq \theta \leq 360°$ for each of the following:

(a) $\sin\theta = -0.23$

(b) $\cos\theta = -0.72$

(c) $\tan\theta = 2.45$

9.4 The sine and cosine rules

The sine and cosine rules can be used with any triangle, not just those containing a right angle.

The angles are denoted by the letters A, B and C and the lengths of the sides opposite these angles are denoted by a, b and c respectively.

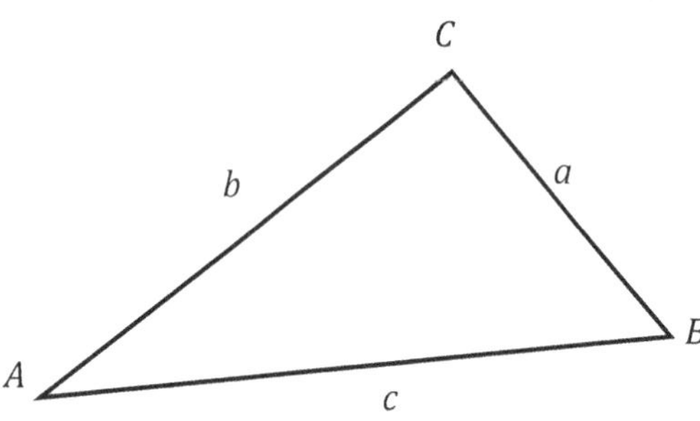

The sine rule states:

$$\frac{a}{\sin A} = \frac{b}{\sin B} = \frac{c}{\sin C}$$

The cosine rule states:

$$a^2 = b^2 + c^2 - 2bc\cos A$$

The sine rule should be used in the most useful form for the given question:

$$\frac{a}{\sin A} = \frac{b}{\sin B} = \frac{c}{\sin C} \text{ or } \frac{\sin A}{a} = \frac{\sin B}{b} = \frac{\sin C}{c}$$

It is important to be able to apply the cosine rule to any triangle. To do this you need to see the pattern in the formula. The right-hand side (i.e. the more complicated side) involves two sides of the triangle and the angle between these two sides (called the included angle). The left-hand side is the square of the remaining side which is opposite the angle being used in the formula.

Smallest and largest sides in a triangle

Where all the angles are different in a triangle, the largest side is always opposite to the largest angle and the smallest side is opposite the smallest angle.

The area of a triangle

If two sides of a triangle are known as well as the included angle, then the area of the triangle can be found using the formula:

Area of triangle = $\frac{1}{2}ab \sin C$

This formula works for all triangles but for areas of right-angled triangles, use the formula

$A = \frac{1}{2} \times base \times height$

Note that you will not be given either formula.

Warning: be careful when using this formula to work out the angle when the area and two sides of the triangle are known. For example, $\sin C = \frac{1}{2}$ can have two solutions 30° and 150°. If another angle in the triangle is known then the obtuse angle may not be a possible solution. Be guided by the wording of the question, so look for the plural 'angles' in the question to see if you are looking for two possible angles.

Note that if the angle between the two included sides is 90°, then in the formula

Area of triangle = $\frac{1}{2}ab \sin C$, $C = 90°$ so we have

Area of triangle = $\frac{1}{2}ab \sin 90$ and since $\sin 90° = 1$ this formula becomes

Area of triangle = $\frac{1}{2}ab$ and this is the familiar formula for the area of a right-angled triangle where a is the length of the base and b is the perpendicular height or vice versa.

Examples

9 The diagram below shows the triangle ABC with $AB = 6$ cm, $AC = 10$ cm and angle $BAC = 150°$.

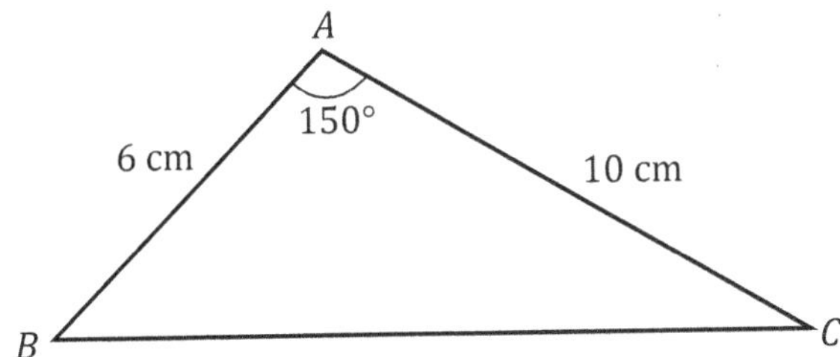

(a) Find the area of triangle ABC.

(b) Find the length of BC correct to three significant figures.

Answer

9 (a) Area of triangle $ABC = \frac{1}{2}bc \sin A$

$= \frac{1}{2} \times 10 \times 6 \sin 150°$

$= 15 \text{ cm}^2$

(b) Using the cosine rule

$BC^2 = 6^2 + 10^2 - 2 \times 6 \times 10 \cos 150°$

$BC^2 = 36 + 100 - 120 \cos 150°$

$BC^2 = 136 + 103.92$

$BC = \sqrt{239.92}$

$BC = 15.5$cm (to 3 s.f.)

10 The triangle ABC has AB = 16 cm, AC = 8 cm and angle ABC = 20°.

The triangle described above can be drawn in the following two ways, one with angle ACB as an obtuse angle and the other with angle ACB as an acute angle.

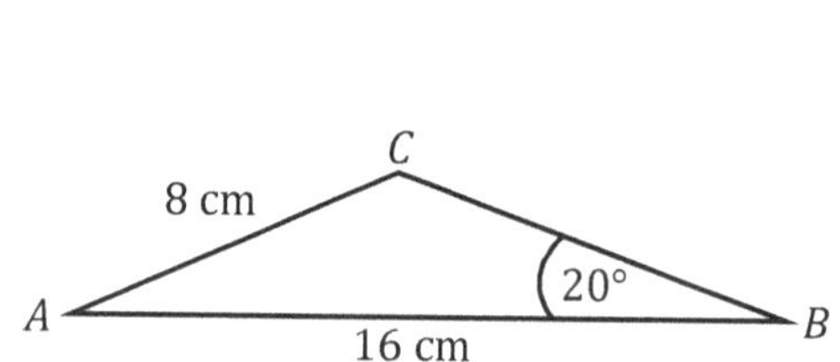

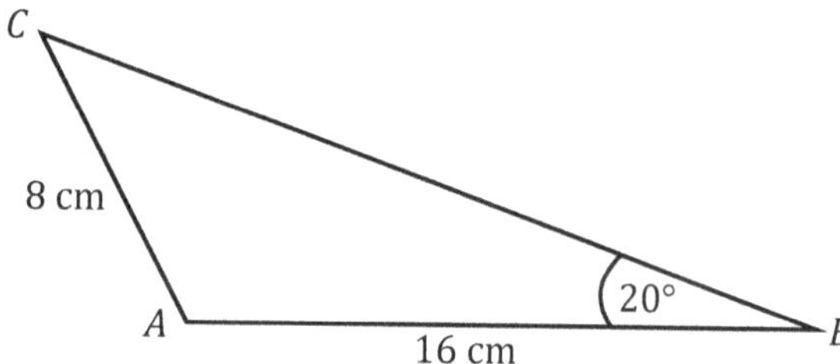

(a) Using the sine rule, determine the two possible sizes of angle ACB giving your answers to the nearest 0.1°.

(b) Hence, determine the two possible lengths of side BC giving your answer to three significant figures.

Answer

10 (a) Let angle $ACB = \theta$

Using the sine rule

$$\frac{16}{\sin\theta} = \frac{8}{\sin 20°}$$

$$\sin\theta = \frac{16\sin 20°}{8}$$

$$\sin\theta = 0.6840$$

$$\theta = 43.16° \text{ or } (180 - 43.16)° = 136.84°$$

$$\theta = 43.2° \text{ or } 136.8°$$

You need to find the two angles which have a sine equal to 0.6840. Use $\sin^{-1}$ (0.6840) to find the angle. Using the CAST method, sine is positive in the first and second quadrants. You could also have used the symmetry of the sine graph to find the obtuse angle.

(b) Angle BAC = (180 – [43.2 + 20]) = 116.8° or (180 – [136.8 + 20]) = 23.2°.

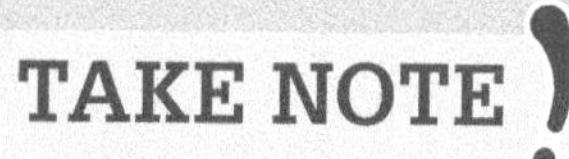

Remember to give your answers to the nearest 0.1°.

We now need to find the side opposite the angle in each of these two situations. The cosine rule could be used here but it is easier to use the sine rule.

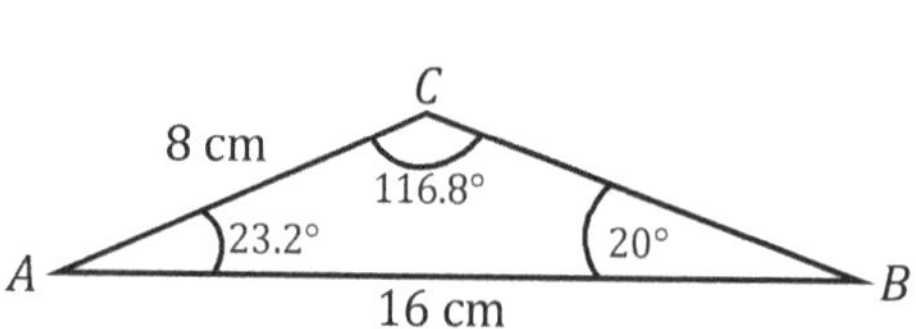

For angle BAC = 23.2° and using the sine rule, we have

$$\frac{BC}{\sin 23.2°} = \frac{8}{\sin 20°}$$

$$BC = \frac{8\sin 23.2°}{\sin 20°}$$

$$BC = 9.2145$$

$$= 9.21 \text{ cm (3 s.f.)}$$

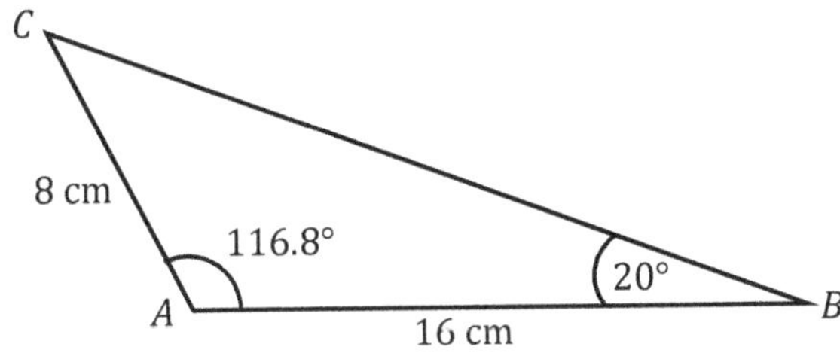

For angle BAC =116.8° and using the sine rule, we have

$$\frac{BC}{\sin 116.8°} = \frac{8}{\sin 20°}$$

$$BC = \frac{8 \sin 116.8°}{\sin 20°}$$

$$BC = 20.8780$$

$$= 20.9 \text{ cm (3 s.f.)}$$

---

11 The triangle ABC with has AB = 8 cm, BC = 15 cm and ABC = 60°.

Here we know the sides and the included angle and want to find the other side. In these situations, the cosine rule is used.

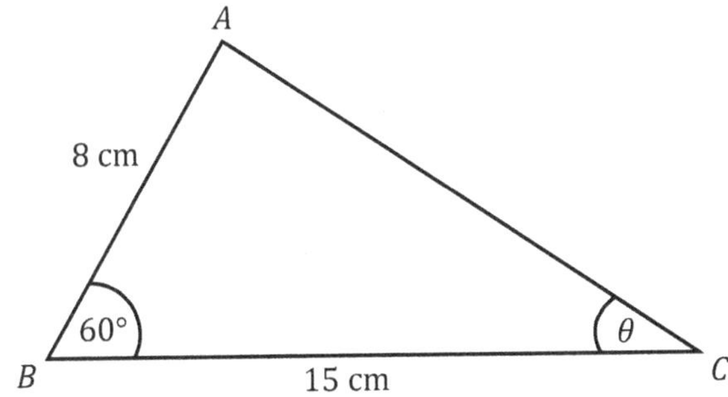

(a) Calculate the length of side AC.

(b) Find the size of angle θ giving your answer to the nearest 0.1°.

Answer

11 (a) Using the cosine rule:

$$AC^2 = 8^2 + 15^2 - 2 \times 8 \times 15 \cos 60°$$

$$AC^2 = 64 + 225 - 240 \times \frac{1}{2}$$

$$AC^2 = 169$$

$$AC = 13 \text{ cm}$$

(b)

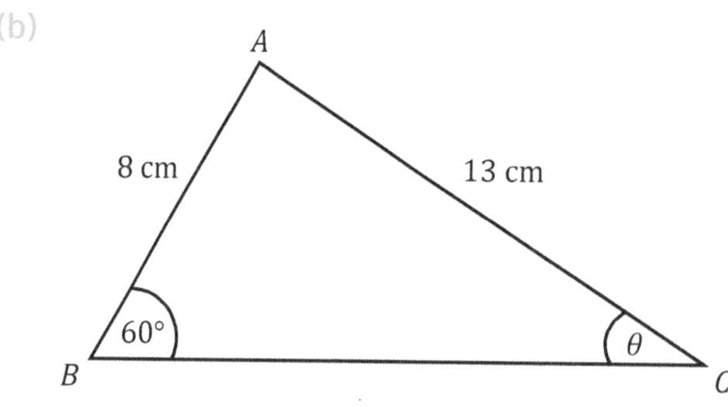

Using the sine rule:

$$\frac{b}{\sin B} = \frac{c}{\sin C}$$

$$\frac{13}{\sin 60°} = \frac{8}{\sin \theta}$$

$$\sin \theta = \frac{8 \times \sin 60°}{13}$$

$$\theta = 32.2° \text{ (nearest } 0.1°)$$

Progress check

9 A triangle has sides 5 cm, 7 cm and 10 cm. Calculate the smallest angle of the triangle to the nearest 0.1°.

10

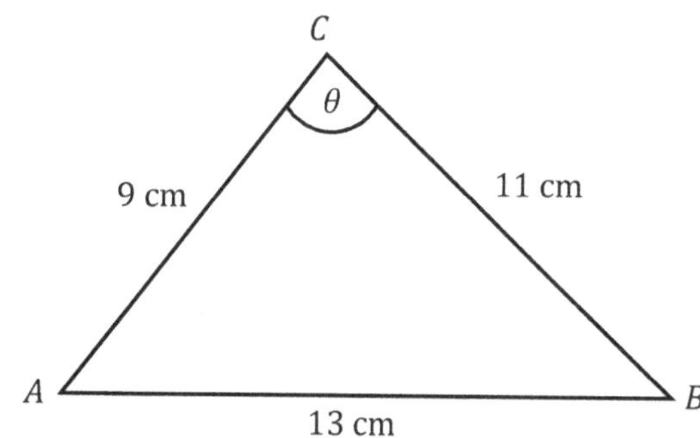

ABC is a triangle with sides *AB*, *BC* and *AC* of length 13 cm, 11 cm and 9 cm respectively.

(a) Calculate the size of the acute angle θ to the nearest 0.1°.

(b) Calculate the area of triangle *ABC* giving your answer to one decimal place.

11

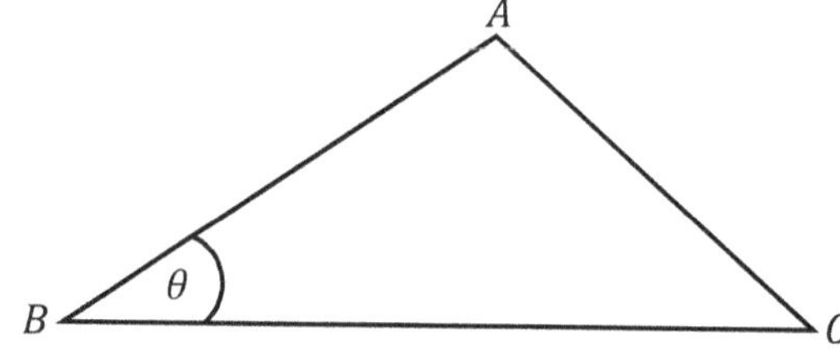

ABC is a triangle with sides *AB* = 25 cm, *BC* = 30 cm and acute angle *ABC* = θ, where $\sin \theta = \frac{3}{5}$.

(a) Calculate the area of triangle *ABC*.

(b) Find the exact value of $\cos \theta$.

(c) Calculate the length of *AC* giving your answer to three significant figures.

Exam practice

1 The angle θ is greater than 90° and less than 360° and $\cos\theta = \frac{2}{3}$.

Find the exact value of $\tan\theta$. [3]

(OCR FSMQ June 2009 q1)

Answer

1 As $\cos\theta = \frac{2}{3}$, this is a positive value so using the CAST method the angle could be in the first or fourth quadrants, but because we are told the angle is greater than 90° this means that it must be in the fourth quadrant. Tan is negative in the fourth quadrant so when the value is obtained, we need to include a minus sign.

By Pythagoras' theorem we have

$3^2 = x^2 + 2^2$

So $9 = x^2 + 4$ giving $x = \sqrt{5}$

$\text{Tan}\ \theta = \frac{\text{opposite}}{\text{adjacent}} = \frac{\sqrt{5}}{2}$

As we know θ is in the fourth quadrant, tan is negative so we have

$\theta = -\frac{\sqrt{5}}{2}$

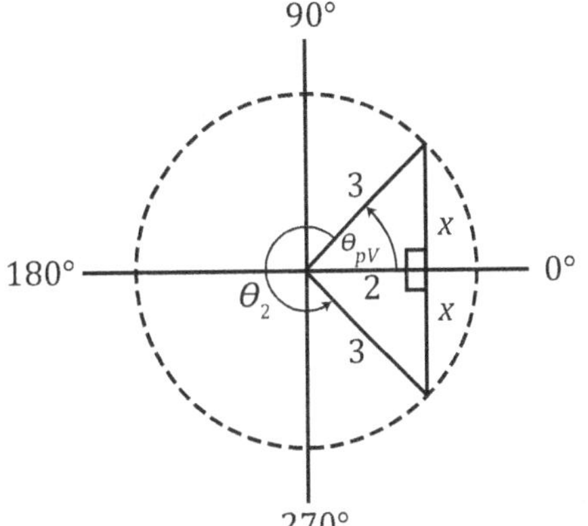

Note that the question asks for the exact value so you must not give your answer as a decimal so the final answer is $-\frac{\sqrt{5}}{2}$.

» TIP

If in a question you are asked for an exact value, then do not work out any roots or fractions. If you did work out your answer as a decimal then you would have to truncate the decimal part so the answer would no longer be exact.

2 John and Jennie are asked to draw a triangle ABC with the following properties.

$AC = 6$ cm, $CB = 4$ cm and the angle $A = 40°$.

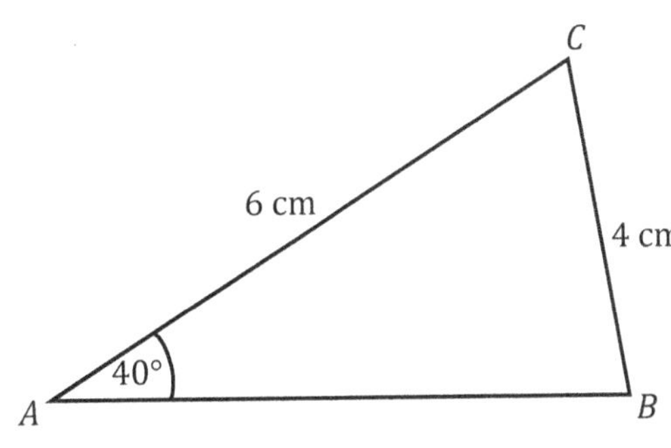

Fig 1

Not to scale

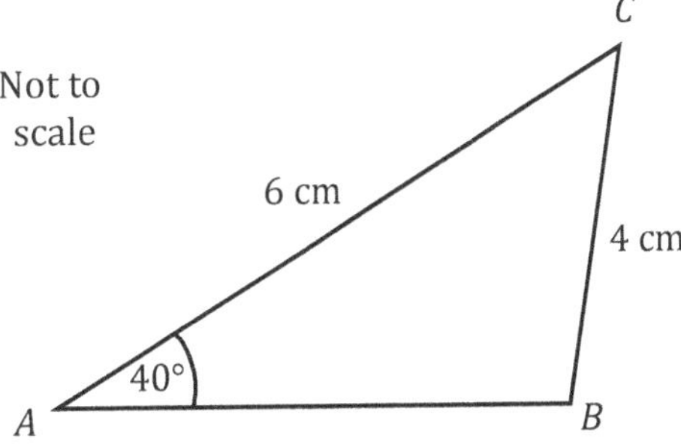

Fig 2

John draws the triangle as shown in Fig 1 and Jennie draws the triangle as shown in Fig 2.

Calculate the angle B in each case. [4]

(OCR FSMQ June 2013 q7)

Answer

2 Using the sine rule we have

$$\frac{4}{\sin 40} = \frac{6}{\sin B}$$

$$\text{Hence } \sin B = \frac{6 \sin 40}{4}$$

$$= 0.9642$$

Drawing the graph of $y = \sin \theta$ we have two places where $\sin \theta = 0.9642$

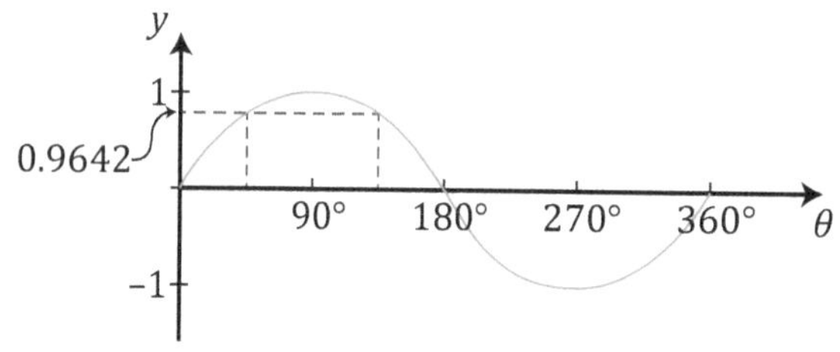

Now angle $B = \sin^{-1}(0.9642)$

$= 74.6°$ or $180 - 74.6 = 105.4°$

The symmetry of the graph is used to find the obtuse angle.

Hence the two possible values of angle B are 74.6° and 105.4°.

Test yourself

1 (a) Copy out the following axes and use them to sketch the graph of $y = \tan \theta$ for values of θ in the range $0° \leq \theta \leq 360°$

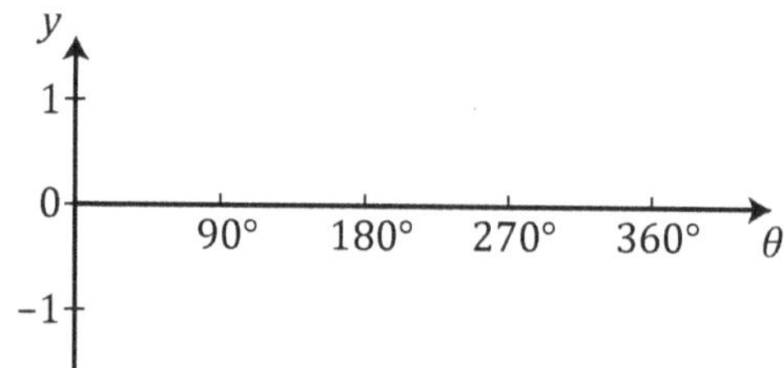

(b) Using the graph you have sketched in part (a) to help you, solve the equation $\tan \theta = 1$ giving all values of θ in the range $0° \leq \theta \leq 360°$.

2 Find all the solutions in the range $0° \leq x \leq 360°$ that satisfy the equation

(a) $\text{Sin } 2x = 1$

(b) $\text{Tan } x = 2$

3 The diagram shows the triangle ABC with $AB = 8$ cm, $AC = 12$ cm and $BAC = 150°$.

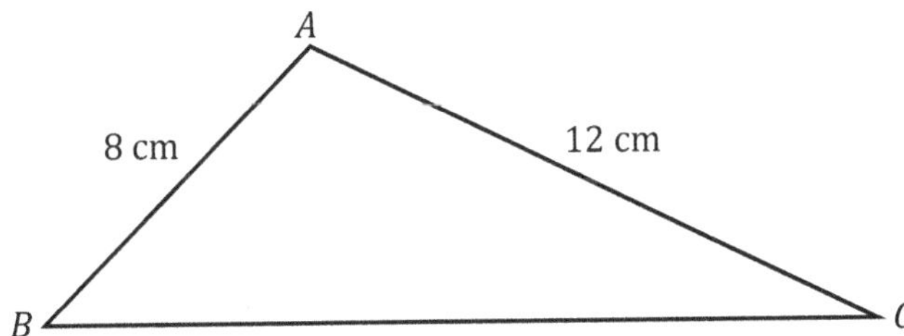

(a) Find the area of triangle ABC.

(b) Find the length of BC correct to one decimal place.

4 The graph shows the curve $y = \sin x$ in the interval $0° \leq x \leq 720°$.

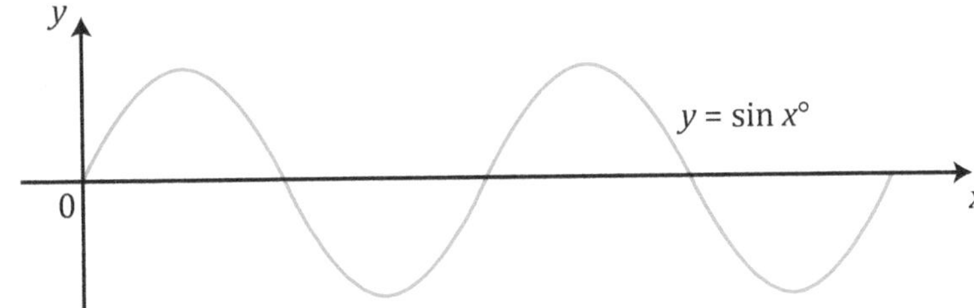

(a) Write down the coordinates of all the points of intersection with the x-axis.

(b) Write down the coordinates of all stationary points for this graph.

5 The acute-angled triangle ABC is shown below.

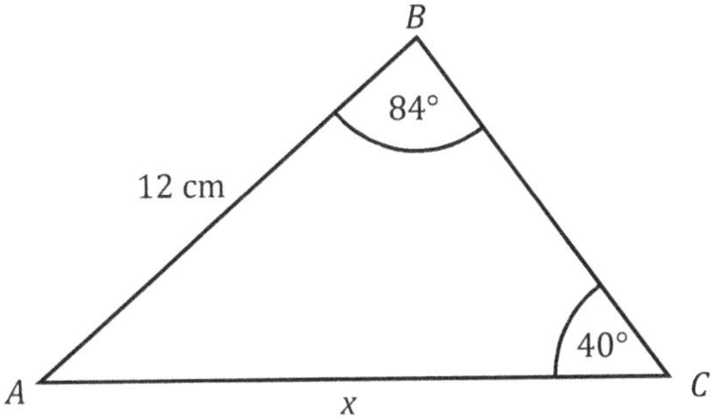

(a) Find x to three significant figures.

(b) Hence find the area of the triangle correct to three significant figures.

Topic summary

Trigonometry is used to find sides and angles in triangles or shapes that can be divided into triangles.

Sine, cosine and tangent functions

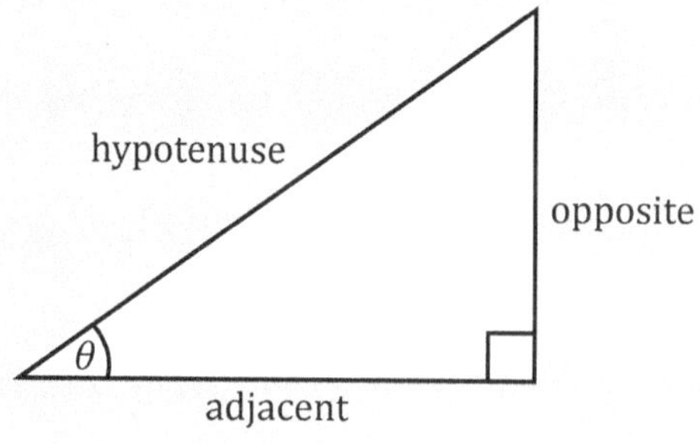

$\sin\theta = \dfrac{\text{opposite}}{\text{hypotenuse}}$

$\cos\theta = \dfrac{\text{adjacent}}{\text{hypotenuse}}$

$\tan\theta = \dfrac{\text{opposite}}{\text{adjacent}}$

The sine and cosine rules and the formula for the area of a triangle

The sine rule states:

$$\frac{a}{\sin A} = \frac{b}{\sin B} = \frac{c}{\sin C}$$

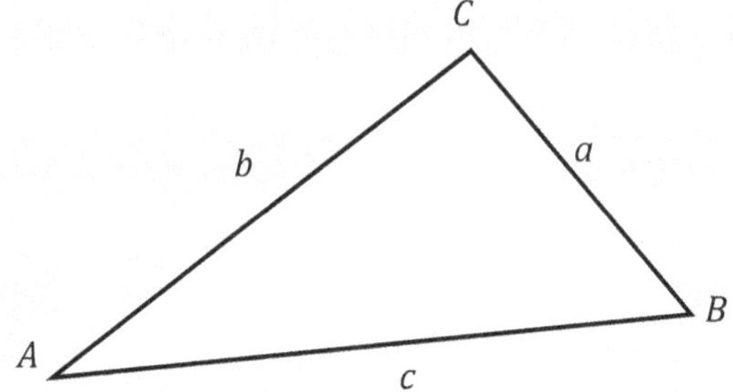

The cosine rule states: $a^2 = b^2 + c^2 - 2bc\cos A$

Area of triangle $= \dfrac{1}{2}ab\sin C$

Trigonometric identities and solving trigonometric equations

The previous topic introduced the use of simple trigonometric ratios and the use of the CAST method and trigonometric graphs to determine angles from their sine, cosine and tangent values in a given interval. You were also introduced to the use of the sine and cosine rules in simple situations. In this topic you will be using all this material to solve more complex trigonometric equations and apply the sine and cosine rules to real-life problems.

This topic covers the following:

10.1 The trigonometric identities $\tan\theta = \dfrac{\sin\theta}{\cos\theta}$ and $\cos^2\theta + \sin^2\theta = 1$

10.2 Solution of simple trigonometric equations in a given interval

10.3 Applying trigonometry to 2- and 3-dimensional problems

10.1 The trigonometric identities $\tan\theta = \dfrac{\sin\theta}{\cos\theta}$ and $\cos^2\theta + \sin^2\theta = 1$

There are two trigonometric identities that you may need to use when solving simple trigonometric equations. These two identities are:

$$\tan\theta = \frac{\sin\theta}{\cos\theta}$$

$$\cos^2\theta + \sin^2\theta = 1$$

You could be asked to prove each of the above identities and this was covered in the previous topic. See if you can prove the above using a right-angled triangle with hypotenuse c and other two sides a and b by combining the use of trigonometry and Pythagoras' theorem.

You will use both $\tan\theta = \dfrac{\sin\theta}{\cos\theta}$ and $\cos^2\theta + \sin^2\theta = 1$ in the examples later on in this topic.

10.2 Solution of simple trigonometric equations in a given interval

The graphs of trigonometric functions can be used to help identify all the solutions of a simple trigonometric equation in a given interval.

Suppose we have to solve the following equation in the interval $0° \le x \le 360°$

$$\sin(2x - 30)° = \frac{1}{2}$$

Draw a sine graph of $y = \sin\theta$. You will need to go a lot further than 360° for your graph so that all the possible solutions are shown.

Note when we have a function such as $(2x - 30)°$ it is best to consider twice the range, since the multiple of the angle involved is 2, i.e. from 0° to 720°.

Here we will go as far as 720°.

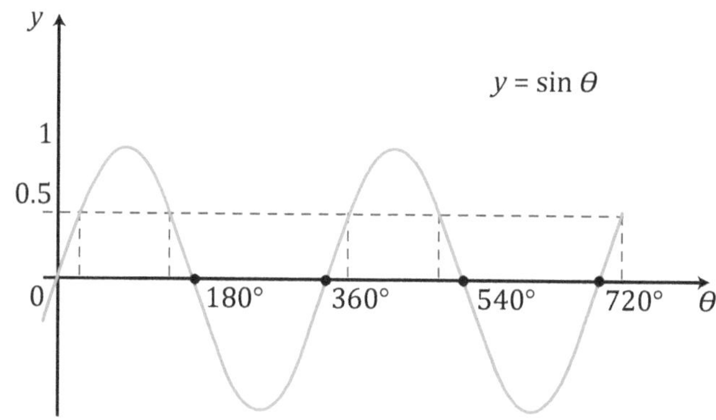

$$2x - 30 = \sin^{-1}\left(\frac{1}{2}\right)$$

Letting $\theta = 2x - 30$

$$\text{So } \theta = \sin^{-1}\left(\frac{1}{2}\right)$$

Using the calculator (or the triangles for the exact values learnt earlier) we have $\theta = 30°$ we can then see from the graph that the line $y = \frac{1}{2}$ also intersects the curve at the following values of θ: $\theta = 150°, 390°, 510°$

When looking for all the solutions, between 0° and 360°, of $\cos(2x - 30) = \frac{1}{2}$, the values of θ that need to be considered will lie between $2 \times 0 - 30$ and $2 \times 360 - 30$, i.e. $-30°$ and $690°$.

In practice, it's probably best to consider twice the range, since the multiple of the angle involved is 2, i.e. from 0° to 720°. It is quicker to do this calculation.

Hence $\theta = 30°, 150°, 390°, 510°$

So $2x - 30 = 30°, 150°, 390°, 510°$

$2x = 60°, 180°, 420°, 540°$

$x = 30°, 90°, 210°, 270°$

So values of x in the required range are $x = 30°, 90°, 210°, 270°$

Sine is positive in the first and second quadrants, therefore $\theta = 30°$ or $\theta = 180 - 30 = 150°$, or (adding 360°) 390° or 510°, etc.

Examples

1 Find the values of x in the range $0° \leq x \leq 360°$, that satisfy the equation

$2 \sin x = \tan x$

Answer

1 $$2 \sin x = \tan x$$

$$2 \sin x = \frac{\sin x}{\cos x}$$

Do not be tempted here to divide both sides by $\sin x$. If you do this then you will lose some solutions of the equation.

$$2 \sin x \cos x - \sin x = 0$$

$$\sin x (2 \cos x - 1) = 0$$

Hence, $\sin x = 0$ or $2 \cos x - 1 = 0$

So $\sin x = 0$ or $\cos x = \frac{1}{2}$

Using the CAST method, e.g. for $\cos x = \frac{1}{2}$, cosine is positive in the first and fourth quadrants, so $x = 60°$ or $x = 360° - 60° = 300°$.

$\sin x = 0$ at $x = 0°, 180°, 360°$

$\cos x = \frac{1}{2}$ at $x = 60°$ or $300°$

Hence, $x = 0°, 60°, 180°, 300°$ or $360°$

2 Find all the values of θ in the range $0° \leq \theta \leq 360°$ satisfying the equation

$(2\cos\theta - 1)(\cos\theta + 1) = 0$

Answer

We take each bracket and put the contents equal to zero.

2 $(2\cos\theta - 1)(\cos\theta + 1) = 0$

$$2\cos\theta - 1 = 0$$

$$2\cos\theta = 1$$

$$\cos\theta = \frac{1}{2}$$

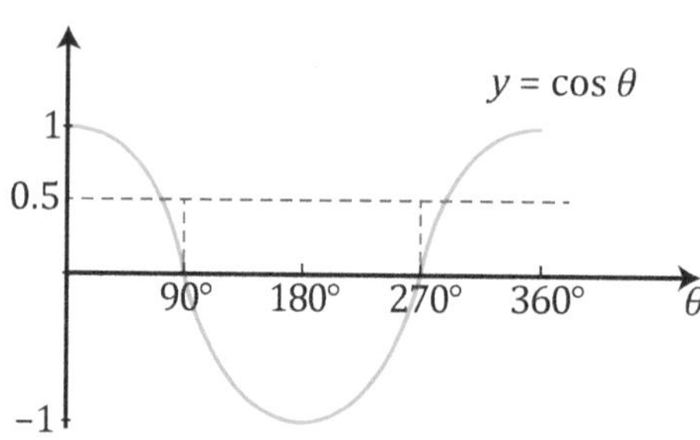

$$\theta = 60°, 300°$$

$$\cos\theta + 1 = 0$$

$$\cos\theta = -1$$

$$\theta = 180°$$

You could have used the CAST method to work out the angles.

Hence, the values of θ in the range are 60°, 180°, 300°

3 Find all the values of θ in the range $0° < \theta \leq 360°$ satisfying the equation

$3\cos^2\theta - \cos\theta - 2 = 0$

Answer

3 $3\cos^2\theta - \cos\theta - 2 = 0$

It is important to spot that this is a quadratic equation in $\cos\theta$. To solve this equation we factorise it and then equate each of the brackets to zero. We then solve each of the resulting equations.

Factorising, we obtain $(3\cos\theta + 2)(\cos\theta - 1) = 0$

Hence $3\cos\theta + 2 = 0$ or $\cos\theta - 1 = 0$

$\cos\theta = -\frac{2}{3}$ or $\cos\theta = 1$

TAKE NOTE !

Always check the range for the allowable values of θ. Cos θ =1 gives $\theta = 0°$ but this lies outside the range $0° < \theta \leq 360°$ so we ignore this value.

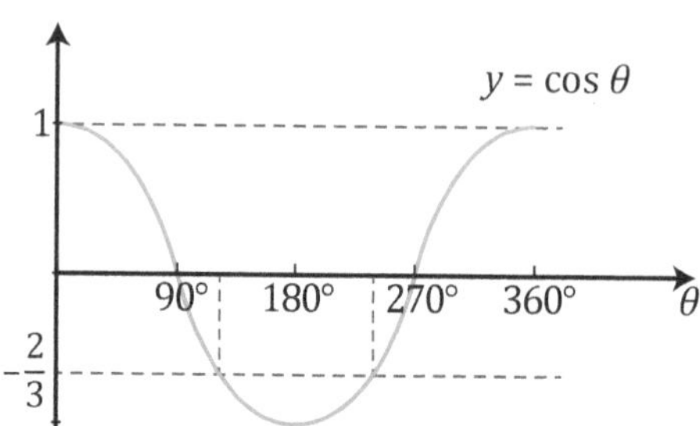

Draw a graph of $y = \cos\theta$ to find the angles.

$\theta = 131.8°$ or $228.2°$ or $\theta = 360°$

Hence values of θ are 131.8°, 228.2°, 360°

Progress check

1. Find all the values of x in the range $0° \leq x \leq 360°$ that satisfy the equation

   $\cos x = -2 \sin x.$

2. Prove the identity $\cos^2 \theta - \sin^2 \theta = 2\cos^2\theta - 1$.

3. If θ is an acute angle and $\cos \theta = \frac{2}{\sqrt{5}}$.

   (a) Find the **exact** value of $\sin \theta$.

   (b) Hence, show that the *exact* value of $\tan \theta$ is $\frac{1}{2}$.

4. Solve the equation $6\cos^2 \theta + 5\cos \theta - 6 = 0$ giving all values of θ in the range $0° \leq \theta \leq 360°$ to the nearest 0.1°.

5. (a) If $5\sin \theta = 3\cos \theta$, find the value of $\tan \theta$ leaving your answer as a fraction.

   (b) If θ is an acute angle, find the value of θ to the nearest degree.

6. Find all values of in the range $0° \leq \theta \leq 360°$ satisfying

   $12 \cos^2 x - 5 \sin x - 10 = 0$

   Give all your values of x to one decimal place.

10.3 Applying trigonometry to 2- and 3-dimensional problems

Two-dimensional problems

Two dimensional problems are problems that can be accurately represented by a drawing on a piece of paper.

Bearings

Bearings are angles measured from due north in a clockwise direction. Bearings are always given as three figures so, for example, if we had angle of 5° clockwise from due north, it would be a bearing of 005°. If you had an angle of 55.5° drawn in clockwise direction from the north line then we would first round the angle to the nearest whole degree and then to convert it to a bearing, you would write it as three figures (i.e. 056°).

It is important to be able to draw lines in the compass directions, north, east, south and west.

Note that from due north, east is on a bearing 090°, south is on a bearing 180° and west is on a bearing of 270°.

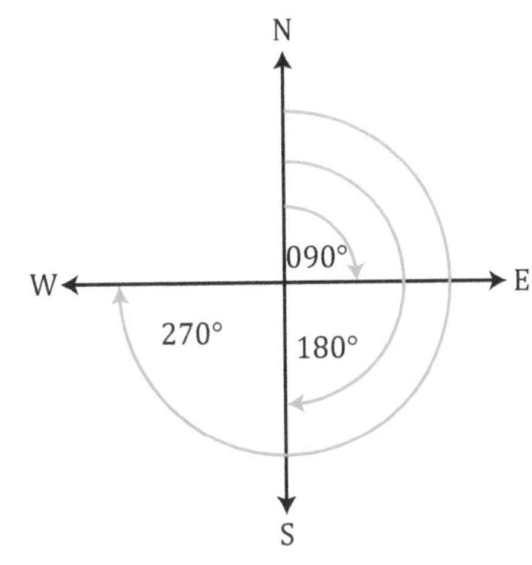

Suppose we have two points A and B at the same level. Point B is on a bearing of 100° from point A and a distance of 10 km from point A. The 'from' part in the question is important because it tells you where you are starting from. So here we have 'from point A' which means you are starting from point A.

This can be represented by the following diagram.

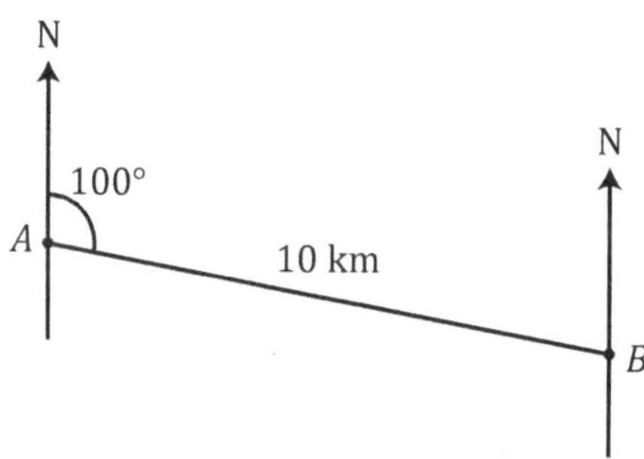

The bearing of point B from point A (i.e. 100°) means that if you were facing due north at point A you would turn 100° in a clockwise direction and then travel 10 km in order to reach point B. Suppose you were at point B and needed to return to point A. We always start from a northerly direction so you would need to turn clockwise through an angle of θ to then travel the 10 km back to A. This is shown here.

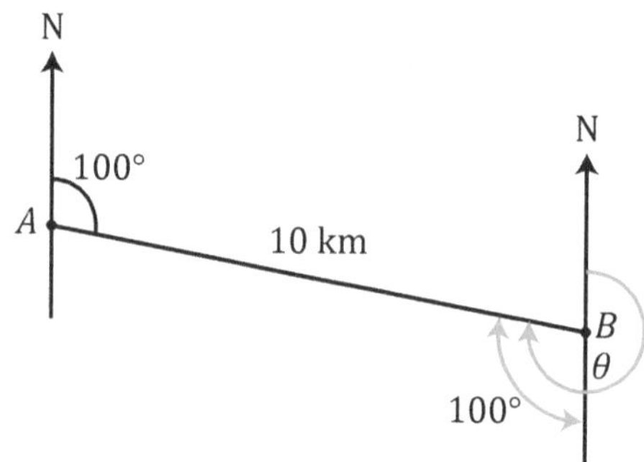

TAKE NOTE

You often need to look for alternate angles when you draw diagrams showing bearings between two or more points.

You can see that there is an alternate angle to the original 100°. This can be marked on the diagram as the two north lines are parallel.

From the diagram $\theta = 180 + 100 = 280°$.

Hence, the bearing of point A from point B is 280°.

TIP

North lines are always parallel so you can use these lines as parallel lines when finding alternating angles.

Example

4 A ship sails due north and 2 hours after leaving port P it is 40 km from P. Another ship leaves P at the same time but travels on a bearing of 050° and after 2 hours it is 50 km from P. Calculate how far the ships are apart 2 hours after leaving P. Give your answer to three significant figures.

Answer

4 Using the cosine rule we have

$x^2 = 40^2 + 50^2 - 2 \times 40 \times 50 \cos 50°$

Get practice in trying to do all of the calculation in one go using your calculator. This will save time in the exam.

Solving we obtain $x = 39.1$ km (3 s.f.)

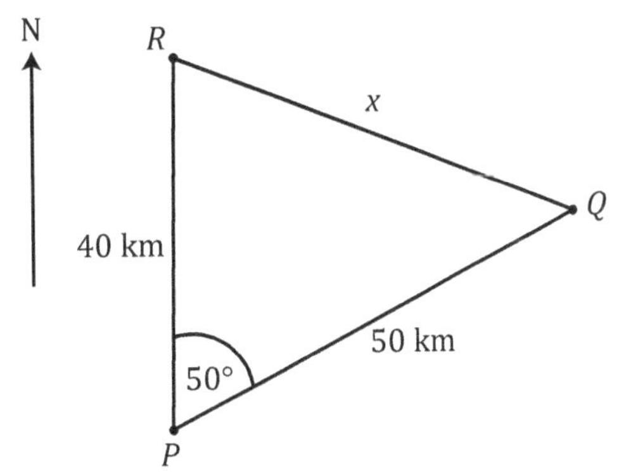

Notice in the diagram that we know the two sides and the included angle and want to find the missing side. In this situation, we need to use the cosine rule.

First draw a diagram showing the positions of the ship (points Q and R) 2 hours after leaving port P.

TIP

Always look at your answer and ask yourself if it is reasonable. Looking at the sizes of the sides and the angle this answer looks reasonable.

Three-dimensional problems

Three dimensional shapes drawn on a two-dimensional surface (i.e. a 3D diagram on a piece of paper) can be quite hard to understand so here are a few tips to make it easier:

- Solid lines are used for any of the edges of the shape you can see.
- Dotted lines are used for any of the edges of the shape you cannot see.
- Lines which go into the plane of the paper are drawn at an angle.
- Sides which are parallel to the plane of the paper are drawn as you would see them if you were drawing them in 2D.

There are also some terms to define before starting this section:

Faces – are the flat surfaces on the outside that make up the shape.

Edges – are where two flat surfaces meet. In a cube, for example, there are 12 edges.

Vertex – the strict mathematical definition of a vertex is where three or more edges meet. Using this definition a cube has eight vertices (vertices is the plural of vertex). However, you will also see the word vertex used to mean the highest point of a shape, so, for example, the tip of a pyramid is called the vertex.

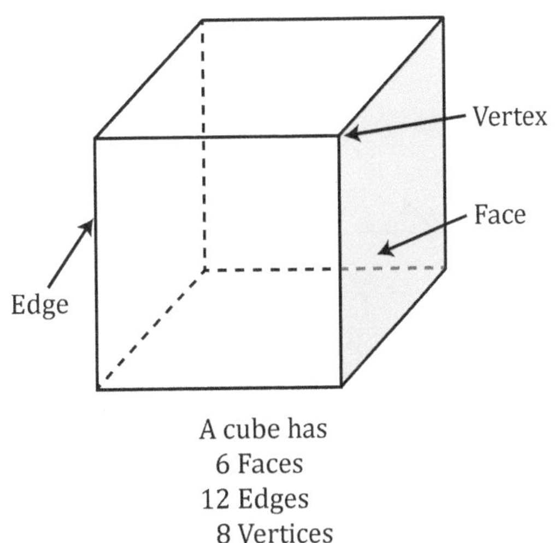

A cube has
6 Faces
12 Edges
8 Vertices

TIP

When dealing with problems in 3D it is always best to draw true shape diagrams by drawing appropriate 2D right-angled triangles separately and then work on these triangles to find missing sides/angles. The following example shows this technique.

In order to answer questions on three-dimensional problems it is important to be able to spot the following:

Isosceles triangles: the line of symmetry of the triangle bisects the base so it forms two equal right-angled triangles which can subsequently be used.

Lines at right-angles to a plane: a line from the vertex of a pyramid will form a right-angle with the plane containing the base.

The line of greatest slope: if you released a ball from the point being considered, then the line of greatest slope is the straight line path the ball would follow when released.

Examples

5 A square-based pyramid has a square base $PQRS$ with side 8 cm. The vertex V is directly above the centre of the base and the height of the vertex above the base is 10 cm.

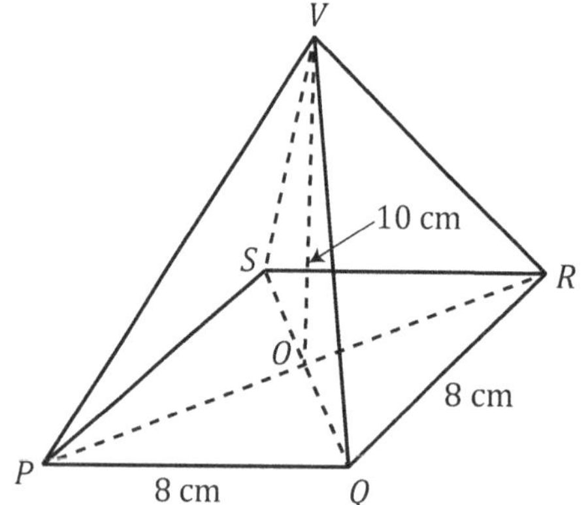

(a) Calculate the distance OP.

(b) Find the angle OP makes with the sloping edge VP.

Answer

5 (a)

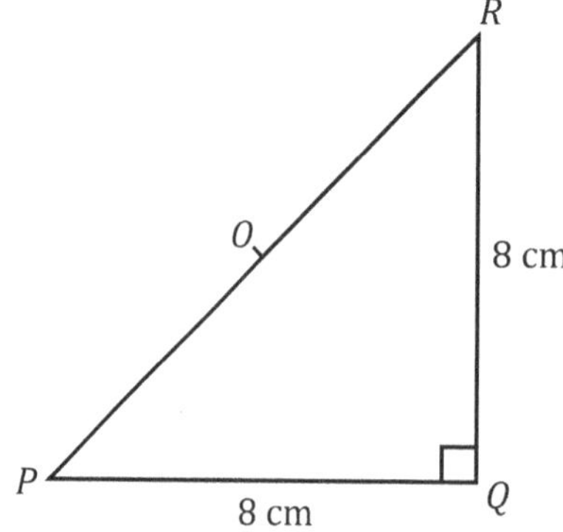

It is important to note that in this question, the vertex is directly above the centre of the base. This is not always the case so be careful to check in the question.

By Pythagoras' theorem $PR^2 = 8^2 + 8^2$

$$PR^2 = 128$$

$$PR = \sqrt{128} = 11.3137 \text{ cm}$$

OP is half of $PR = 0.5 \times 11.3137 = 5.6569 = 5.66$ cm (3 s.f.)

(b)

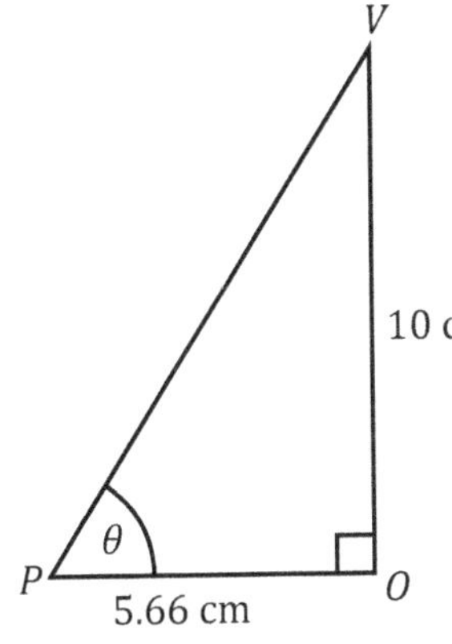

$$\tan\theta = \frac{10}{5.66}$$

$$\theta = \tan^{-1}\left(\frac{10}{5.66}\right)$$

$$= 60.5° \text{ (nearest } 0.1°)$$

6 A wheelchair ramp *ABCDEF* made of wood is shown below with $BC = 1.8$ m, $CF = 0.1$ m and $AB = 1.5$ m. Edges *DE* and *CF* are perpendicular to the plane *ABCD*.

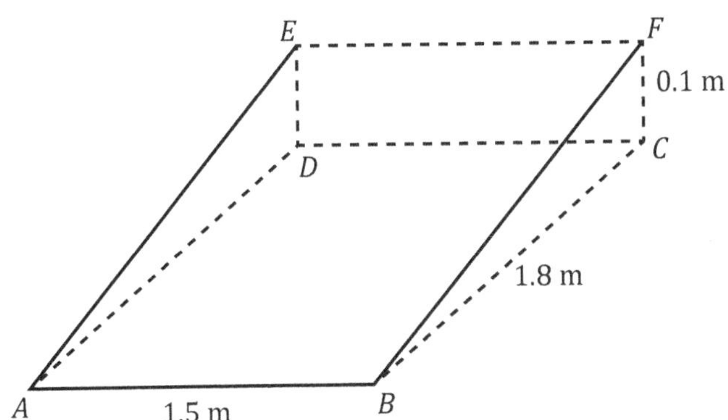

Look at the diagram carefully identifying the right-angled triangles and rectangles so that Pythagoras' theorem and trigonometry can be used.

(a) Calculate the length of the diagonal of the rectangular base *AC*.

(b) Calculate the length of *AF*.

(c) Calculate the angle *CAF* to the nearest 0.1°.

(d) Calculate the greatest angle up the slope to the nearest 0.1°.

Answer

6 (a) By Pythagoras' theorem

$$AC^2 = 1.5^2 + 1.8^2$$

Giving $AC = 2.343$ cm

$= 2.34$ m (3 s.f.)

(b) By Pythagoras' theorem

$$AF^2 = 0.1^2 + 2.343^2$$

Giving $AF = 2.345$ m

$= 2.35$ m (3 s.f.)

(c)

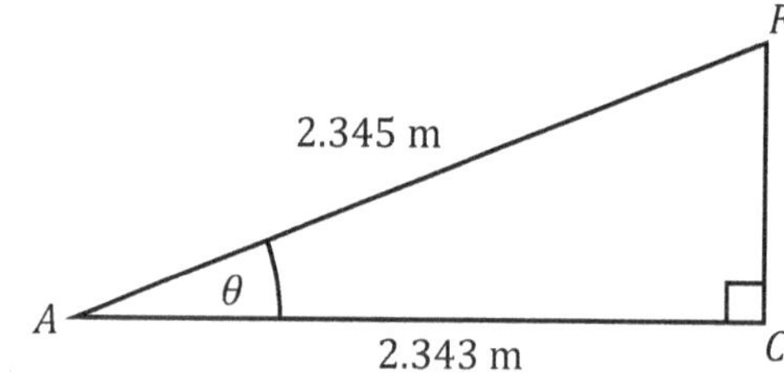

Let angle $CAF = \theta$

$$\text{Cos } \theta = \frac{2.343}{2.345}$$

$$\theta = 2.4° \text{ (to the nearest } 0.1°)$$

(d) In order to obtain the greatest angle down the slope think of the path a ball would take if it was released at the top of the slope.

It would follow a line parallel to the lines AE or BF.

We can use triangle BCF to find this angle.

Let angle $CBF = \alpha$ so $\tan \alpha = \frac{0.1}{1.8}$ giving $\alpha = 3.2°$ (nearest 0.1°)

Progress check

7 John sets out from A at 09.00 and walks at a steady speed of 6 km/h due north for 3 hours. Amy also sets out from point A at the same time and walks a distance of 15 km on a bearing of 050° which takes her 3 hours.

Calculate the distance they are apart in km to one decimal place, 3 hours after starting their walks.

> You will need to use the formula speed = $\frac{\text{distance}}{\text{time}}$ in this question.

8 The top of a fence post is made of wood in the shape of a pyramid. The base of the pyramid is a square of side 9 cm. The vertex, V, of the pyramid is directly above the centre of the base O and the distance VO is 8 cm.

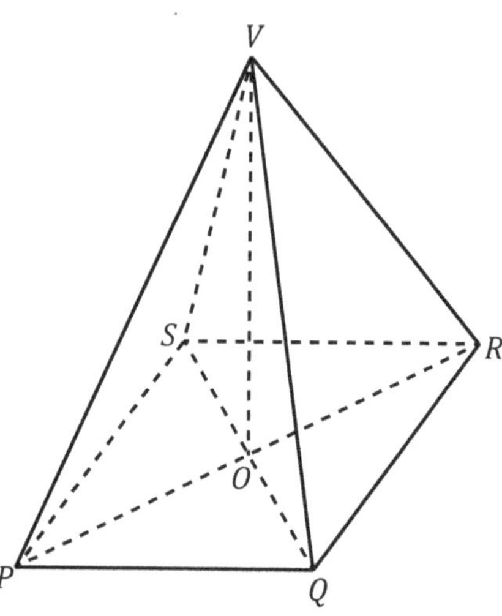

(a) Show that the length of one of the diagonals of the square base is $9\sqrt{2}$ cm.

(b) Show that the length of the edge VP is 10.2 cm to three significant figures.

(c) Calculate the size of the angle that side VP makes with the base giving your answer to the nearest 0.1°.

9 A wedge $ABCDEF$ made of wood is shown below with BC = 6 cm, CF = 4 cm and AB = 9 cm. Edges DE and CF are perpendicular to the plane $ABCD$.

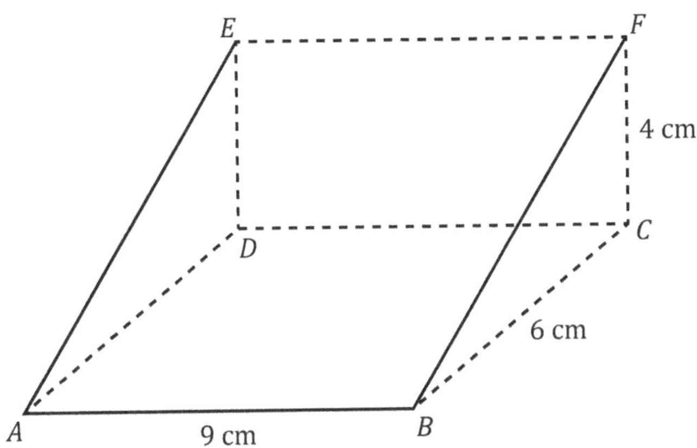

(a) Calculate the length of AC giving your answer in cm to three significant figures.

(b) Calculate the length of AF giving your answer in cm to three significant figures.

(c) Calculate the least angle up the slope which is angle CAF to the nearest 0.1°

(d) Calculate the greatest angle up the slope to the nearest 0.1°.

10 A boat sets sail from a harbour H on a bearing of 040° and travels in a straight line for 8 km. The boat then turns and travels in a straight line for 10 km on a new bearing of 010°.

(a) Draw a diagram showing the path of the boat.

(b) Calculate the straight line distance back to the harbour.

(c) On what bearing would the boat sail in order to return to the harbour travelling in a straight line?

TAKE NOTE!

When you obtain your answer always ask yourself if the question asks for the answer to be given to a certain number of decimal places or significant figures.

Exam practice

1 A yachtsman wishes to sail from a port A, to another port, B, which is 9 km due east of A. Because of the wind he is unable to sail directly east and sails 8 km on a bearing of 070° to point C.

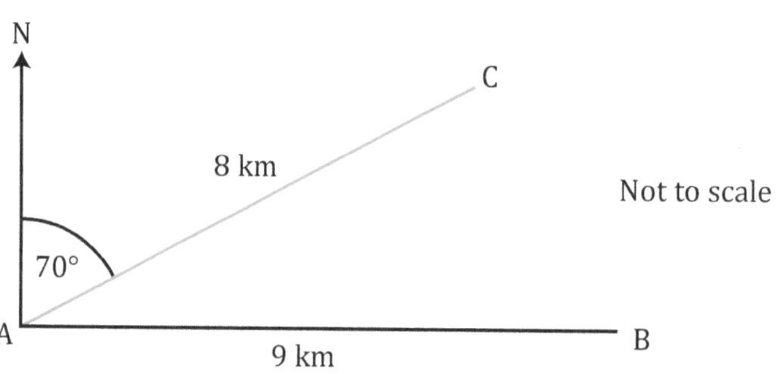

Calculate

(i) the distance he now is from port B, [3]

(ii) the angle ABC and hence the bearing on which he must sail to reach port B from point C, correct to the nearest degree. [4]

(OCR FSMQ May 2012 q7)

Note that we are given two sides and the included angle and we are asked to determine the length of the other side. For this type of situation, we use the cosine rule.

Answer

1 (i) Angle $BAC = 90 - 70 = 20°$

Using the cosine rule we have

$$BC^2 = 8^2 + 9^2 - 2 \times 8 \times 9 \cos 20°$$

Solving gives $BC = 3.112$ km

Hence distance = 3.11 km (3 s.f.)

(ii) Using the sine rule we obtain

$$\frac{8}{\sin ABC} = \frac{3.11}{\sin 20°}$$

Hence $\sin ABC = \dfrac{8 \sin 20°}{3.11}$

So, angle $ABC = 61.62°$

$= 61.6°$ (nearest 0.1°)

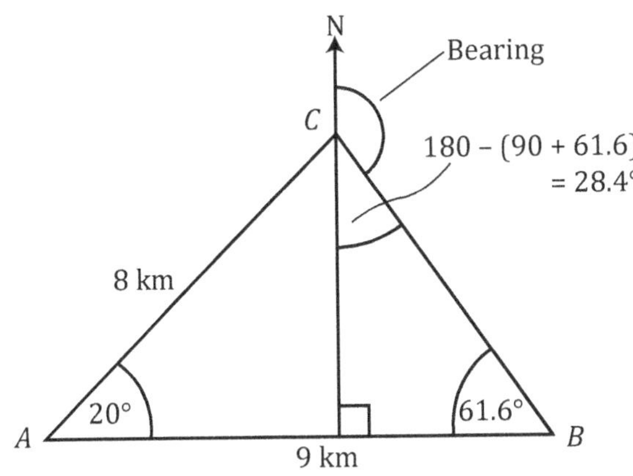

To work out the bearing from C back to B we draw a north line through C meeting the base of the triangle and forming a right-angled triangle.

The top angle of the right-angled triangle = 180 – (90 + 61.6) = 28.4°.

Bearing = 180 – 28.4 = 151.6° = 152°

Remember that bearings must only have three figures.

---

2 (i) Show that the equation $3\cos^2\theta = \sin\theta + 1$ can be written as

$$3\sin^2\theta + \sin\theta - 2 = 0.$$ [2]

(ii) Solve this equation to find values of θ in the range $0° < \theta < 360°$ that satisfy

$3\cos^2\theta = \sin\theta + 1.$ [4]

(OCR FSMQ May 2012 q5)

Answer

2 (i) Notice that in the second equation there are no terms in $\cos\theta$. This means we need to remove the $\cos^2\theta$ by using a rearrangement of the identity $\cos^2\theta + \sin^2\theta = 1$.

$$\cos^2\theta = 1 - \sin^2\theta.$$

Hence, $3\cos^2\theta = \sin\theta + 1$

$$3(1 - \sin^2\theta) = \sin\theta + 1$$

$$3 - 3\sin^2\theta = \sin\theta + 1$$

Rearranging, we obtain $3\sin^2\theta + \sin\theta - 2 = 0$

This is a quadratic in sin θ which needs to be factorised and solved.

(ii) Replacing the equation with the result from part (i) we have

$$3\sin^2\theta + \sin\theta - 2 = 0$$

$$(3\sin\theta - 2)(\sin\theta + 1) = 0$$

Hence $\sin\theta = \frac{2}{3}$ or $\sin\theta = -1$

$\theta = \sin^{-1}\left(\frac{2}{3}\right)$ giving = 41.8° or 138.2° (using the graphs or the CAST method)

$\theta = \sin^{-1}(-1)$ giving $\theta = 270°$.

Hence $\theta = 41.8°, 138.2°$ or $270°$.

---

3 The height above the ground of a seat on a fairground big wheel is h metres. At time t **minutes** after the wheel starts, h is given by

$$h = 7 - 5\cos(480t)°.$$

(i) Write down the initial height above the ground of the seat (when $t = 0$). [1]

(ii) Find the greatest height reached by the seat. [2]

(iii) Calculate the time of the first occasion when the seat is 9 metres above the ground. Give your answer correct the nearest second. [4]

(OCR FSMQ May 2012 q9)

Answer

3 (i) When $t = 0$, $h = 7 - 5\cos(0)°$ and as $\cos 0° = 1$, $h = 7 - 5 = 2$ m

(ii) The greatest value of $\cos\theta$ is 1. The smallest value of $\cos\theta$ is – 1.

Now if $\cos(480t)° = -1$, this will change $-5\cos(480t)°$ to $+5$ so the greatest value of h will be $h = 7 + 5 = 12$ m.

(iii) $h = 7 - 5\cos(480t)°$

Substituting $h = 9$ into the above equation we obtain

$$9 = 7 - 5\cos(480t)°$$

Rearranging gives $\cos(480t)° = -\frac{2}{5}$

$$480t = \cos^{-1}\left(-\frac{2}{5}\right)$$

$$480t = 113.578$$

$$t = \frac{113.578}{480}$$

$= 0.2366$ min

$= 0.2366 \times 60$ seconds

$= 14.196$ seconds

$= 14$ seconds (nearest second)

 In the triangle PQR, $PQ = 8$ cm, $RQ = 9$ cm and $RP = 7$ cm.

(i) Find the size of the largest angle. [4]

(ii) Calculate the area of the triangle. [3]

(OCR FSMQ June 2011 q3)

Answer

4 (i)

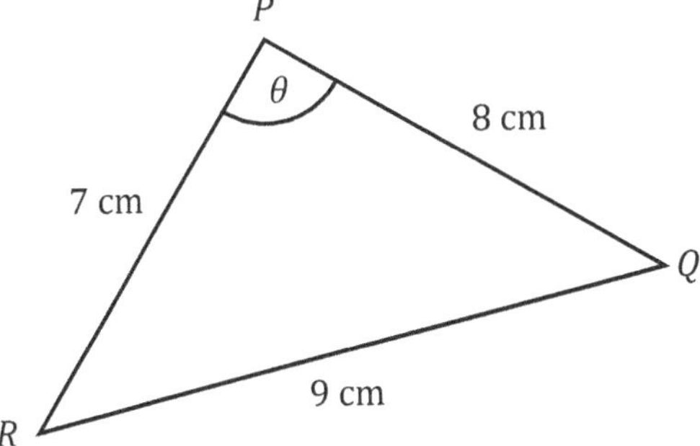

Remember the largest side in a triangle is always opposite the largest angle. As the largest side is RQ the largest angle must be angle RPQ.

Using the cosine rule we have

$$9^2 = 7^2 + 8^2 - 2 \times 7 \times 8 \cos\theta$$

$$81 = 49 + 64 - 112\cos\theta$$

Rearranging and solving for θ gives $\theta = 73.4°$ (nearest 0.1°)

(ii) Area of triangle $PQR = \frac{1}{2} \times 8 \times 7 \sin 73.4°$

$= 26.8\text{ cm}^2$ (3 s.f.)

5 Solve the equation $5 \sin 2x = 2 \cos 2x$ in the interval $0° \leq x \leq 360°$

Give your answer correct to one decimal place. [5]

(OCR FSMQ June 2011 q4)

Answer

5 $5\sin 2x = 2 \cos 2x$

Dividing both sides by cos $2x$

$$\frac{5\sin 2x}{\cos 2x} = 2$$

Dividing both sides by 5

$$\frac{\sin 2x}{\cos 2x} = \frac{2}{5}$$

Now, $\frac{\sin 2x}{\cos 2x} = \tan 2x$

$$\tan 2x = \frac{2}{5}$$

$$\text{Hence, } 2x = \tan^{-1}\left(\frac{2}{5}\right)$$

$$2x = 21.80°$$

$$x = 10.9°$$

Using the CAST method to find the other solutions. Tan x is positive in the first and third quadrants.

Dividing both angles by 2 to find the values of x.

Hence for the third quadrant $2x = 180 + 21.80 = 201.80°$.

Hence $x = 100.9°$

We need to go further than this as the angles are being divided by 2. So we might need to go as far as 720° to find all the solutions.

Hence $2x = 360 + 21.8 = 381.8°$ giving $x = 190.9°$ or

$2x = 360 + 201.80 = 561.8°$ giving $x = 280.9°$.

Hence $x = 10.9°, 100.9°, 190.9°, 280.9°$.

6 One leg of a cross-country race is from A to B. The checkpoint B is at the end of a wall that runs due east–west as shown in the diagram. A is a point 1000 m due south of a point C on the wall. $BC = 2400$ m.

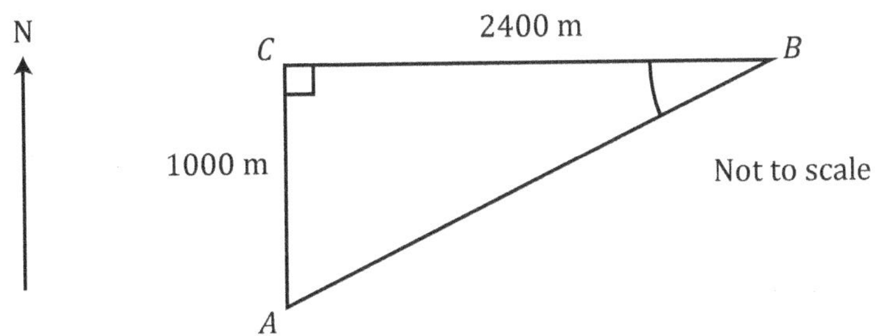

(i) What bearing should a runner take to travel from A to B and what is the distance AB? [4]

John sets off from A unable to see the checkpoint, B. He heads out on a bearing of 055° and when he reaches the wall at point D he knows he has to go east along the wall to reach the point B, as shown in the diagram.

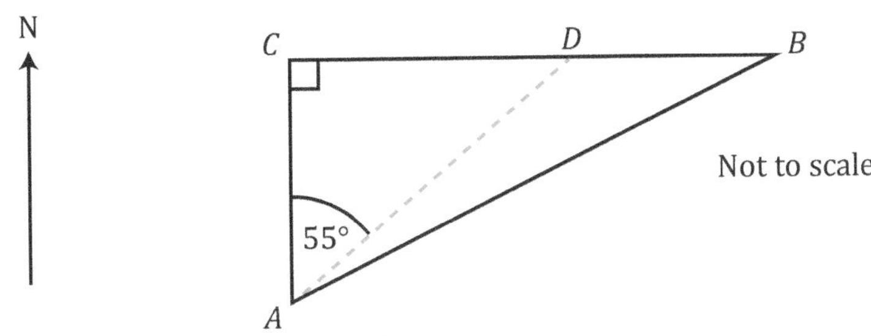

(ii) How much further than the distance AB does John run? [3]

(OCR FSMQ June 2013 q10)

Answer

6 (i)

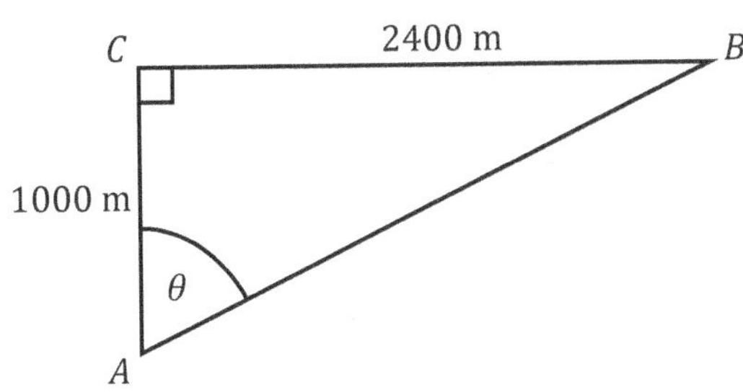

Bearing from A to B is angle θ.

$$\text{Tan } \theta = \frac{2400}{1000} \text{ so } \theta = \tan^{-1}\left(\frac{2400}{1000}\right) = 67.4°$$

Bearing = 067°

By Pythagoras' theorem, $AB^2 = 2400^2 + 1000^2$

Solving, gives $AB = 2600$ m

Remember than bearings are always given as three figures to the nearest degree.

We need to find the lengths *AD* and *DB*. Note that to find *DB* we need to first find *CD* and then subtract the length from 2400 m.

(ii)

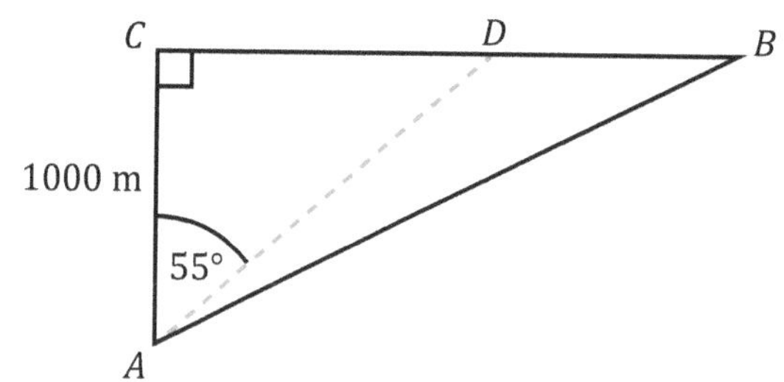

By trigonometry, $\frac{CD}{1000} = \tan 55°$

$CD = 1000 \tan 55° = 1428.1$ m

$DB = 2400 - 1428.1 = 971.9$ m

By trigonometry, $\frac{1000}{AD} = \cos 55°$, giving $AD = 1743.4$ m

Total distance John runs = 1743.4 + 971.9 m

= 2715.3 m

Extra distance John runs = 2715.3 − 2600 = 115.3 m = 115 m

Test yourself

1. Find the values of θ in the range $0° \le \theta \le 360°$, that satisfy the equation

   $3\sin^2\theta + 5\cos\theta - 5 = 0,$

   giving your answers to the nearest 0.1°.

2. Find the values of x in the range $0° \le x \le 360°$, that satisfy the equation

   $$\sin 2x = \sqrt{3}\cos 2x$$

   giving your answers to the nearest 0.1°.

3. A cruise ship sets sail from port A at 1700 on a bearing of 030° and travels at a constant speed of 24 knots (1 knot is a speed of 1 nautical mile per hour) in a straight line. At 1900 the cruise ship is at point B where there is a lighthouse 5 nautical miles due east of the ship.

   (a) Calculate the distance AB in nautical miles.

   (b) Calculate the distance in nautical miles from port A to the lighthouse.

   (c) Calculate the bearing of port A from the lighthouse.

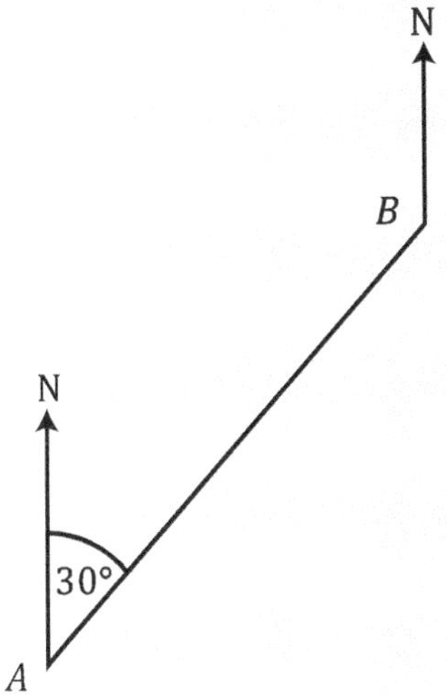

4. Find the values of θ in the range $0° \le \theta \le 360°$ that satisfy the equation

   $$\sin\theta = -3\cos\theta.$$

5. In the pyramid $VPQR$, sides VP, VQ are equal to 20 cm.

   Point V is directly above point R.

   $QR = PR = 16$ cm and side $PQ = 24$ cm.

   (a) Calculate the vertical height VR.

   (b) Point S is the mid-point of PQ. Find the lengths of VS and RS.

   (c) Using your answers to part (a), find the angle between the line VS and the plane PQR.

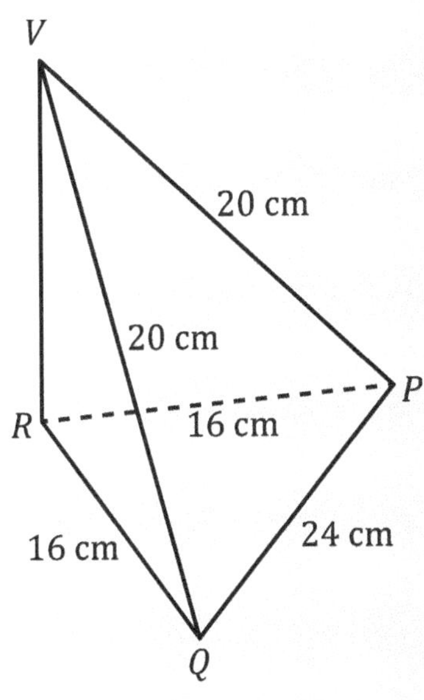

Topic summary

This topic expands on the material in Topic 9 and there are two new identities you will need to remember as well as how to draw and use the graphs of trigonometric functions to find angles.

Trigonometric identities

$$\tan\theta = \frac{\sin\theta}{\cos\theta}$$

$$\cos^2\theta + \sin^2\theta = 1$$

Graphs of the trigonometric functions

The sine graph ($y = \sin\theta$) where θ is measured in degrees

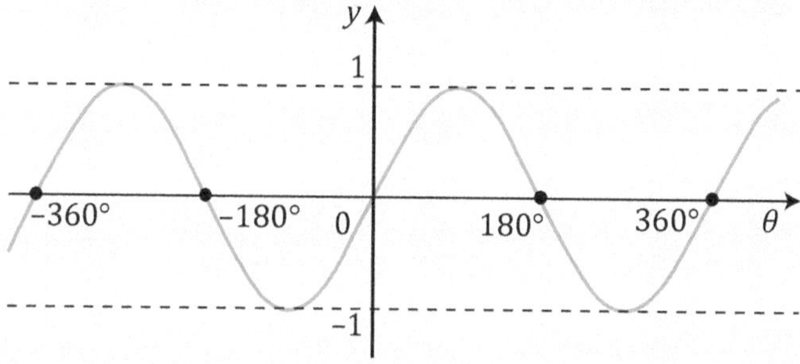

The cosine graph ($y = \cos\theta$) where θ is measured in degrees

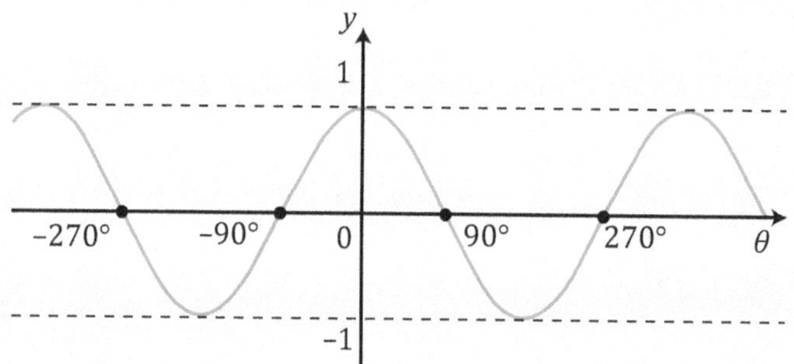

The tangent graph ($y = \tan\theta$) where θ is measured in degrees

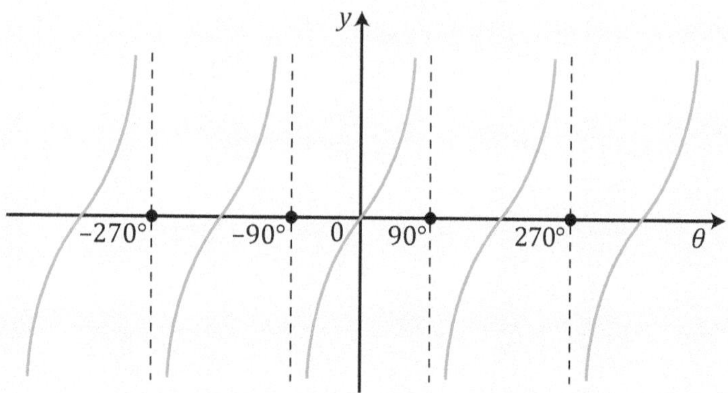

4 Calculus

Differentiation

This topic introduces you to differentiation which is about rates of change and calculating gradients of points on curves. Using differentiation you can also find the points where the peaks (called maximums) and troughs (called minimums) occur on some curves and this helps when sketching curves.

This topic covers the following:

11.1 Differentiation of kx^n and related sums

11.2 The gradient $\left(\text{i.e. } \frac{dy}{dx}\right)$ of a curve

11.3 Differentiating to find equations of tangents and normals

11.4 Stationary points

11.5 Determining the nature of stationary points

11.6 Sketching a curve with known stationary points

11.1 Differentiation of kx^n and related sums

What is differentiation?

Unlike a straight line, which has a fixed gradient, a curve has a variable gradient depending on the point on the curve where the gradient is taken. The gradient at a point on the curve is the gradient of the tangent to the curve at that point. A tangent is a straight line that touches the curve at a point $P(x, y)$.

Tangent

$P(x, y)$

> The gradient of the curve at the point $P(x, y)$ is the same as the gradient of the tangent to the curve at this point. We find the gradient of the curve by determining $\frac{dy}{dx}$. This means the change in y divided by the change in x and the 'd' in $\frac{dy}{dx}$ stands for delta and is shorthand for a small change.

Differentiation is the process of finding a general expression for the gradient of a curve at any point. This general expression for the gradient is known as the derivative, and can be expressed in two ways:

$\frac{dy}{dx}$ or $f'(x)$

Differentiation from first principles

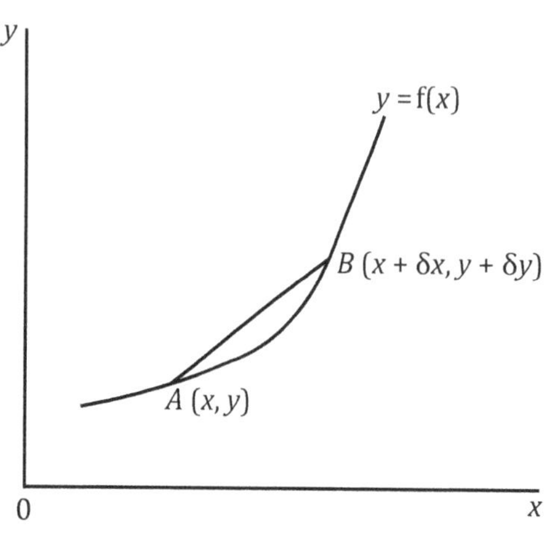

The line joining points A and B is called a chord. Notice that there is a small horizontal distance δx and a small vertical distance δy between points A and B. As A and B move closer together the gradient of the chord AB becomes nearer the true gradient of the tangent to the curve at point A. As $\delta x \to 0$ (i.e. as δx approaches zero) the chord will tend to become the tangent to the curve at point A and the gradient of the curve at point A will be the limit of the gradient of the chord.

This can be expressed in the following way:

$$\frac{dy}{dx} = \underset{\delta x \to 0}{\text{limit}} \frac{\delta y}{\delta x} = \underset{\delta x \to 0}{\text{limit}} \left(\frac{f(x + \delta x) - f(x)}{\delta x} \right)$$

Suppose we want to find $\frac{dy}{dx}$ for $y = 4x^2 - 2x + 1$

Increasing x by a small amount δx will result in y increasing by a small amount δy.

Substituting $x + \delta x$ and $y + \delta x$ into the equation we have:

$y + \delta y = 4(x + \delta x)^2 - 2(x + \delta x) + 1$

$y + \delta y = 4(x^2 + 2x\delta x + (\delta x)^2) - 2x - 2\delta x + 1$

$y + \delta y = 4x^2 + 8x\delta x + 4(\delta x)^2 - 2x - 2\delta x + 1$

But $y = 4x^2 - 2x + 1$

Subtracting these equations gives

$$\delta y = 8x\delta x + 4(\delta x)^2 - 2\delta x$$

Dividing both sides by δx

$$\frac{\delta y}{\delta x} = 8x + 4\delta x - 2$$

Letting $\delta x \to 0$

$$\frac{dy}{dx} = \underset{\delta x \to 0}{\text{limit}} \frac{\delta y}{\delta x} = 8x - 2$$

Differentiation

To differentiate a power of x: multiply by the index and then reduce the index by one.

For example in $4x^3$, the index is the power of x, which is 3 in this case. So multiplying by the index we multiply the coefficient (4 in this case) by 3 to give 12 and then reduce the power of x by 1. So when differentiated, $4x^3$ becomes $12x^2$.

If $y = kx^n$ then the derivative $\frac{dy}{dx} = nkx^{n-1}$

$\frac{dy}{dx}$ is referred to as the derivative of y with respect to x.

It is useful to remember this in words as follows: To find the derivative (i.e. $\frac{dy}{dx}$) you multiply by the index and then reduce the index by one.
So, for example, if $y = x^5$ to find $\frac{dy}{dx}$ you would multiply by the index 5 and then reduce the index by 1 (i.e. to give 4). Hence we have $\frac{dy}{dx} = 5x^4$
$\frac{dy}{dx}$ is often called the gradient function as it is a function representing the gradient at any point on the curve. If an x-coordinate is known, then the number can be substituted into the gradient function to find the numerical value of the gradient.

Using the above rule, here are some functions and their derivatives:

If $y = x^3$ then $\frac{dy}{dx} = 3x^2$.

If $y = 4x$ then $\frac{dy}{dx} = 4$.

If $y = 3$ then $\frac{dy}{dx} = 0$.

Differentiating terms with a single x, i.e. x^1, gives $x^{1-1} = x^0$ which equals 1. So differentiating $2x$ gives 2, and differentiating x gives 1.

Constant terms (i.e. those terms that are just numbers) give zero when differentiated as they do not change as x changes.

Examples

1 If $y = 6x^3 + \frac{1}{2}x^2 - 5x + 4$, find $\frac{dy}{dx}$.

Answer

1 Differentiating gives

$$\frac{dy}{dx} = (3)6x^2 + (2)\frac{1}{2}x - 5$$

$$\frac{dy}{dx} = 18x^2 + x - 5$$

TAKE NOTE !

This step shows the working. You should show your working because if you make an arithmetic error, then you may still get marks for your method.

2 If $y = 20x^4 + 5x^2 + 8x - 7$, find $\frac{dy}{dx}$.

Answer

2 Differentiating gives

$$\frac{dy}{dx} = (4)20x^3 + (2)5x + 8$$

$$\frac{dy}{dx} = 80x^3 + 10x + 8$$

3 If $y = (3x - 1)(x + 5)$, find $\frac{dy}{dx}$.

Answer

3 We first need to multiply out the brackets, so

$$y = 3x^2 + 15x - x - 5$$

$$y = 3x^2 + 14x - 5$$

$$\frac{dy}{dx} = 6x + 14$$

4 If $y = (x - 1)(x + 5)(x - 3)$, find $\frac{dy}{dx}$.

Answer

4 We first need to multiply out last two pairs of brackets, so

$$y = (x - 1)(x^2 - 3x + 5x - 15)$$

$$y = (x - 1)(x^2 + 2x - 15)$$

Now multiply the entire contents of the second bracket by x and then by -1 to give the following.

$$y = x^3 + 2x^2 - 15x - x^2 - 2x + 15$$

$$y = x^3 + x^2 - 17x + 15$$

Differentiating gives $\frac{dy}{dx} = 3x^2 + 2x - 17$

TAKE NOTE !

Sometime students, after getting the equation into a form that can be differentiated, forget to differentiate the equation. Watch out for this.

Progress check

1 Find $\frac{dy}{dx}$ for each of the following:

(a) $y = 4x^3 + 6x^2 - 3x + 1$

(b) $y = 6x^5 + 8x^4 - 3x^3 + 1$

(c) $y = 7x^4 + 8x^3 - 9x^2 + 1$

(d) $y = 10x^3 - 7x^2 - 9x + 11$

(e) $y = 20x^2 - 7x - 21$

(f) $y = 5x^2 - 7x - 5$

2 Multiply out the brackets and then find $\frac{dy}{dx}$:

(a) $y = (x + 2)(x + 1)$

(b) $y = (x + 4)(x + 2)$

(c) $y = (x - 3)(x + 2)$

(d) $y = (x - 4)(x - 2)$

(e) $y = (x - 4)^2$

(f) $y = (x + 2)(x - 2)$

(g) $y = (x + 5)^2$

(h) $y = x(x^2 + 2x + 1)$

(i) $y = x(3x^2 + 6x + 9)$

(j) $y = x^2(x^2 + 6x + 9)$

(k) $y = (3x + 2)(2x - 5)$

(l) $y = (5x - 1)(4x - 7)$

(m) $y = (2x + 3)^2$

(n) $y = (3x - 2)^2$

3 Multiply out the brackets and then find $\frac{dy}{dx}$:

(a) $y = (x + 1)(x^2 + 3x + 1)$

(b) $y = (x - 1)(x^2 + 5x - 1)$

(c) $y = (x - 5)(x^2 - 2x + 4)$

(d) $y = (2x + 1)(x^2 - 2x + 4)$

(e) $y = (4x - 3)(x^2 + 5x - 3)$

(f) $y = (5x - 1)(x^2 + 5x - 3)$

(g) $y = (x + 2)(x + 3)(x + 5)$

(h) $y = (x + 6)(x + 5)(x + 7)$

(i) $y = (x - 3)(x - 2)(x + 1)$

(j) $y = (x + 1)^2(x + 2)$

(k) $y = (2x - 1)^2(x - 3)$

(l) $y = (3x + 4)^2(x - 1)$

11.2 The gradient $\left(\text{i.e. } \frac{dy}{dx}\right)$ of a curve

Curves have changing gradients. Depending on the x-coordinate of a point on the curve the gradient as given by $\frac{dy}{dx}$ can have a positive, negative or zero value.

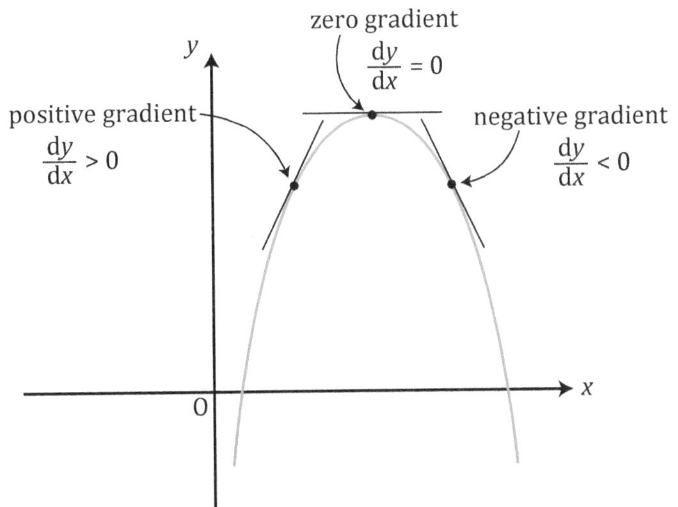

$\frac{dy}{dx}$ can be regarded as a rate of change as it is a measure of the change in y divided by the change in x. Rates of change of distance with time and velocity with time are covered in Topic 14.

11.3 Gradients of tangents and normals, and their equations

A tangent to a curve is a line which just touches the curve at a certain point which is A in the diagram shown below. A normal is a line drawn at right angles to the tangent at the point where the tangent touches the curve.

The gradient of the tangent at point A is the same as the gradient of the curve at point A.

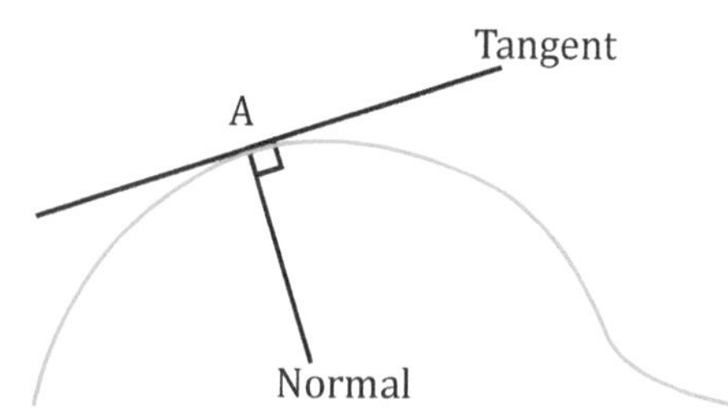

Note that this is just an application of $m_1m_2 = -1$ (i.e. the products of the gradients of two lines at right-angles to each other is always -1).

The tangent to a curve and the normal to the curve at the same point are perpendicular to each other so they make an angle of 90°. If two lines are perpendicular, the product of their gradients is -1. Hence we have

Gradient of tangent × gradient of normal at the same point = -1

TAKE NOTE!

You may need to look back at Topic 6 on coordinate geometry and straight lines before looking at the rest of this section.

To find the equation of the tangent at a point $P(x, y)$

1 Differentiate the equation of the curve to find the gradient function $\frac{dy}{dx}$.

2 Substitute the x-coordinate of P into $\frac{dy}{dx}$ to obtain the value of the gradient of the tangent at P, m.

3 Using the formula for the equation of a straight line: $y - y_1 = m(x - x_1)$

Substitute the gradient m, and the coordinates of point P for x_1 and y_1 into the above formula.

To find the equation of a normal at a point $P(x, y)$ to a curve

1 Differentiate the equation of the curve to find the gradient function $\frac{dy}{dx}$.

2 Put the x-coordinate for P into $\frac{dy}{dx}$ to obtain the value of the gradient, m_1, of the tangent at P.

3 Find the gradient of the normal using $m_1m_2 = -1$, i.e. $m_2 = -\frac{1}{m_1}$.

4 Using the formula for the equation of a straight line.

$y - y_1 = m(x - x_1)$ substitute the gradient m_2 for m, and the coordinates of point P for x_1 and y_1 into the above formula.

Example

5 The curve C has equation $x^3 + 3x^2 - 2$. The point P has coordinates (1, 2) and lies on C.

Find the equation of the **normal** to C at P.

Answer

5 $y = x^3 + 3x^2 - 2$

$\frac{dy}{dx} = 3x^2 + 6x$

First differentiate the equation of the curve to find the derivative/gradient function.

When $x = 1$

$\frac{dy}{dx} = 3(1)^2 + 6(1)$

$= 9$

This is the value for the gradient of the tangent. This is then used to determine the gradient of the normal which is at right angles to the tangent.

To find the gradient of the normal we use $m_1 m_2 = -1$ where $m = 9$.

So, $(9)\ m_2 = -1$ (where m_2 is the gradient of the normal)

Giving the gradient of the normal $m_2 = -\frac{1}{9}$

Equation of a straight line having gradient m and passing through the point (x_1, y_1) is given by:

$y - y_1 = m(x - x_1)$. In this case $m = -\frac{1}{9}$ and $(x_1, y_1) = (1, 2)$, so

$y - 2 = -\frac{1}{9}(x - 1)$

$9y - 18 = -x + 1$

We multiply both sides of the equation by 9 to remove the fraction.

Hence, equation of the normal at P is $9y + x - 19 = 0$

Progress check

4. Find the equation of the tangent to the curve $y = 3x^2 - 2x + 5$ at the point (2, 13).

5. Find the equations of the tangent and the normal to the curve $y = x^3 + 4x^2 - 8x + 2$

   at the point P where $x = 2$.

6. The equation of a curve is $y = 2x^3 - 3x^2 - 4x + 2$. Find the equation of the tangent to the curve at the point (2, −2).

7. A curve has the equation $y = x^2 - 3x + 2$.

   (a) Find the gradients of the tangents to the curve at the points where $x = 1$ and $x = 2$.

   (b) Find the equations of the tangents to the curve at $x = 1$ and $x = 2$.

   (c) P is the point where the two tangents at $x = 1$ and $x = 2$ intersect. Find the coordinates of point P.

11.4 Stationary points

TAKE NOTE!

Stationary points are also known as turning points.

A stationary point is a point on a curve where the gradient is zero. A tangent to the curve at a stationary point will have zero gradient and therefore be parallel to the x-axis.

To find the stationary points on a curve you first differentiate the equation of the curve and then set the derivative equal to zero. The resulting equation is solved to find the x-coordinate or coordinates of the stationary points.

Maximum and minimum points

Look carefully at the graph drawn here and notice the way the sign of the gradient changes either side of a stationary point for a maximum and minimum.

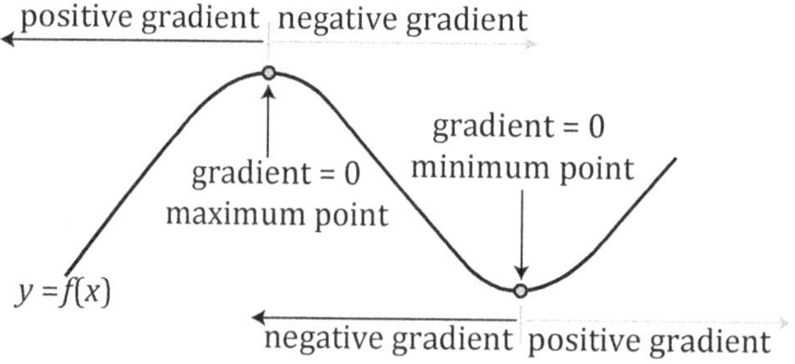

11.5 Determining the nature of stationary points

Stationary points are points on a curve where the function is neither increasing nor decreasing.

At a stationary point the gradient is zero so $\frac{dy}{dx} = 0$.

Determining the nature of stationary points means finding whether a particular point is a maximum or minimum point. As you will see later in this topic, finding stationary points and their nature is important if you need to sketch the curve.

Suppose you have found that the stationary points are at $x = 3$ and $x = 7$ and you want to find the nature of these points, one method involves finding the gradient of a point either side of each stationary point. So for $x = 3$ we can investigate the gradient at $x = 2$ and $x = 4$. If the gradient at $x = 2$ is positive and the gradient at $x = 4$ is negative then we know that the stationary point at $x = 3$ is a maximum point. If however the gradient at $x = 2$ is negative and the gradient at $x = 4$ is positive, then the point is a minimum point.

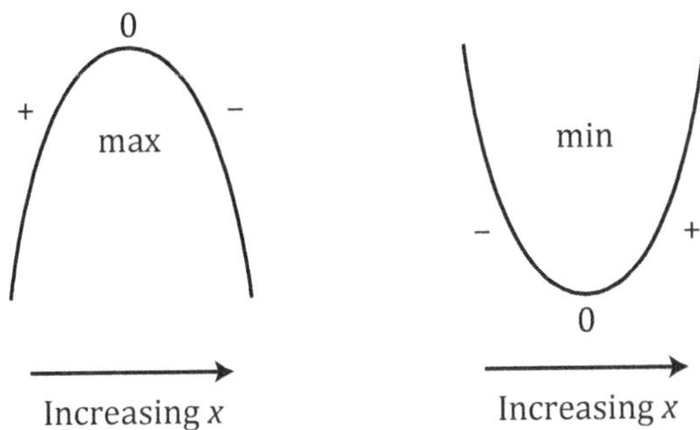

Notice the way the gradient changes sign in the above situations. For a maximum the gradient changes from + to 0 to – and for a minimum it changes from – to 0 to +.

There is another method for finding the nature of the stationary points and it involves finding the second order derivative and this is covered in the next section.

The second order derivative

In order to find the second derivative (i.e. $\frac{d^2y}{dx^2}$ or $f''(x)$) you take the first derivative (i.e. $\frac{dy}{dx}$ or $f'(x)$) and differentiate it again.

The second derivative gives the following information about the stationary points:

If $\frac{d^2y}{dx^2}$ or $f''(x) < 0$ the point is a maximum point.

If $\frac{d^2y}{dx^2}$ or $f''(x) > 0$ the point is a minimum point.

If $\frac{d^2y}{dx^2}$ or $f''(x) = 0$ this gives no further information about the nature of the point and further investigation is necessary.

Suppose we found that $\frac{d^2y}{dx^2} = x^3 - 3x$ and we also knew there was a stationary point at $x = 3$.

We then substitute $x = 3$ in the expression for $\frac{d^2y}{dx^2}$ to determine the sign.

Hence, $\frac{d^2y}{dx^2} = 3^3 - 3(3) = 27 - 9 = 18$.

As $\frac{d^2y}{dx^2}$ is positive, it means the stationary point at $x = 3$, is a minimum point.

TAKE NOTE!

The reason for finding the second derivative is to determine the nature of any stationary points.

Example

6 The curve C has equation: $y = -2x^3 + 3x^2 + 12x - 5$

Find the coordinates and nature of each of the stationary points of C.

TAKE NOTE !

Note that when you differentiate and put the derivative equal to zero, the x-coordinate(s) are found so it is necessary to substitute these coordinates in turn into the equation for the curve in order to find the corresponding y-coordinates.

Answer

6

$$y = -2x^3 + 3x^2 + 12x - 5$$

$$\frac{dy}{dx} = -6x^2 + 6x + 12 = -6(x^2 - x - 2) = -6(x - 2)(x + 1)$$

At the stationary points, $\frac{dy}{dx} = 0$, so

$-6(x - 2)(x + 1) = 0$

Solving gives $x = 2$ or -1

To find the corresponding y-values, each of these values is substituted into the equation for the curve.

When $x = 2$, $y = -2(2)^3 + 3(2)^2 + 12(2) - 5 = 15$

When $x = -1$, $y = -2(-1)^3 + 3(-1)^2 + 12(-1) - 5 = -12$

Stationary points are $(2, 15)$ and $(-1, -12)$

To find the nature of the stationary points, $\frac{dy}{dx}$ is differentiated again.

$$\frac{d^2y}{dx^2} = -12x + 6$$

Each x-value is entered in turn to determine whether the second derivative is positive or negative. If negative, the point is a maximum, and if positive, the point is a minimum.

Hence when $x = 2$, $\frac{d^2y}{dx^2} = -12(2) + 6 = -18 < 0$ showing there is a maximum point at $x = 2$.

When $x = -1$, $\frac{d^2y}{dx^2} = -12(-1) + 6 = 18 > 0$ showing there is a minimum point at $x = -1$.

Hence $(2, 15)$ is a maximum point and $(-1, -12)$ is a minimum point.

11.6 Sketching a curve with known stationary points

Simple curve sketching

To sketch a curve when you are given its equation, you need to determine the following:

- The coordinates of the stationary points on the curve and their nature (i.e. whether they are maximum or minimum points).
- The coordinates of the points where the curve intersects (i.e. crosses) the x-axis.
- The coordinates of the point(s) where the curve intersects the y-axis.

You have already come across how to find the coordinates and the nature of the stationary points.

To find where a curve cuts the x-axis you substitute $y = 0$ and then solve the resulting equation in x.

To find where a curve cuts the y-axis you substitute $x = 0$ into the equation of the curve, and then solve the resulting equation in y.

Once you have all these coordinates you can plot them on a suitable set of axes. The graph does not have to be drawn accurately as it is only a sketch but you have to include the coordinates of the points mentioned above and make sure that the curve is drawn smoothly.

The following example shows all these techniques.

 **TIP**

Drawing a sketch does not mean that you do not need to use a ruler to draw the set of axes.

Example

7 A curve C has the equation $y = x^2 - 2x - 3$

(a) Find the coordinates and nature of the stationary point of C.

(b) Sketch the curve $y = x^2 - 2x - 3$.

Answer

7 (a)

$$y = x^2 - 2x - 3$$

$$\frac{dy}{dx} = 2x - 2$$

At the stationary point $\frac{dy}{dx} = 0$

Hence, $2x - 2 = 0$

Solving for x gives $x = 1$

Substituting $x = 1$ into the equation of the curve to find the corresponding y-coordinate gives

$$y = 1^2 - 2(1) - 3 = -4$$

Hence the coordinates of the stationary point are $(1, -4)$

Differentiating again to find the nature of the stationary point:

$$\frac{d^2y}{dx^2} = 2$$

The second order derivative is positive, showing that $(1, -4)$ is a minimum point.

(b) To determine where the curve cuts the x-axis, substitute $y = 0$ into the equation of the curve.

> The x-axis has the equation $y = 0$ so you solve this equation and the equation of the curve to find an equation just in x which can then be solved to find the x-coordinates of the points of intersection.

$0 = x^2 - 2x - 3$

Factorising gives $(x - 3)(x + 1) = 0$

Solving gives $x = 3$ or -1

To determine where the curve cuts the y-axis, put $x = 0$ into the equation of the curve.

$y = (0)^2 - 2(0) - 3 = -3$

You now need to draw a set of axes making sure that all the important points you have just found are shown on the graph.

Label numbers on each axis where the curve cuts and make sure you mark on the curve the coordinates of the stationary points.

Remember to label both axes and to write the equation next to the curve.

The curve can now be sketched like this:

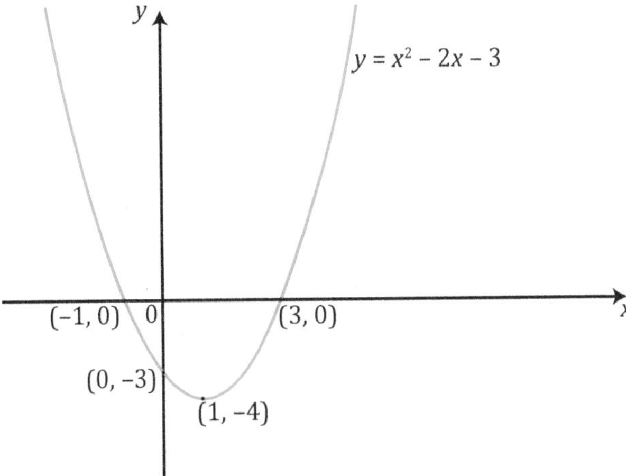

Exam practice

1 The curve C has equation $y = x^2 - 8x + 6$. The point A has coordinates (1, 2).

(a) Find the equation of the tangent to C at A.

(b) Find the equation of the normal to C at the point A.

TAKE NOTE !

To find the equation of a tangent you need the coordinates of a point through which it passes and also the gradient of the curve at that point. You then use the formula $y - y_1 = m(x - x_1)$ to find the equation of the tangent.

Answer

1 (a) $y = x^2 - 8x + 6$

Differentiating the equation of the curve to find the gradient gives

$$\frac{dy}{dx} = 2x - 8$$

At A (1, 2) the gradient is found by substituting $x = 1$ into the expression for $\frac{dy}{dx}$.

Hence, the gradient of the tangent at A, $\frac{dy}{dx} = 2(1) - 8 = -6$

The equation of the tangent is found using the formula:

$y - y_1 = m(x - x_1)$. In this case $m = -6$ and $(x_1, y_1) = (1, 2)$, so

$$y - 2 = -6(x - 1)$$

$$y - 2 = -6x + 6$$

$$6x + y - 8 = 0$$

(b) The tangent and normal are perpendicular to each other, so using $m_1m_2 = -1$ we have

$(-6)\,m = -1$ giving $m = \frac{1}{6}$.

Equation of the normal having gradient $\frac{1}{6}$ and passing through $A(1, 2)$ is

$$y - 2 = \frac{1}{6}(x - 1)$$

$$6y - 12 = x - 1$$

$$x - 6y + 11 = 0$$

---

2 The curve $y = x^3 - 3x^2 - 9x + 7$ has two turning points, one of which is where $x = 3$.

(i) Find the coordinates of the other turning point and determine whether it is a maximum or minimum point. [5]

(ii) Sketch the curve. [1]

(OCR FSMQ June 2010 q5)

Answer

2 (i) $y = x^3 - 3x^2 - 9x + 7$

Differentiating the equation of the curve to find the gradient gives

$$\frac{dy}{dx} = 3x^2 - 6x - 9$$

At the stationary points, $\frac{dy}{dx} = 0$

Hence, $3x^2 - 6x - 9 = 0$.

Dividing both sides by 3 we obtain

$x^2 - 2x - 3 = 0$.

Factorising gives $(x - 3)(x + 1) = 0$.

Hence $x = 3$ or -1

When $x = -1$, $y = (-1)^3 - 3(-1)^2 - 9(-1) + 7 = 12$

The other stationary point is at $(-1, 12)$

Differentiating again to find the nature of the stationary point:

$$\frac{d^2y}{dx^2} = 6x - 6$$

When $x = -1$, $\frac{d^2y}{dx^2} = 6(-1) - 6 = -12$

The second derivative is negative showing that $(-1, 12)$ is a maximum point.

(ii) To find the point where the curve cuts the y-axis we substitute $x = 0$ into the equation of the curve. Hence we have $y = (0)^3 - 3(0)^2 - 9(0) + 7 = 7$. So the curve cuts the y-axis at $(0, 7)$.

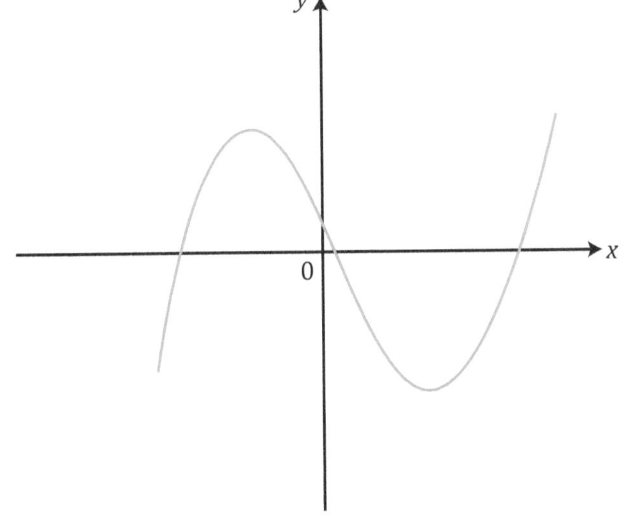

All that is required for this sketch, is to show that the stationary points are in the correct quadrants of the graph and that the curve cuts the y-axis at a positive value of y.

Always check to see if a quadratic equation can divided by a number because if it can it will make factorisation easier.

Note that in the question you are told that $x = 3$, so this means $(x - 3)$ is a factor.

TAKE NOTE !

Be guided by the marks allocated for this sketch. If they wanted the stationary points marked as well as the intersects on the x- and y-axes marked then you would expect more than one mark and the question will have stated that this is required.

3 Use calculus to find the x-coordinate of the minimum point on the curve

$$y = x^3 - 2x^2 - 15x + 30.$$

Show your working clearly, giving the reasons for your answer.

(OCR FSMQ June 2007 q5)

Answer

3 $y = x^3 - 2x^2 - 15x + 30$

Differentiating the equation of the curve to find the gradient gives

$$\frac{dy}{dx} = 3x^2 - 4x - 15$$

At the stationary points, $\frac{dy}{dx} = 0$

Hence, $3x^2 - 4x - 15 = 0$

To solve each bracket is made equal to zero.

Factorising, we obtain $(3x + 5)(x - 3) = 0$.

Solving gives $x = -\frac{5}{3}$ or $x = 3$

Differentiating again to find the nature of the stationary point:

$$\frac{d^2y}{dx^2} = 6x - 4$$

We have chosen to substitute $x = 3$ into the expression for the second differential as it is easier to substitute than $-\frac{5}{3}$.

When $x = 3$, $\frac{d^2y}{dx^2} = 6(3) - 4 = 14$

The second derivative is positive showing that the stationary point at $x = 3$ is a minimum point.

---

4 The equation of a curve is $y = x^3 - x^2 - 2x - 3$.

Find the equation of the tangent to this curve at the point (3, 9). [5]

(OCR FSMQ June 2011 q2)

Answer

4 $y = x^3 - x^2 - 2x - 3$

Differentiating the equation of the curve to find the gradient gives

$$\frac{dy}{dx} = 3x^2 - 2x - 2$$

At $x = 3$, $\frac{dy}{dx} = 3(3)^2 - 2(3) - 2 = 19$

Gradient of a tangent with gradient m and passing through the point (x_1, y_1) is given by

$$y - y_1 = m(x - x_1)$$

Here we have $m = 19$ and $(x_1, y_1) = (3, 9)$

$y - 9 = 19(x - 3)$

$y - 9 = 19x - 57$

$y = 19x - 48$

---

5 A curve has equation $y = 4x^3 - 5x^2 + 1$ and passes through the point $A\ (1, 0)$.

(i) Find the equation of the normal to the curve at A. [5]

(ii) This normal also cuts the curve in two other points B and C. Show that the coordinates of the three points where the normal cuts the curve are given by the equation $8x^3 - 10x^2 + x + 1 = 0$. [2]

(iii) Show that the point $B\left(\frac{1}{2}, \frac{1}{4}\right)$ satisfies the normal and the curve. [2]

(iv) Find the coordinates of C. [3]

(OCR FSMQ June 2013 q14)

Answer

5 (i) $y = 4x^3 - 5x^2 + 1$

Differentiating the equation of the curve to find the gradient gives

$$\frac{dy}{dx} = 12x^2 - 10x$$

At $x = 1$, $\frac{dy}{dx} = 12(1)^2 - 10(1) = 2$

This is the gradient of the tangent.

The tangent and normal are perpendicular to each other, so using $m_1 m_2 = -1$ we have

$(2)\ m = -1$ giving $m = -\frac{1}{2}$.

Equation of the normal having gradient $-\frac{1}{2}$ and passing through A(1, 0) is

$$y - 0 = -\frac{1}{2}(x - 1)$$

$$2y = -x + 1$$

$$2y + x = 1$$

(ii) Rearranging the equation of the normal for y we have $y = \frac{1 - x}{2}$

At the points of intersection between the normal and the curve, the y-values will be the same.

Equating the y-values we obtain

$$\frac{1 - x}{2} = 4x^3 - 5x^2 + 1$$

Multiply both sides by two to remove the denominator.

$$1 - x = 8x^3 - 10x^2 + 2$$

So, $8x^3 - 10x^2 + x + 1 = 0$

(iii) For the line $2y + x = 1$ LHS $= 2\left(\frac{1}{4}\right) + \frac{1}{2} = 1$ giving $\frac{1}{2} + \frac{1}{2} = 1$.

LHS = RHS so the point $\left(\frac{1}{2}, \frac{1}{4}\right)$ satisfies the equation of the normal.

For the curve $y = 4x^3 - 5x^2 + 1$ LHS $= 4\left(\frac{1}{2}\right)^3 - 5\left(\frac{1}{2}\right)^2 + 1$

giving $\frac{1}{4} = \frac{1}{2} - \frac{5}{4} + 1$.

LHS = RHS so the point $\left(\frac{1}{2}, \frac{1}{4}\right)$ satisfies the equation of the curve.

(iv) As $x = \frac{1}{2}$ and $x = 1$ are solutions of the equation $8x^3 - 10x^2 + x + 1 = 0$

then $(2x - 1)$ and $(x - 1)$ are factors of this equation.

Let $(2x - 1)(x - 1)(ax + b) = 8x^3 - 10x^2 + x + 1$

Equating coefficients of x^3 we have $2a = 8$, giving $a = 4$.

Equating coefficients independent of x we have $b = 1$.

Hence the other factor is $(4x + 1)$

Now $4x + 1 = 0$ giving $x = -\frac{1}{4}$.

To find the y-coordinate we substitute the x-coordinate into the equation of the curve.

When $x = -\frac{1}{4}$, $y = 4\left(-\frac{1}{4}\right)^3 - 5\left(-\frac{1}{4}\right)^2 + 1 = \frac{5}{8}$

Hence, the coordinates of C are $\left(-\frac{1}{4}, \frac{5}{8}\right)$.

Test yourself

1. The curve C has the following equation

$$y = 4x^2 - 30x - 3$$

   (a) Find the value of $\frac{dy}{dx}$ when $x = 4$.

   (b) Find the equation of the normal to C at the point where $x = 4$.

2. A curve has the equation $y = x^3 + 3x^2 - 9x - 8$

   (a) Show that the curve has a stationary point at $x = 1$.

   (b) Determine whether the stationary point at $x = 1$ is a maximum or minimum point.

3. The curve C has equation $y = x^3 - 6x^2 + 9x + 1$.

   (a) Find $\frac{dy}{dx}$

   (b) Determine the gradient at the point where $x = 3$.

   (c) Find the coordinates of the stationary points on the curve.

   (d) Determine the nature (i.e. maximum or minimum) of each stationary point.

4. The curve C has equation: $y = \frac{2}{3}x^3 + \frac{1}{2}x^2 - 6x$

   Find the coordinates of the stationary points of C and determine the nature of these points.

5. Curve C with equation: $y = x^3 - 6x^2 + 12x + 1$ has only one stationary point. Find the coordinates of this point.

Topic summary

Differentiating

To differentiate terms of a polynomial expression: multiply by the index and then reduce the index by one.

If $y = kx^n$ then the derivative $\frac{dy}{dx} = nkx^{n-1}$

Finding a stationary point

Put $\frac{dy}{dx} = 0$ and solve the resulting equation to find the value or values of x. Substitute the value or values of x into the equation of the curve to find the corresponding y-coordinate(s).

Finding whether a stationary point is a maximum or minimum

Differentiate the first derivative $\left(\text{i.e. } \frac{dy}{dx}\right)$ to find the second order derivative $\left(\text{i.e. } \frac{d^2y}{dx^2}\right)$ at stationary points.

Substitute the x-coordinate of the stationary point into the expression for $\frac{d^2y}{dx^2}$.

If the resulting value is negative then the stationary point is a maximum point but if the resulting value is positive, then the stationary point is a minimum point. If $\frac{d^2y}{dx^2} = 0$, then the result is inconclusive and further investigation is required.

Curve sketching

Find the points of intersection with the x- and y-axes by putting $y = 0$ and $x = 0$ in turn and then solving the resulting equations.

Find the stationary points and their nature (i.e. maximum and minimum).

Plot the above on a set of axes.

Integration

Indefinite integration is the reverse process of differentiation. If the differential of a function is known then you can get back to the original equation by integration provided that you also know the coordinates of a point lying on the curve.

This topic covers the following:

12.1 Indefinite integration

Indefinite integration is the reverse process of differentiation and is represented by the symbol $\int$.

For example: If $y = x^2 + 3x + 5$, then $\frac{dy}{dx} = 2x + 3$, so $\int 2x + 3 \, dx = x^2 + 3x + c$.

Notice a constant of integration called c is needed. When differentiating, constant terms disappear so when integrating it is impossible to know the value of any constant term, hence the use of c. So a constant is added. You will see later how to find the value of this constant.

To integrate x^n you increase the index by one and then divide by the new index. It is important to note that this works for all values of n provided $n \neq -1$. For indefinite integration you must always remember to include the constant of integration, called c.

TAKE NOTE!

Note that $\int y \, dx$ means integrate y with respect to x.

TAKE NOTE !

It is a good idea to think of integration as undoing the process of differentiation.

This can be expressed in the following way:

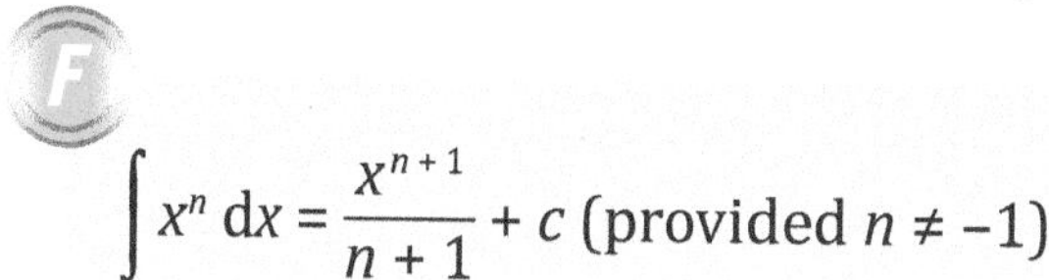

$$\int x^n \, dx = \frac{x^{n+1}}{n+1} + c \text{ (provided } n \neq -1)$$

Note that when there are no numbers on the integral sign, it is an indefinite integral and a constant of integration needs to be included.

Note that the integral symbol $\int$ must be used with dx in the examples shown below to show that you are integrating the function with respect to x.

You will see how this works by looking at the following examples:

1 $\int x \, dx = \frac{x^2}{2} + c$

2 $\int x^2 \, dx = \frac{x^3}{3} + c$

3 $\int x^3 \, dx = \frac{x^4}{4} + c$

4 $\int 1 \, dx = x + c$

The x in the integral is to the power 1. When integrating this is increased by 1 to 2 and then the resulting x^2 is divided by this new index 2 to give $\frac{x^2}{2}$. A constant of integration, c, is added.

A constant term is multiplied by x when it is integrated.

» TIP

Students in exams often forget to include the constant of integration, *c*, in their answers.

12.2 Integration of kx^n

If k is a constant (e.g. a number such as 3, −2, or $\frac{2}{3}$) then kx^n is integrated in the following way:

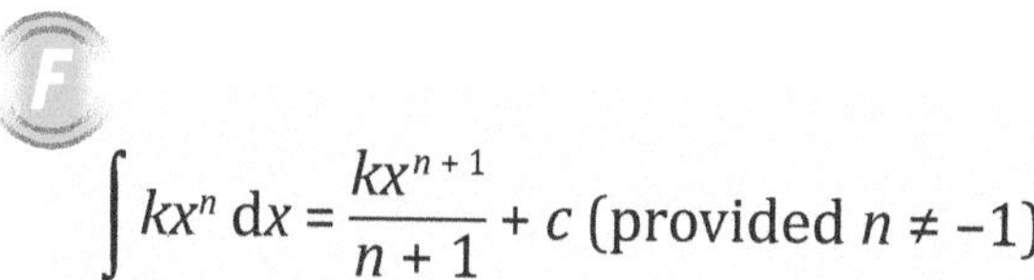

$$\int kx^n \, dx = \frac{kx^{n+1}}{n+1} + c \text{ (provided } n \neq -1)$$

You will see how this works by looking at the following:

1 $\int 2x \, dx = \frac{2x^2}{2} + c = x^2 + c$

2 $\int 4 \, dx = 4x + c$

3 $\int 3x^2 \, dx = \frac{3x^3}{3} + c = x^3 + c$

4 $\int 0.6x^2 \, dx = \frac{0.6x^3}{3} + c = 0.2x^3 + c$

5 $\int \frac{1}{2}x^2 \, dx = \frac{x^3}{2 \times 3} + c = \frac{x^3}{6} + c$

To integrate we increase the index by one and divide by this new index and we must remember to add the constant of integration, c.

Constant terms are multiples of x^0, as $x^0 = 1$. Applying the integration rule we have $\frac{4x^{0+1}}{1} = 4x$.

The x^2 term becomes x^3 when integrated. You then need to divide by the new index but there is already a 2 in the denominator. The new index (i.e. 3) is multiplied by the 2 in the denominator to become 6.

The following expression is integrated as follows:

$$\int (x^3 + 4x^2 - x + 2) \, dx = \frac{x^4}{4} + \frac{4x^3}{3} - \frac{x^2}{2} + 2x + c$$

This is called an indefinite integral because there are no numbers on the integral sign so you must remember to add a constant of integration c.

Examples

1 Find $\int (x^3 + 3x^2 - 2x + 1)\, dx$

Answer

$$\int (x^3 + 3x^2 - 2x + 1)\, dx$$
$$= \frac{x^4}{4} + \frac{3x^3}{3} - \frac{2x^2}{2} + x + c$$
$$= \frac{x^4}{4} + x^3 - x^2 + x + c$$

2 Find $\int (5x^4 + 4x^3 - 2x^2 + x - 1)\, dx$

Answer

$$\int (5x^4 + 4x^3 - 2x^2 + x - 1)\, dx$$
$$= \frac{5x^5}{5} + \frac{4x^4}{4} - \frac{2x^3}{3} + \frac{x^2}{2} - x + c$$
$$= x^5 + x^4 - \frac{2x^3}{3} + \frac{x^2}{2} - x + c$$

3 Find $\int (x - 1)(x + 8)\, dx$

Answer

3 We need to prepare the function ready for integration by multiplying out the brackets.

Hence $(x - 1)(x + 8) = x^2 + 8x - x - 8 = x^2 + 7x - 8$

$$\int (x - 1)(x + 8)\, dx = \int (x^2 + 7x - 8)\, dx$$
$$= \frac{x^3}{3} + \frac{7x^2}{2} - 8x + c$$

4 Find $\int \left(\frac{x^2}{5} - \frac{x}{2}\right) dx$

Answer

4 $$\int \left(\frac{x^2}{5} - \frac{x}{2}\right) dx = \frac{x^3}{5 \times 3} - \frac{x^2}{2 \times 2} + c$$
$$= \frac{x^3}{15} - \frac{x^2}{4} + c$$

TIP

Students frequently lose marks because they differentiate instead of integrating. Another way they lose marks is forgetting to include the constant of integration.

Progress check

1. Integrate each of the following with respect to x:
   (a) $4x^3$
   (b) $5x$
   (c) 3
   (d) $-6x^2$
   (e) $16x^3$
   (f) 1

2. Integrate each of the following with respect to x:
   (a) $5x^2 + 3x - 5$
   (b) $7x^3 - 4x^2 + 8x - 1$
   (c) $\frac{1}{2}x^2 + 5x - 3$
   (d) $(x - 3)(x + 2)$
   (e) $(x - 3)^2$
   (f) $x(x^2 + 6x - 5)$

3. Find each of the following integrals in terms of x:
   (a) $\int 4x^3\,dx$
   (b) $\int 6x^2\,dx$
   (c) $\int (2x + 1)\,dx$
   (d) $\int (8x^2 + 4x - 1)\,dx$
   (e) $\int (5x^4 + 4x^3 - 6x)\,dx$
   (f) $\int (x^2 + 4x - 5)\,dx$
   (g) $\int (x + 5)(x + 1)\,dx$
   (h) $\int (x - 1)(x + 1)\,dx$
   (i) $\int (2x - 5)(x + 1)\,dx$
   (j) $\int (x + 5)^2\,dx$
   (k) $\int x(x + 1)\,dx$
   (l) $\int x^2(2x + 1)\,dx$
   (m) $\int (6x^5 + 20x^4 - 6x^2 - x + 9)\,dx$

TAKE NOTE!
This question is just another way of asking you to integrate each of the following.

4. Find $\int \left(\frac{x^3}{4} - \frac{x^2}{2}\right) dx$

5. Find the following indefinite integrals:
   (a) $\int (5x^4 - 6x^2 + 9)\,dx$
   (b) $\int (8x^3 - 6x^2 + 10x + 5)\,dx$
   (c) $\int (4 - x)^2\,dx$
   (d) $\int \frac{x^4}{3}\,dx$
   (e) $\int \left(\frac{x^2}{2} + \frac{x}{3}\right) dx$

12.3 Finding the constant of integration

To find the constant of integration you need a pair of values (such as x and y) that fit the original equation. These values are substituted into the equation obtained after integration so that the value of the constant, c, can be found.

Example

5 If $y = \int (3x^2 - 10x + 4)\ \mathrm{d}x$, find the integral if it is know that when $x = 2, y = 4$.

Answer

5
$$y = \int (3x^2 - 10x + 4)\ \mathrm{d}x$$
$$= \frac{3x^3}{3} - \frac{10x^2}{2} + 4x + c$$
$$= x^3 - 5x^2 + 4x + c$$

Now when $x = 2, y = 4$ so substituting these values into the above equation we obtain

$$4 = (2)^3 - 5(2)^2 + 4(2) + c$$

Solving gives $c = 8$

Hence $y = x^3 - 5x^2 + 4x + 8$

12.4 Finding the equation of a curve, given its gradient function and one point

Integrating a gradient function will reveal an equation similar to the actual equation of the curve but it will involve the constant c. If you want to find the actual equation of the curve then it is necessary to find the numerical value of c. If a point (x, y) lies on the curve then the coordinates will satisfy the equation of the curve. This can then be used to find the value of c. The following example shows these steps.

Example

6 The gradient of a curve is given by $\frac{\mathrm{d}y}{\mathrm{d}x} = 18x^2 + x - 5$.

Find the equation of the curve given that the curve passes through the point (2, 20).

Answer

6 $\frac{\mathrm{d}y}{\mathrm{d}x} = 18x^2 + x - 5$

So, $y = \int (18x^2 + x - 5)\ \mathrm{d}x$

Integrating with respect to x gives $y = \frac{18x^3}{3} + \frac{x^2}{2} - 5x + c$

$$y = 6x^3 + \frac{x^2}{2} - 5x + c$$

TAKE NOTE !

Integration is the reverse of differentiation so if you have $\frac{\mathrm{d}y}{\mathrm{d}x}$ you can get back to the original equation by integrating $\frac{\mathrm{d}y}{\mathrm{d}x}$, including a constant c which then needs to be found.

Now as the point (2, 20) lies on the curve the coordinates will satisfy the equation of the curve. So,

> Notice that we now have an equation with c, the constant of integration as the unknown.

$$20 = 6(2)^3 + \frac{(2)^2}{2} - 5(2) + c$$

$$20 = 6 \times 8 + \frac{4}{2} - 10 + c$$

$$= 48 + 2 - 10 + c$$

Giving $c = -20$

> The value of c (i.e. −20) is now substituted into the equation for the curve.

Hence, the equation of the curve is $y = 6x^3 + \frac{x^2}{2} - 5x - 20$.

Progress check

6 Integrate each of the following with respect to x:

(a) $3x^2$

(b) $16x^3$

(c) $\frac{1}{3}x^2$

(d) 5

7 If $\frac{dy}{dx} = 4x + 5$, find the equation of the curve given that it passes through the point (2, 9).

8 If $\frac{dy}{dx} = 6x^2 + 10x + 2$, find y given that when $x = 1, y = 1$.

9 The gradient function of a curve is given by $\frac{dy}{dx} = 2x - 2$.

(a) Find the equation of the curve given that it passes through the point (3, –5).

(b) Find the coordinates of the points where the curve cuts the x-axis.

(c) Using the gradient function, find the coordinates of the minimum point.

Exam practice

1 The gradient function of a curve is given by $\frac{dy}{dx} = 3x^2 - 2x + 4$.

Find the equation of the curve, given that it passes though the point (2, 2). [4]

(OCR FSMQ June 2011 q9)

Answer

1 $\frac{dy}{dx} = 3x^2 - 2x + 4$

Integrating both sides with respect to x we obtain

$$y = \int (3x^2 - 2x + 4)\, dx$$

$$= \frac{3x^3}{3} - \frac{2x^2}{2} + 4x + c$$

$$= x^3 - x^2 + 4x + c$$

Now the curve passes through (2, 2) so these coordinates will satisfy the above equation.

Hence, $2 = 2^3 - 2^2 + 4(2) + c$

Solving gives $c = -10$

Equation of the curve is

$y = x^3 - x^2 + 4x - 10$

---

2 The gradient function of a curve is $\frac{dy}{dx} = x^2 + 2x - 8$. The curve passes through the point $P(3, 0)$.

(a) Show that the equation of the curve is $\frac{x^3}{3} + x^2 - 8x + 6$.

(b) Find the coordinates of the stationary points of this curve.

(c) Sketch the curve showing the stationary points and the intercept on the y-axis.

Answer

2 (a) $\frac{dy}{dx} = x^2 + 2x - 8$

So, $y = \int (x^2 + 2x - 8)\, dx$

Integrating both sides with respect to x gives

$$y = \frac{x^3}{3} + \frac{2x^2}{2} - 8x + c$$

$$y = \frac{x^3}{3} + x^2 - 8x + c$$

Now as the point (3, 0) lies on the curve the coordinates will satisfy the equation of the curve. So,

$$0 = \frac{(3)^3}{3} + (3)^2 - 8(3) + c$$

Solving gives $c = 6$.

So $y = \frac{x^3}{3} + x^2 - 8x + 6$

TAKE NOTE !

Make sure you do not get differentiation and integration mixed up. Plenty of students do in the exam.

TIP

If the question wanted just the x-coordinate it would have specified it. If you are asked for the coordinates of the stationary points, you must give both the x- and y-coordinates.

(b) At the stationary points, $\frac{dy}{dx} = 0$ so $x^2 + 2x - 8 = 0$.

Factorising the quadratic equation gives $(x - 2)(x + 4) = 0$.

Hence, $x = 2$ or -4

When $x = 2$, $y = \frac{(2)^3}{3} + (2)^2 - 8(2) + 6 = -3\frac{1}{3}$

When $x = -4$, $y = \frac{(-4)^3}{3} + (-4)^2 - 8(-4) + 6 = 32\frac{2}{3}$

(c) Finding the intercept on the y-axis by substituting $x = 0$ into the equation of the curve

we have $y = \frac{(0)^3}{3} + (0)^2 - 8(0) + 6 = 6$.

Note that you could easily do the above calculation mentally.

Adding the points to the sketch we have.

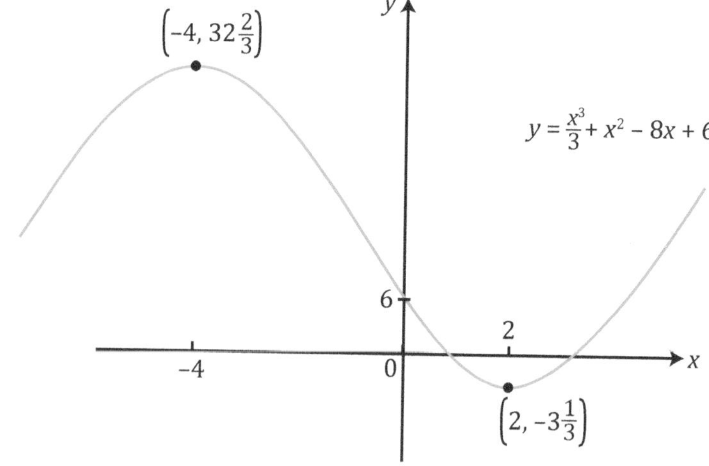

3 The gradient function of a curve is given by $\frac{dy}{dx} = a + bx$.

Find the values of a and b and the equation of the curve given that it passes through the points (0, 2), (1, 8) and (−1, 2). [7]

(OCR FSMQ June 2005 q7)

Answer

3 $\frac{dy}{dx} = a + bx$

$$y = \int (a + bx)\,dx$$

$$y = ax + \frac{bx^2}{2} + c$$

As the curve passes through the point (0, 2) these two coordinates will satisfy the equation of the curve. Hence we have

$$2 = 0 + \frac{b(0)^2}{2} + c$$

So, $c = 2$

Substituting the coordinates (1, 8) into the equation of the curve and also the value of c (i.e. 2), we have

$$8 = a(1) + \frac{b(1)^2}{2} + 2$$

$$8 = a + \frac{b}{2} + 2$$

$$6 = a + \frac{b}{2}$$

Multiplying both sides of the equation by 2 in order to remove the fraction, we have

$$12 = 2a + b \quad \text{.......................} \quad (1)$$

Substituting the coordinates (−1, 2) and $c = 2$ into the equation of the curve, we have

$$2 = a(-1) + \frac{b(-1)^2}{2} + 2$$

$$0 = -a + \frac{b}{2}$$

Multiplying both sides of the equation by 2 in order to remove the fraction, we have

$$0 = -2a + b \quad \text{.......................} \quad (2)$$

Adding equations (1) and (2) so as to eliminate a we obtain

$$12 = 2b$$

Giving $b = 6$.

Substituting $b = 6$ into equation (1) gives

$$12 = 2a + 6$$

Giving $a = 3$.

Hence $a = 3$, $b = 6$ and $c = 2$

The equation of the curve is $y = 3x + 3x^2 + 2$

TAKE NOTE !

Simultaneous equations crop up throughout the course. Make sure that you fully master them.

Test yourself

1 The gradient function of a curve is given by $\frac{dy}{dx} = 4 - 2x - 3x^2$.

Find the equation of the curve given that it passes through the point (0, 1).

2 Integrate each of the following functions with respect to x.

(a) $4x - 3x^3$

(b) $2x(3x^2 - 5x + 1)$

(c) $\frac{1}{2}x^2 - x + \frac{1}{2}$

3 Integrate the following expression with respect to t.

$25t^4 - 12t^3 + 15t^2 - 9t + 2$

4 Integrate the following expression with respect to x.

$\frac{2}{15}(x^2 - 30)$

5 Find $\int (6t^2 - 2t + 1)\,dt$

6 Curve C has a gradient given by $\frac{dy}{dx} = 15x^2 + 8x + 1$. Given that curve C passes through the point (1, 3), find the equation of curve C.

7 The curve shown below has the gradient function $\frac{dy}{dx} = 3 - 2x$.

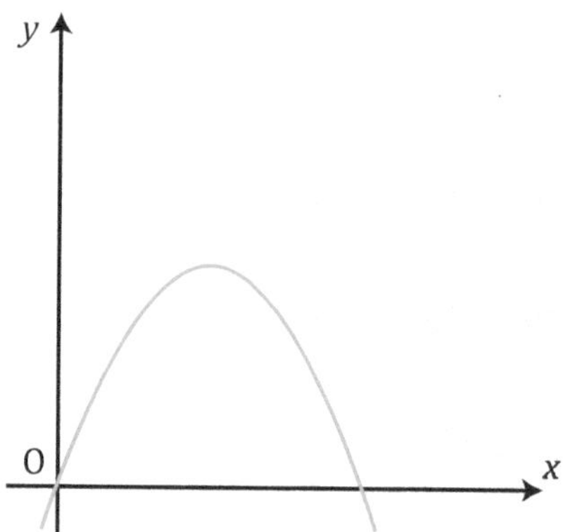

(a) Find the equation of the curve if it passes through the origin.

(b) The curve cuts the x-axis at two points. One of the points is the origin. Find the coordinates of the other point

Topic summary

Integration of x^n

Indefinite integration is the reverse process to differentiation. When integrating indefinitely you must remember to include the constant of integration.

$$\int x^n\,dx = \frac{x^{n+1}}{n+1} + c \text{ (provided } n \neq -1)$$

Integration of kx^n

$$\int kx^n\,dx = \frac{kx^{n+1}}{n+1} + c \text{ (provided } n \neq -1)$$

Definite integration

Definite integration is similar to indefinite integration except this time there is no constant of integration and you obtain a number as your answer rather than an algebraic expression. This topic covers the following:

13.1 The difference between indefinite and definite integrals

TAKE NOTE!
Indefinite integrals do not have limits whereas definite integrals do.

Integrals that contain a constant of integration are called indefinite integrals.

When there is no constant of integration, the integral is found as a numerical value and this is called a definite integral.

Definite integration uses limits which are numbers that you put into the algebraic expression to obtain the final numerical answer. The main use of definite integration is to find the areas under curves.

Integrals in the form $\int_a^b y\,\mathrm{d}x$ are called definite integrals because the result will be a definite answer, usually a number, with no constant of integration.

13.2 Evaluation of definite integrals

The definite integral is found by substituting the limits (the numbers a and b) into the result of the integration and subtracting the value corresponding to the lower limit from the value corresponding to the upper limit.

Definite integrals represent an area under the curve $y = f(x)$ as you will see later.

Examples

1 Find $\int_1^2 (3x^2 - x + 4)\, dx$

Answer

Once you have integrated, put square brackets around the result and add the limits as shown here.

1 $\int_1^2 (3x^2 - x + 4)\, dx$

$= \left[\frac{3x^3}{3} - \frac{x^2}{2} + 4x\right]_1^2$

You should cancel any fractions that appear.

$= \left[x^3 - \frac{x^2}{2} + 4x\right]_1^2$

Two pairs of brackets are used. The first contains the top limit substituted for x. The second contains the bottom limit substituted for x. A minus sign is inserted between the two brackets.

$= \left[\left(2^3 - \frac{2^2}{2} + 4(2)\right) - \left(1^3 - \frac{1^2}{2} + 4(1)\right)\right]$

$= \left[(8 - 2 + 8) - \left(1 - \frac{1}{2} + 4\right)\right]$

$= 14 - 4\frac{1}{2} = 9\frac{1}{2}$

2 Find $\int_0^3 \left(\frac{4x^3}{3} - \frac{x^2}{2}\right) dx$

Answer

2 $\int_0^3 \left(\frac{4x^3}{3} - \frac{x^2}{2}\right) dx = \left[\frac{4x^4}{12} - \frac{x^3}{2 \times 3}\right]_0^3$

$= \left[\frac{x^4}{3} - \frac{x^3}{6}\right]_0^3$

$= \left[\left(\frac{3^4}{3} - \frac{3^3}{6}\right) - (0)\right]$

$= \left[\left(27 - \frac{3^3}{6}\right) - (0)\right]$

$= 22.5$

If one of the limits is zero then if all the terms in the bracket to which this limit refers contain x, then you can simply replace the whole bracket with a zero.

3 Find $\int_0^1 \frac{2}{3}(5x - 6)\,dx$

Answer

3 $\int_0^1 \frac{2}{3}(5x - 6)\,dx = \frac{2}{3}\int_0^1 (5x - 6)\,dx$

$= \frac{2}{3}\left[\frac{5x^2}{2} - 6x\right]_0^1$

$= \frac{2}{3}\left[\left(\frac{5(1)^2}{2} - 6(1)\right) - (0)\right]$

$= \frac{2}{3}(-3.5)$

$= -2.33$

Note that you can remove the fraction outside the integral sign which will make the integration easier.

Combining two integrals

Provided the limits are the same, two integrals can be combined as the following example shows.

Suppose we need to subtract two integrals such as:

$$\int_0^1 (3x^2 + 4x - 1)\,dx - \int_0^1 (2x - 3)\,dx$$

We now collect the terms to produce the following:

$$\int_0^1 (3x^2 + 2x + 2)\,dx = \left[\frac{3x^3}{3} + \frac{2x^2}{2} + 2x\right]_0^1$$

$$= \left[x^3 + x^2 + 2x\right]_0^1$$

$$= [(1^3 + 1^2 + 2(1)) - (0)]$$

$$= 4$$

Note that we can do the sum $4x - 2x = +2x$ and also $-1 - (-3) = -1 + 3 = +2$.

Note that the alternative, and longer, method is to find the value of each integral separately.

Hence $\int_0^1 (3x^2 + 4x - 1)\,dx - \int_0^1 (2x - 3)\,dx$

$= \left[x^3 + 2x^2 - x\right]_0^1 - \left[x^2 - 3x\right]_0^1$

$= [(1 + 2 - 1) - (0)] - [(1 - 3) - (0)]$

$= 2 - (-2)$

$= 4$

You can see that there is a lot more calculation involved when you do not combine the integrals.

Progress check

1. Find $\int_0^1 (6x^2 - 2x + 5)\,dx$
2. Find $\int_2^3 (3x^2 - 4x - 5)\,dx$
3. If $y = \frac{1}{3}(2x - 3x^2)$, find $\int_0^{0.5} y\,dx$ giving your answer to three significant figures.
4. Show that $\int_0^2 (x^2 + 4x - 3)\,dx = 4\frac{2}{3}$.
5. Find $\int_0^3 (x^2 + 6x + 4)\,dx - \int_0^3 (x^2 - 4x)\,dx$
6. Find the value of $\int_0^1 (x + 5)(x + 6)\,dx$ giving your answer to three significant figures.

13.3 Finding the area between a curve, two ordinates and the *x*-axis

Definite integrals represent the area under the curve $y = f(x)$ between the two x-values $x = a$ and $x = b$. Note that the lines parallel to the y-axis, $x = a$ and $x = b$ are called ordinates.

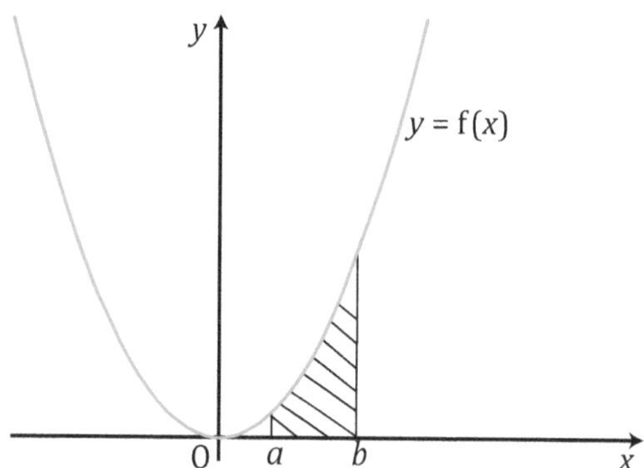

A definite integral is positive for areas above the x-axis and negative for areas below the x-axis. A final area must always be given as a positive value.

The area under the graph between the two ordinates (i.e. the two vertical lines) having equations $x = a$ and $x = b$ is written in the following way.

Shaded area $= \int_a^b y\,dx$

If the curve had the equation $y = 3x^2$ and we wanted to find the area bound by the curve and the two ordinates $x = 1$ and $x = 3$, then we proceed in the following way:

$$\text{Shaded area} = \int_1^3 3x^2\,dx$$

$$= \left[\frac{3x^3}{3}\right]_1^3$$

$$= \left[x^3\right]_1^3$$

$$= [(3^3) - (1^3)]$$

$$= 27 - 1$$

$$= 26$$

Examples

4

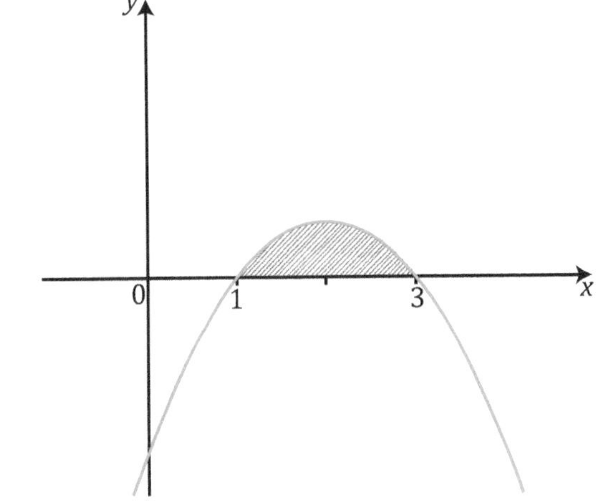

The diagram shows a sketch of the curve $y = (1 - x)(x - 3)$. If the curve cuts the x-axis at $x = 1$ and $x = 3$, find the area of the shaded region.

To find where the curve cuts the x-axis we equate the equation of the curve to zero. Hence, in this case we have $(1 - x)(x - 3) = 0$ which is solved to give $x = 1$ and $x = 3$.

Answer

$$\text{Shaded area} \int_1^3 y\,dx = \int_1^3 (1 - x)(x - 3)\,dx$$

$$= \int_2^3 (-3 + 4x - x^2)\,dx$$

$$= \left[-3x + 2x^2 - \frac{x^3}{3}\right]_1^3$$

$$= \left[(-9 + 18 - 9) - \left(-3 + 2 - \frac{1}{3}\right)\right]$$

$$= 0 - \left(-\frac{4}{3}\right)$$

$$= \frac{4}{3}$$

5 (a) Draw a sketch of the curve $y = x^3$.

(b) Find $\int_{-2}^{0} x^3\,dx$.

(c) Find the area enclosed by the curve and the ordinates $x = -2$ and $x = 2$.

Answer

5 (a)

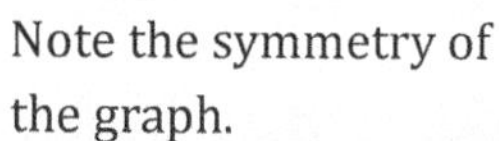

Note the symmetry of the graph.

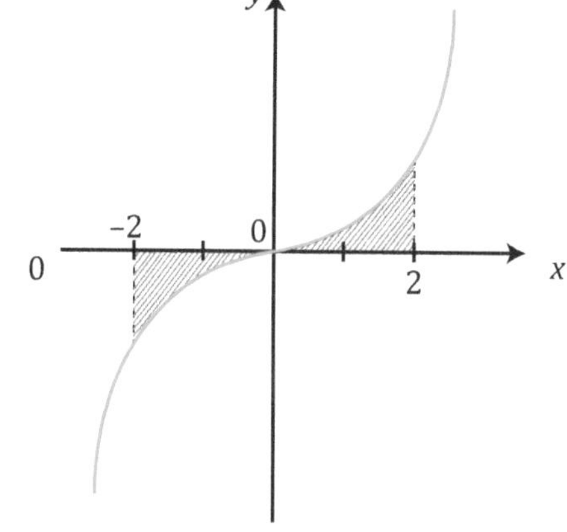

Note that the area is negative as areas below the x-axis are always negative.

(b) $\int_{-2}^{0} x^3\,dx = \left[\frac{x^4}{4}\right]_{-2}^{0} = \left[\left(\frac{(0)^4}{4}\right) - \left(\frac{(-2)^4}{4}\right)\right] = -4$

Looking at the sketch in part (a) and marking on it the two areas, you can see that one of the areas is below the x-axis. This will give a negative answer. The positive area above the x-axis is equal in magnitude so if we integrate between the limits -2 and 2 it will give the area as zero.

(c) You could integrate between 0 and 2 and then add the result to that obtained in part (a) but this is not necessary.

Owing to the symmetry, the area of the graph is double the answer obtained in part (a) but we remove the negative sign.

Hence, required area = 8

The area between a curve and a straight line

To find the area enclosed between a curve and a straight line, first find the points of intersection if they are not already given. Then integrate the curve between the two x-coordinates to find the area under the curve. Then find the area of the remaining shape, usually a triangle or a trapezium and then either add or subtract the two areas to find the required shaded area. The following diagrams show how the area is found in different situations.

In this situation, the shaded region in the first diagram is below the straight line and above the curve. To obtain the required area we subtract the area under the curve from the area of the triangle.

TIP

Simply look at the graphs and think logically about the area you are finding. You can then make the decision about the shapes you need to add or subtract to give the required area.

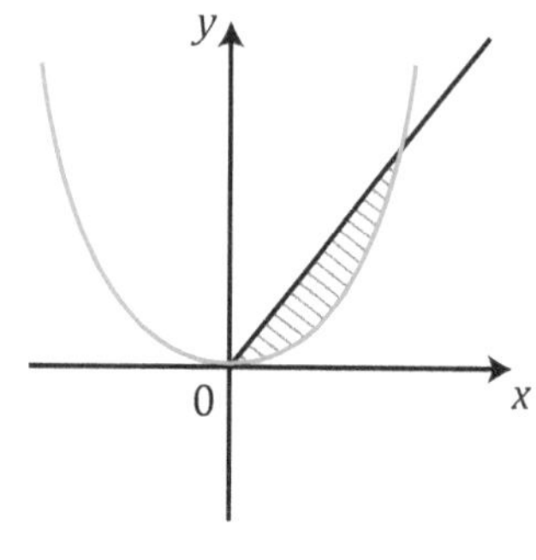

Required Area =

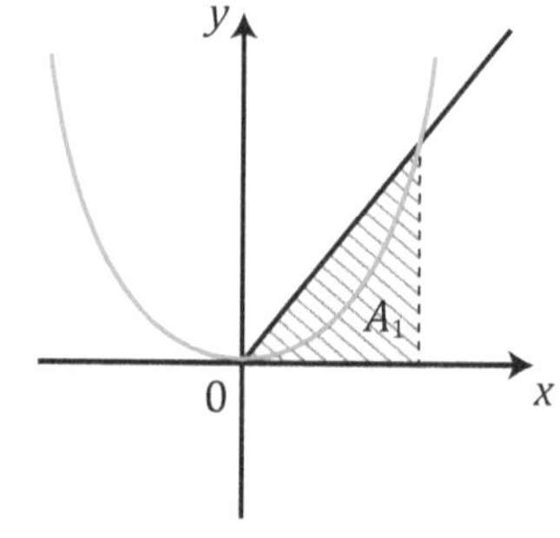

Area of triangle A_1 −

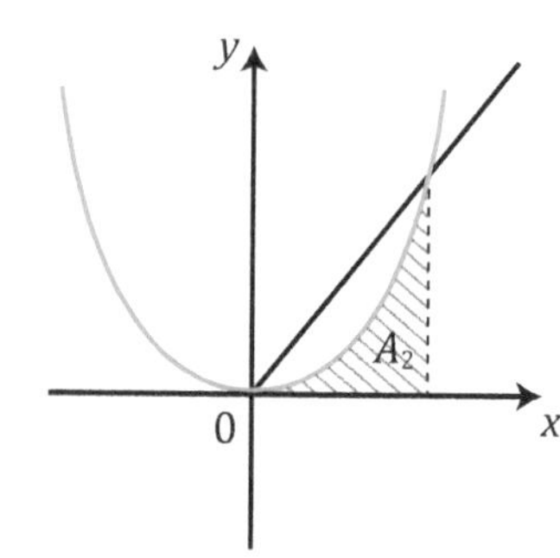

Area under curve A_2

In this situation the shaded region in the first diagram below is above the straight line and below the curve. To obtain the required area we subtract the area of the triangle from the area under the curve.

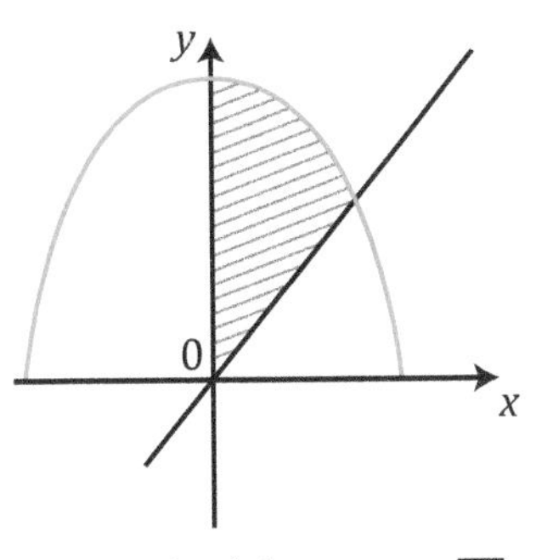

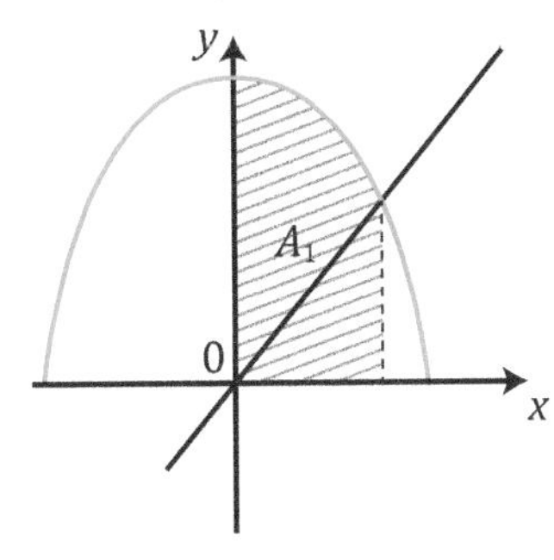

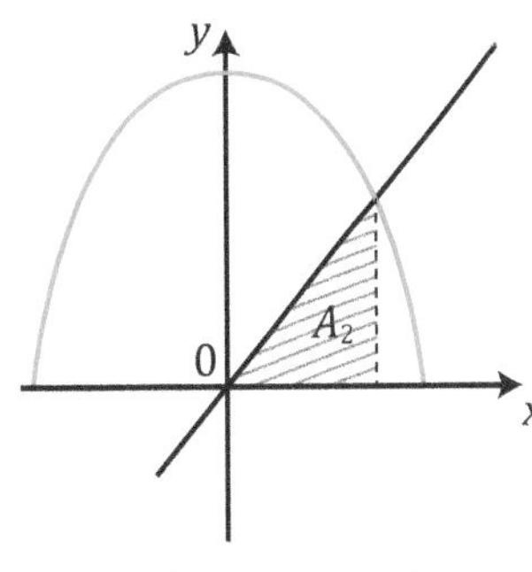

Required Area = Area under curve A_1 − Area under triangle A_2

Suppose we are required to find the shaded area in the graph below:

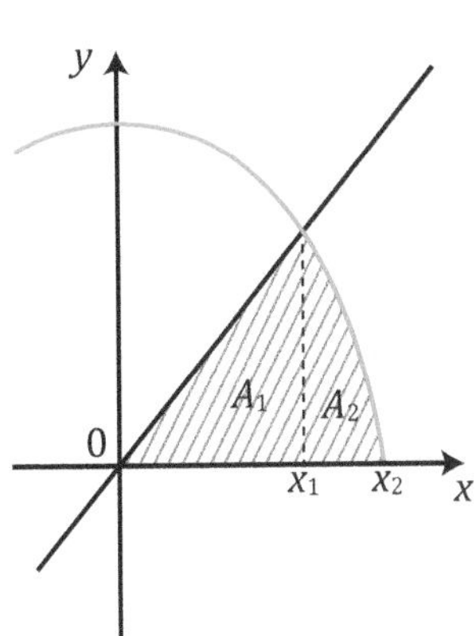

You would need to first find the coordinates of the points of intersection between the straight line and the curve by solving their two equations simultaneously.

The area of the triangle A_1 can be found using the formula

$A_1 = \frac{1}{2} \times \text{base} \times \text{height}.$

The area under the curve, A_2, between the points x_1 and x_2 can be found by integrating the equation of the curve between the limits x_1 and x_2.

The required area is then obtained by adding the two areas A_1 and A_2.

Hence required area = $A_1 + A_2$.

TAKE NOTE !

It is always advisable to draw diagrams showing the areas representing the parts you are going to use to find the required area.

Example

6 The graph below shows the curve with equation $y = x^2$ and the straight line with equation $y = 2x$. They both intersect at the origin and point A.

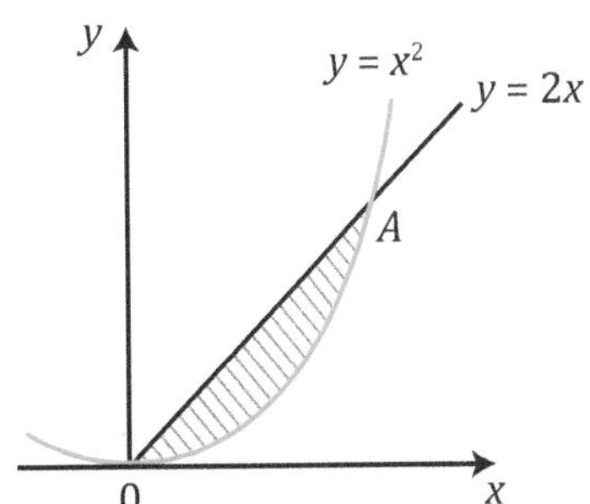

(a) Find the coordinates of point A.

(b) Calculate the area of the shaded region.

TIP

Do not divide both sides by x as you will lose one of the solutions if you do this.

Answer

6 (a) Equating the y-values of the curve and the straight line we obtain.

$$x^2 = 2x$$

$$x^2 - 2x = 0$$

$$x(x - 2) = 0$$

Solving, gives $x = 0$ or $x = 2$.

When $x = 2$, $y = 2(2) = 4$.

Hence, coordinates of A are (2, 4).

(b)

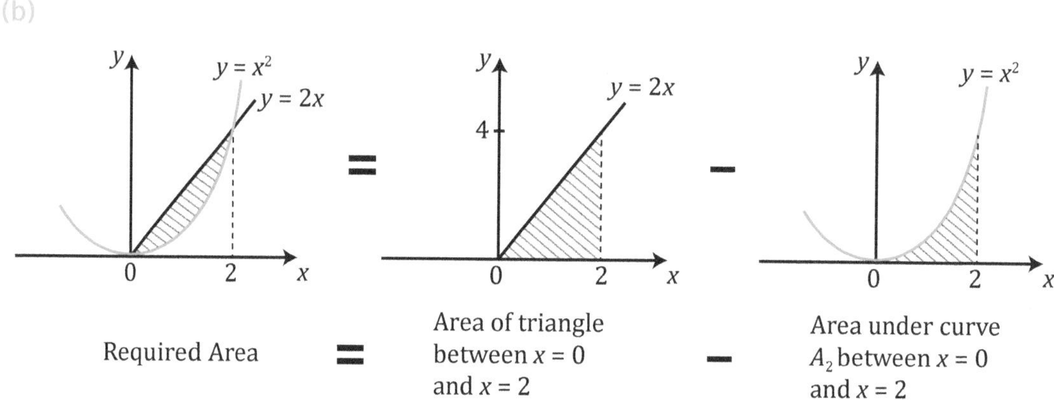

$$\text{Area of triangle} = \frac{1}{2} \times \text{base} \times \text{height}$$

$$= \frac{1}{2} \times 2 \times 4$$

$$= 4$$

$$\text{Area under curve} = \int_0^2 x^2\,dx$$

$$= \left[\frac{x^3}{3}\right]_0^2$$

$$= \frac{8}{3}$$

Hence required area $= 4 - \frac{8}{3} = \frac{4}{3}$ or $1\frac{1}{3}$

13.4 Finding the area between two curves

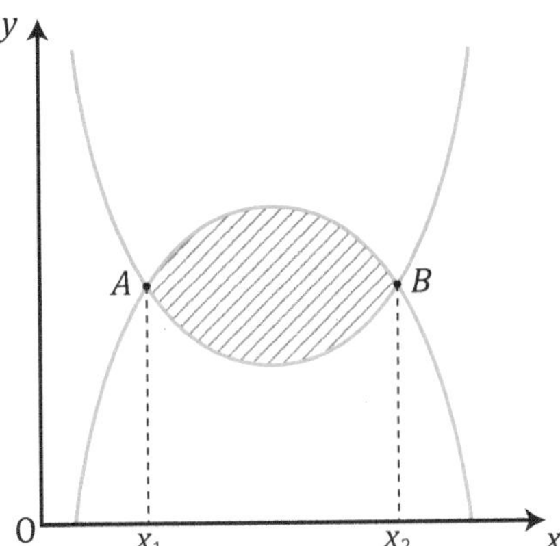

TAKE NOTE!

You usually have to find the points of intersection of the curves and this can be done by solving the two equations simultaneously.

To find the shaded area between two curves, as in the diagram above, first find the x-coordinate of the points of intersection (points A and B on the diagram) by solving the two equations of the curves simultaneously and then use integration to find the areas between the limits x_1 and x_2.

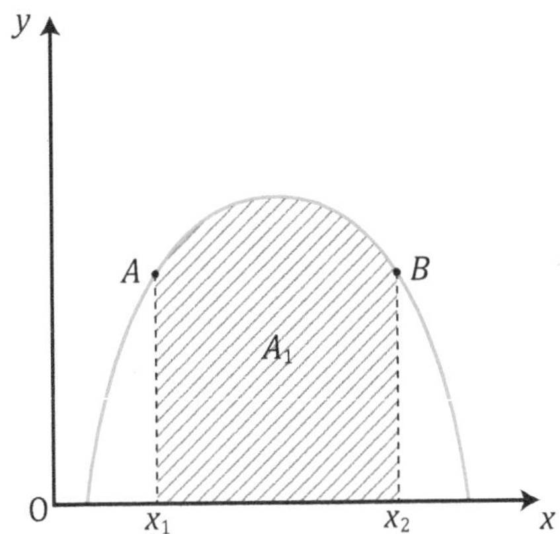

The equation of the ∩-shaped curve is integrated between the limits x_1 and x_2 to give area A_1 as shown above.

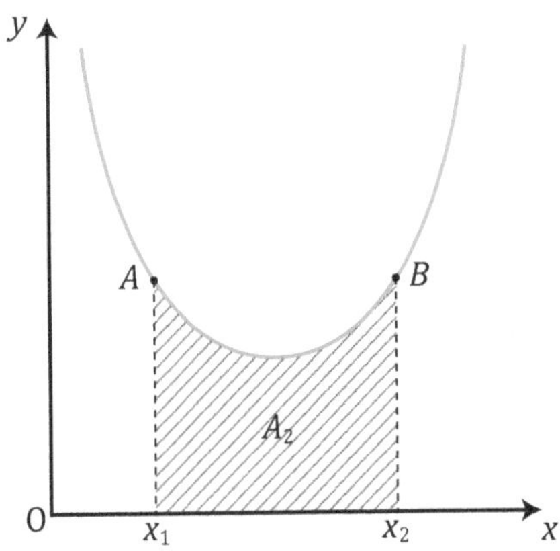

The equation of the U-shaped curve is integrated between the limits x_1 and x_2 to give area A_2 as shown above.

The areas are subtracted to give the required shaded area.

Required area = $A_1 - A_2$

Progress check

7 The curve below shows part of the graph of $y = 9 - x^2$.

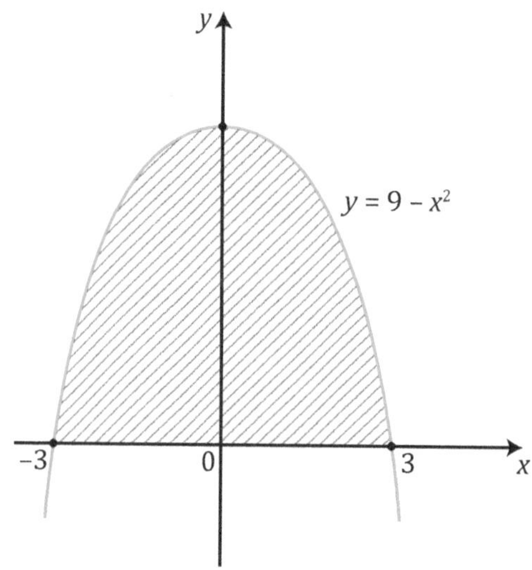

Calculate the shaded area shown.

8 (a) Sketch the curve with equation $y = x^2 - 4$ showing the points where the curve cuts the x-axis.

(b) Find $\int_2^3 \left(x^2 - 4\right) dx$ and $\int_0^2 \left(x^2 - 4\right) dx$.

(c) Explain why one of these values is positive and the other is negative.

These questions all require a good knowledge of drawing curves and finding their points of intersection with the x-axis. Check you are competent at both before attempting these questions.

9

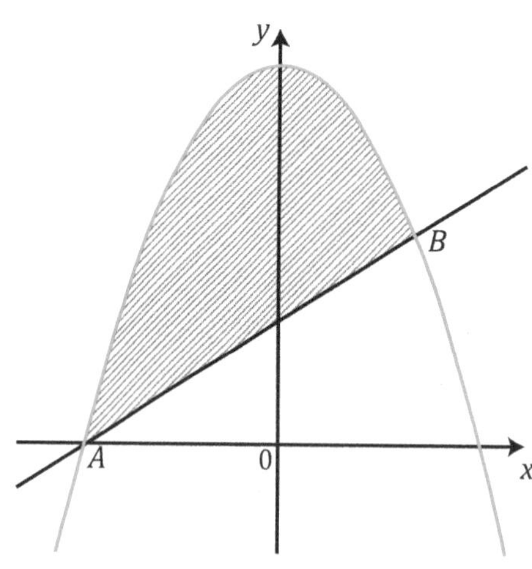

The diagram shows a sketch of the curve $y = 9 - x^2$ and the line $y = x + 3$.

The line and the curve intersect at the points A and B.

(a) Find the coordinates of A and B.

(b) Find the area of the shaded region.

Exam practice

1 The figure shows the graphs of $y = 4x - x^2$ and $y = x^2 - 4x + 6$.

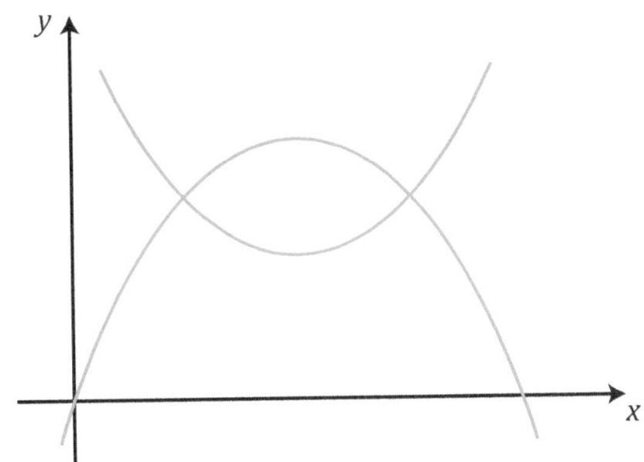

To find the point of intersection of two curves we solve their equations simultaneously.

(i) Use an algebraic method to find the x-coordinates of the points where the curves intersect. [3]

(ii) Calculate the area enclosed by the two curves. [4]

(OCR FSMQ June 2007 q8)

Answer

1 (i) $y = 4x - x^2$ .... (1)

$y = x^2 - 4x + 6$ .... (2)

Solving the two equations above simultaneously by equating the y-values we have

$4x - x^2 = x^2 - 4x + 6$

$2x^2 - 8x + 6 = 0$

Dividing both sides by 2 we obtain

$x^2 - 4x + 3 = 0$

Factorising, we obtain $(x - 1)(x - 3) = 0$

Solving gives $x = 1$ or $x = 3$.

Substituting $x = 1$ into equation (1) we obtain

$y = 4(1) - (1)^2$

$= 3$

Substituting $x = 3$ into equation (1) we obtain

$y = 4(3) - (3)^2$

$= 3$

Hence, the points of intersection are (1, 3) and (3, 3).

(ii) Shaded area $\int_1^3 y\,dx = \int_1^3 \left(4x - x^2\right) dx$.

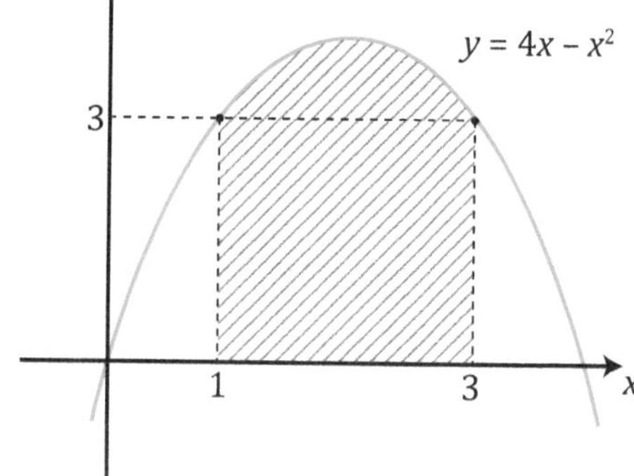

$= \left[2x^2 - \frac{x^3}{3}\right]_1^3$

$= \left[\left(18 - 9\right) - \left(2 - \frac{1}{3}\right)\right]$

$= 9 - 1\frac{2}{3}$

$= 7\frac{1}{3}$

Shaded area $\int_1^3 y\,dx = \int_1^3 \left(x^2 - 4x + 6\right) dx$

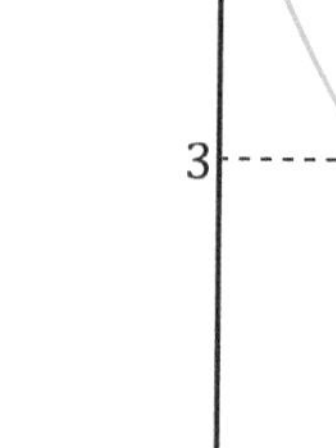

$= \left[\frac{x^3}{3} - 2x^2 + 6x\right]_1^3$

$= \left[\left(9 - 18 + 18\right) - \left(\frac{1}{3} - 2 + 6\right)\right]$

$= 9 - 4\frac{1}{3}$

$= 4\frac{2}{3}$

Required area $= 7\frac{1}{3} - 4\frac{2}{3}$

$= 2\frac{2}{3}$

TAKE NOTE !

Remember that any area below the x-axis is negative but when adding the area to another area to make up a larger area, we remove the negative sign and add the separate areas.

2 (i) Show that $\int_0^2 (x^2 + 2x - 3)\,dx = \frac{2}{3}$ [3]

The diagram shows part of the curve $y = x^2 + 2x - 3$.

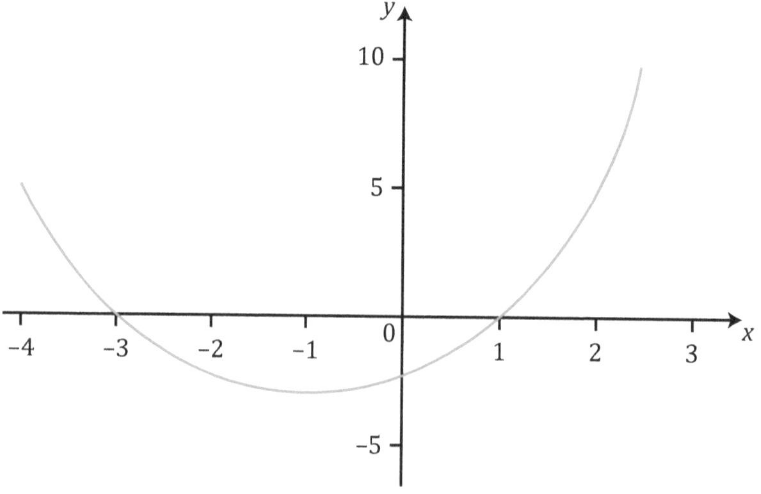

(ii) Marc claims that the total area between the curve, the x-axis and the lines $x = 0$ and $x = 2$ is $\frac{2}{3}$. Explain why he is wrong. [1]

(iii) Calculate the total area between the curve, the x-axis and the lines $x = 0$ and $x = 2$. [3]

(OCR FSMQ May 2012 q8)

Answer

2 (i) $\int_0^2 \left(x^2 + 2x - 3\right) dx = \left[\frac{x^3}{3} + x^2 - 3x\right]_0^2$

$$= \left[\left(\frac{2^3}{3} + 2^2 - 3(2)\right) - (0)\right]$$

$$= \frac{8}{3} - 2$$

$$= \frac{2}{3}$$

(ii) There are two sections to the curve between these two limits. One section is below the x-axis and will therefore give a negative area and the section above the x-axis will give a positive area. Because they have been integrated between 0 and 2 both these areas will have been combined to give $\frac{2}{3}$.

(iii) Area below the x-axis $= \int_0^1 \left(x^2 + 2x - 3\right) dx = \left[\frac{x^3}{3} + x^2 - 3x\right]_0^1$

$$= \left[\left(\frac{1^3}{3} + 1^2 - 3(1)\right) - (0)\right]$$

$$= -\frac{5}{3}$$

Changing this to a positive area, area $= \frac{5}{3}$

Area above the x-axis $= \int_1^2 \left(x^2 + 2x - 3\right) dx = \left[\frac{x^3}{3} + x^2 - 3x\right]_1^2$

$$= \left[\left(\frac{2^3}{3} + 2^2 - 3(2)\right) - \left(\frac{1^3}{3} + 1^2 - 3(1)\right)\right]$$

$$= \left(\frac{8}{3} + 4 - 6\right) - \left(\frac{1}{3} + 1 - 3\right)$$

$$= 2\frac{1}{3}$$

Hence, required area $= \frac{5}{3} + 2\frac{1}{3} = 4$

» TIP

Students often make the mistake of adding areas without removing any negative signs thus leading to the wrong answer.

3 The shape ABCD below represents a leaf.

The curve ABC has equation $y = -x^2 + 8x - 9$.

The curve ADC has equation $y = x^2 - 6x + 11$.

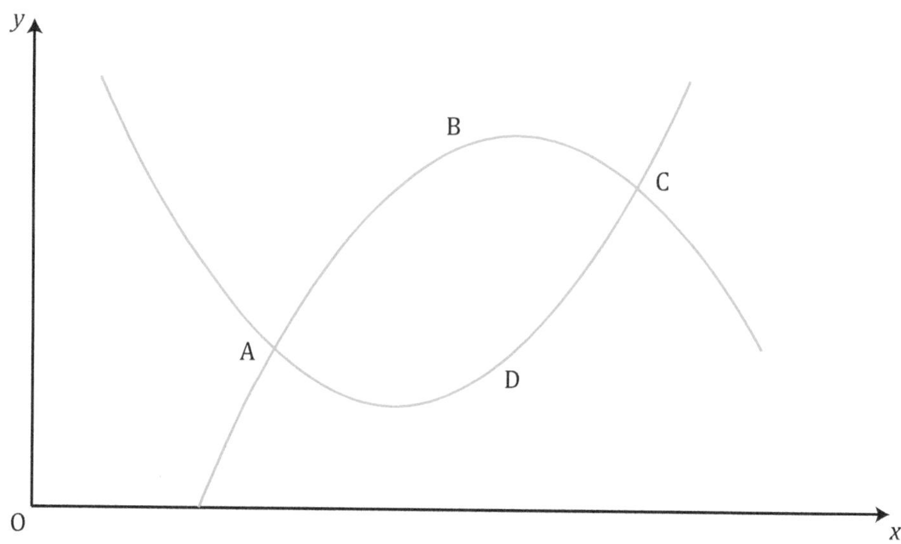

(i) Find algebraically the coordinates of A and C, the points where the curves intersect. [5]

(ii) Find the area of the leaf. [7]

(OCR FSMQ June 2009 q11)

Answer

Note that at each point of intersection the x- and y-coordinates for each curve will be the same.

3 (i) Equating the y-values, we obtain

$$-x^2 + 8x - 9 = x^2 - 6x + 11$$

$$2x^2 - 14x + 20 = 0$$

$$x^2 - 7x + 10 = 0$$

$$(x - 5)(x - 2) = 0$$

We now find the corresponding x-coordinates by substituting them into the equation of either one of the curves.

Solving we obtain $x = 2$ or $x = 5$

When $x = 2, y = -(2)^2 + 8(2) - 9 = 3$

When $x = 5, y = -(5)^2 + 8(5) - 9 = 6$

Hence, A is the point (2, 3) and C is the point (5, 6).

Note that the limits are the x-coordinates of points A and C.

(ii) Area of leaf = area under curve ABC – area under curve ADC

$$= \int_2^5 (-x^2 + 8x - 9)\,dx - \int_2^5 (x^2 - 6x + 11)\,dx$$

To reduce the maths, we can combine these integrals.

$$= \int_2^5 (-2x^2 + 14x - 20)\, dx$$

$$= \left[-\frac{2x^3}{3} + 7x^2 - 20x\right]_2^5$$

$$= \left[\left(-\frac{250}{3} + 175 - 100\right) - \left(-\frac{16}{3} + 28 - 40\right)\right]$$

$$= 9$$

» TIP

You can only combine integrals if the limits of integration are the same.

---

4 The side of a fairground slide is in the shaded shape as shown in the diagram. Units are metres.

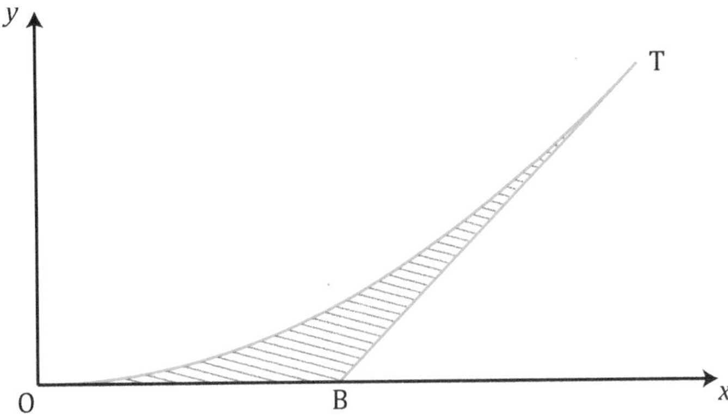

The curve has equation $y = \lambda x^2$.

T has coordinates (4, 2). The line BT is a tangent to the curve at T. It meets the x-axis at the point B.

(i) Find the value of λ. [1]

(ii) Find the equation of the tangent BT and hence find the coordinates of the point B. [6]

(iii) Find the area of the shaded portion of the graph. [3]

(OCR FSMQ June 2008 q11)

Answer

4 (i) Coordinates (4, 2) lie on the curve so these coordinates will satisfy the equation of the curve.

Hence $y = \lambda x^2$ so $2 = \lambda(4)^2$.

Solving, gives $\lambda = \frac{1}{8}$

(ii) Equation of curve is $y = \frac{1}{8}x^2$

$\frac{dy}{dx} = (2)\frac{1}{8}x = \frac{x}{4}$

Gradient of tangent at T $= \frac{4}{4} = 1$

Equation of tangent BT which has gradient 1 and passes through the point (4, 2) is $y - 2 = 1(x - 4)$

$$y = x - 2$$

At point B, $y = 0$ so we have $0 = x - 2$ giving $x = 2$.

Hence B is the point (2, 0).

(iii) The shaded area shown in the second diagram below can be obtained by finding the area under the curve between $x = 0$ and $x = 4$. This is the area A_1. The area of the triangle A_2 shown in the third diagram can then be found. The required area is then found by subtracting the area of the triangle from the area under the curve (i.e. $A_1 - A_2$).

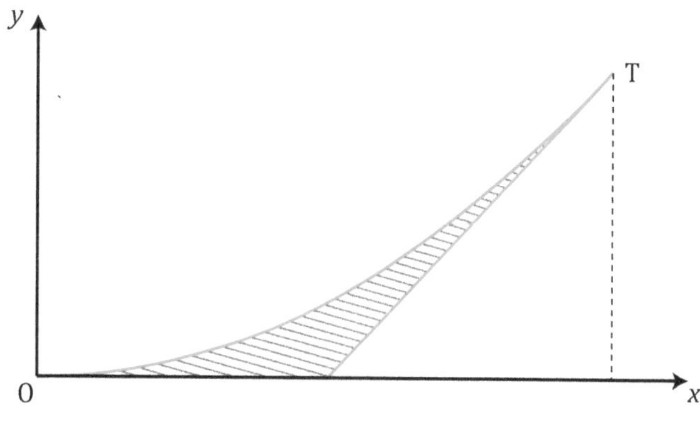

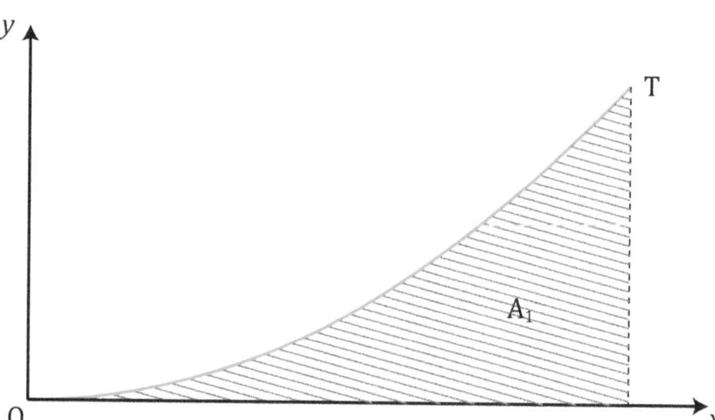

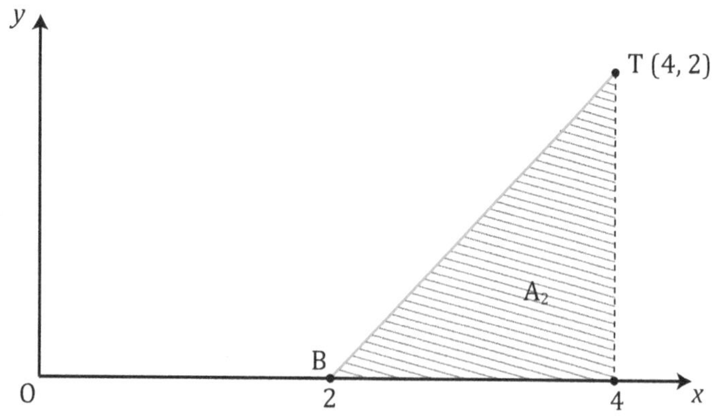

Area under curve, $A_1 = \int_0^4 \frac{1}{8}x^2\,dx$

$= \left[\frac{x^3}{24}\right]_0^4$

$= \left[\frac{4^3}{24} - 0\right]$

$= 2\frac{2}{3}$

Area of triangle, $A_2 = \frac{1}{2} \times \text{base} \times \text{height}$

$= \frac{1}{2} \times 2 \times 2$

$= 2$

Required shaded area $= A_1 - A_2 = 2\frac{2}{3} - 2 = \frac{2}{3}\text{ m}^2$

Test yourself

1 Find $\int_1^4 (6x^2 - 2)\,dx$

2 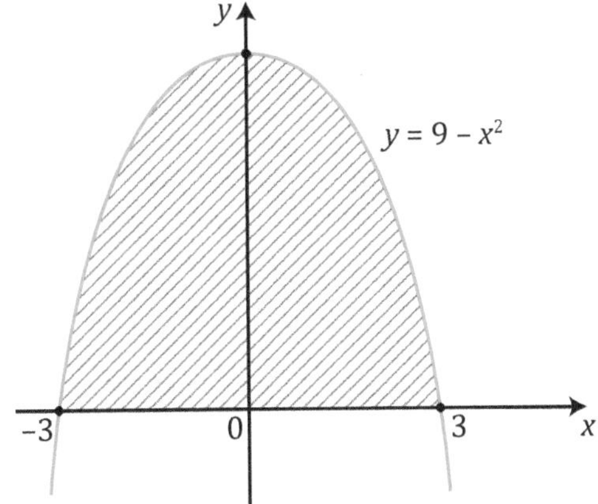

The above graph shows the curve $y = 9 - x^2$.

Calculate the shaded area bounded by the curve and the x-axis.

3 (a) Find $\int_0^2 (x^2 - 4x + 2)\,dx$

(b) Explain the significance of the sign to your answer to part (a).

4 Find $\int_{-1}^2 (x - 3)(x + 4)\,dx$

5 The graph shows the curve $y = x^2 + 1$.

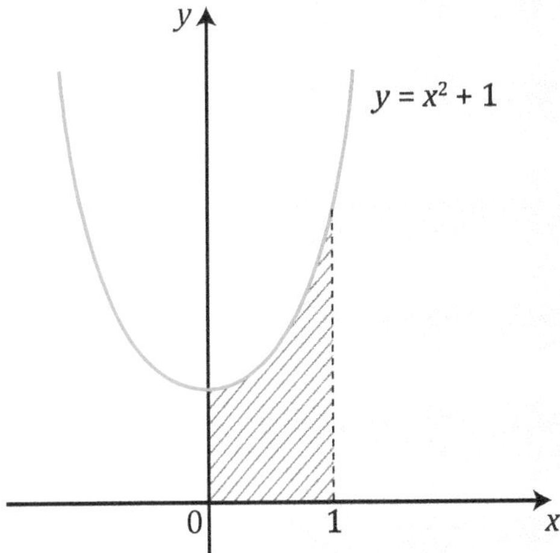

Find the shaded area bounded by the curve and the lines $x = 0$ and $x = 1$.

6 (a) Find $\int_0^2 x(x^2 - 6x + 3)\,dx$

(b) Find $\int_0^2 \frac{(x-3)}{3}\,dx$

(c) Find $\int_{-2}^2 (12x^2 - 4x + 1)\,dx$

Topic summary

The difference between definite and indefinite integration

With indefinite integration there are no limits of integration and a constant of integration is included after integration.

With definite integration, limits of integration are included and the final answer is a number.

Definite integration

To integrate an expression you raise the index by 1 and then divide by the new index.

A definite integral involves limits e.g. $\int_a^b y \, dx$ where a and b are numbers called the limits.

The definite integral is found by substituting the limits (the numbers a and b) into the result of the integration and subtracting the value corresponding to the lower limit from the value corresponding to the upper limit.

Definite integration to find the area under a curve

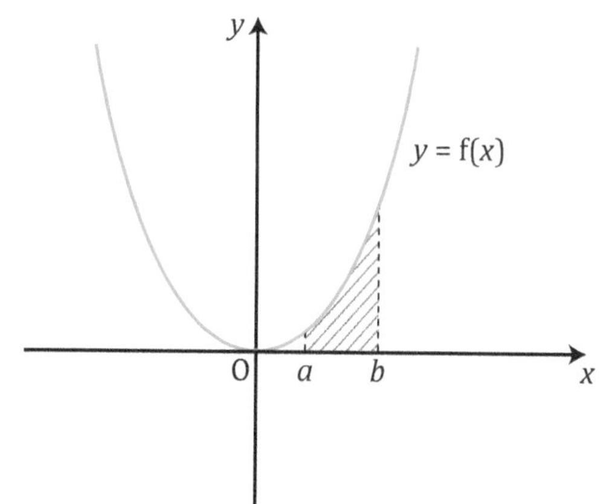

Shaded area = $\int_a^b y \, dx$ where a and b are the limits.

A definite integral is positive for areas above the x-axis and negative for areas below the x-axis.

A final area must always be given as a positive value.

Application of calculus to kinematics

Kinematics deals with the motion of objects without considering the masses or the forces that produce the motion. In this topic you will be considering motion in a straight line (called rectilinear motion) under either constant acceleration or under variable acceleration.

This topic covers the following:

14.1 Use of constant acceleration formulae

14.2 Using differentiation and integration with respect to time to solve simple problems involving acceleration

14.3 Solving problems using the constant acceleration formulae

14.1 Use of constant acceleration formulae

This section looks at motion under constant acceleration. Constant acceleration has a fixed size and direction. Both the displacement–time and velocity–time graphs for motion under constant acceleration will be straight lines.

Some important definitions of terms used

The following terms are used to describe motion and you need to understand their meanings:

Distance – this is the length that is travelled and is measured in metres (m). If you walked in a straight line from A to B and then back to A, then the distance travelled would be twice the distance from A to B. Distance is scalar quantity because it has size only.

Displacement – is a measure of distance but it also takes the direction into account.

Displacement is a vector quantity, which means it has both magnitude (i.e. size) and direction. Displacement can therefore be positive or negative. For example, if you walked in a straight line from A to B and then back to A, the displacement would be zero. This is because the displacement one way would be positive and the displacement in the opposite direction would be negative. Displacement is measured in metres (m).

Speed – is a scalar quantity so it has no direction. Speed is the distance travelled divided by the time taken (i.e. the rate of change of distance with time) and is measured in metres per second (ms^{-1}).

Hence speed $= \dfrac{\text{distance}}{\text{time}}$ or using symbols $s = \dfrac{d}{t}$.

Velocity – is a vector quantity so it has both size and direction. If the velocity is uniform, then velocity is the change in displacement divided by the time taken (i.e. the rate of change of displacement with time) and is measured in metres per second (ms^{-1}).

Hence velocity $= \dfrac{\text{change in displacement}}{\text{change in time}}$.

Acceleration – is a vector quantity and is the change in velocity divided by the time taken. It is measured in metres per second squared (ms^{-2}).

» TIP

Scalar quantities such as distance and speed have a size only. Vector quantities such as displacement, velocity and acceleration have both size and direction.

Displacement–time graphs

Displacement–time graphs depend on the type of motion.

If a graph of displacement against time is plotted for an object then the shape of the graph depends on the type of motion of the object.

Object stationary

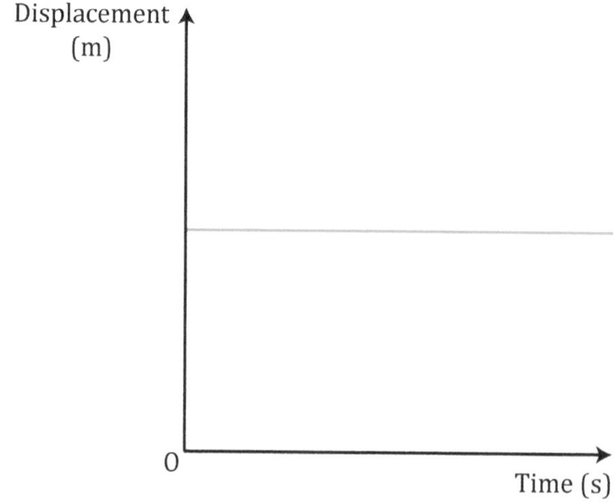

Notice that the displacement stays the same with time so the object is stationary. The gradient of the line is zero and this represents zero velocity.

Object moving with constant velocity

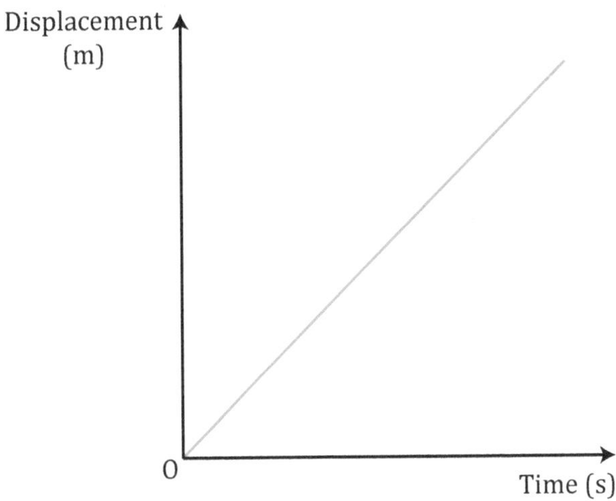

The gradient of the line represents the velocity. The gradient of the line is constant and represents constant velocity so there is no acceleration.

Object accelerating

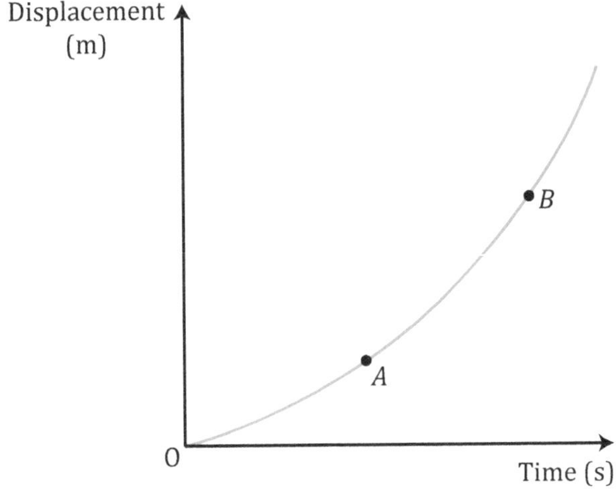

The curve has a steeper gradient at B compared to A. As the gradient represents the velocity, the velocity is increasing, showing the object is accelerating.

TAKE NOTE!

Examination questions frequently ask you to draw these graphs applied to a particular situation so make sure you understand the important parts such as the gradient and the area under the graph.

Object decelerating

The curve has a steeper gradient at A compared to B showing that the velocity of the object is decreasing. The object is therefore decelerating.

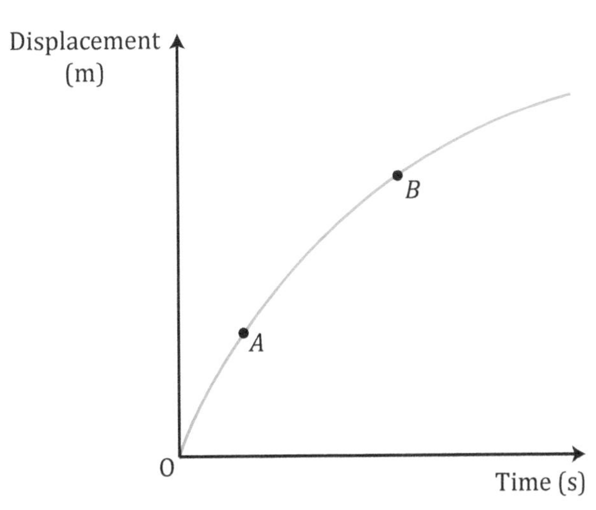

Velocity–time graphs

Velocity–time graphs depend on the type of motion.

If a graph of velocity against time is plotted for an object then the shape of the graph depends on the type of motion of the object.

Object moving with constant velocity (i.e. no acceleration)

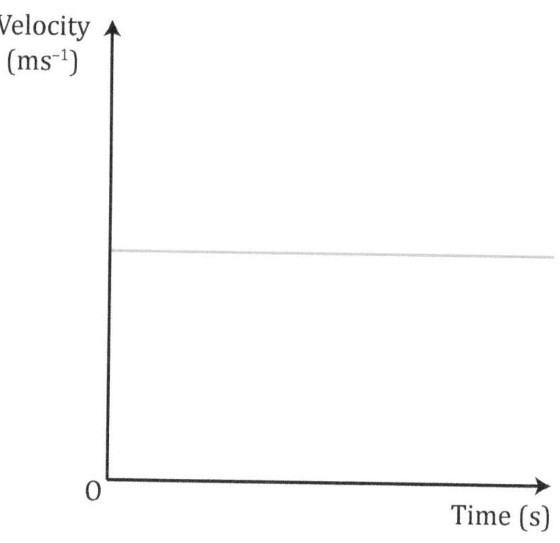

The graph is a straight line parallel to the time axis. This means the velocity stays at the same value as time proceeds. Horizontal lines (i.e. parallel to the time axis) represent constant velocity.

Object moving with constant acceleration

The graph representing an object moving with constant acceleration is a straight line with a positive gradient. Here the object starts with a velocity u and then accelerates with a constant acceleration to a higher velocity v.

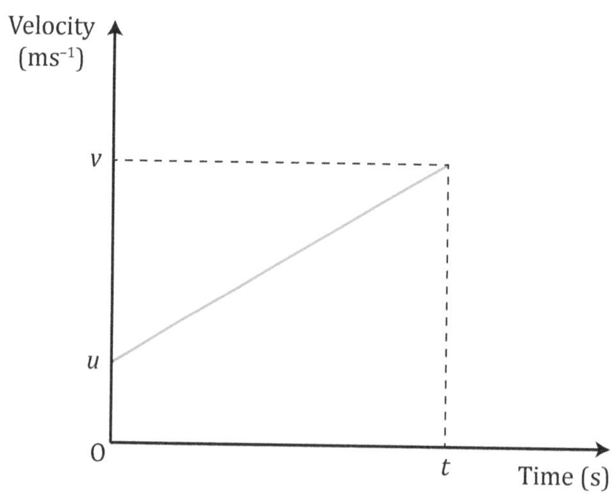

The main features of a velocity–time graph are:

- The gradient represents the acceleration. From the graph $a = \frac{v - u}{t}$.
  A negative gradient represents a deceleration.
- The area under the line represents the distance travelled or displacement. From the graph, distance travelled or displacement = area under the graph (i.e. the area of the trapezium) = $\frac{1}{2}(u + v)t$. If the area is below the time axis, this area represents a negative displacement.

TAKE NOTE

Area of trapezium = $\frac{1}{2}$ (sum of the parallel sides) × perpendicular distance between them.

Objects moving with constant deceleration

The graph representing an object moving with constant deceleration is a straight line with a negative gradient. Here the object starts with a velocity u and then decelerates with a constant deceleration to a lower velocity v.

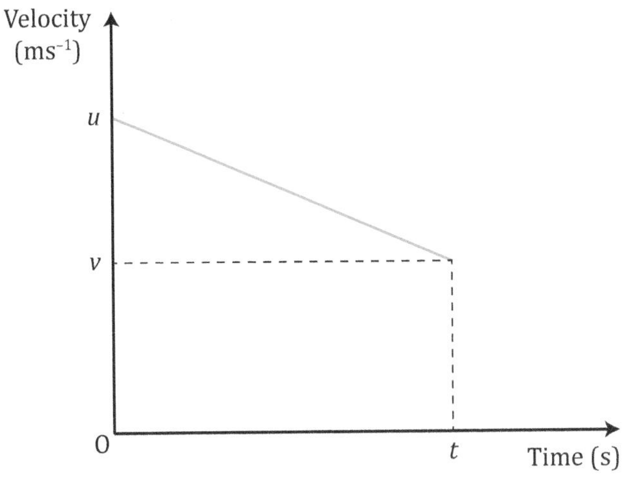

For a velocity–time graph, a positive gradient represents acceleration and a negative gradient represents deceleration. Zero gradient represents no acceleration (i.e. constant velocity).

The velocity–time graph for a journey

The following graph represents a journey:

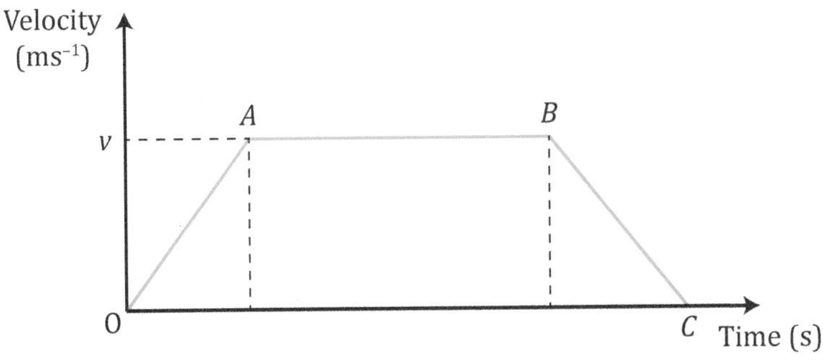

The gradient of line OA represents the acceleration.

Line AB represents travelling at constant velocity.

The gradient of line BC represents the acceleration. Because the gradient is negative, the acceleration will be negative, showing a deceleration.

Examples

1 The velocity–time graph shown below represents the four stages of motion of a vehicle moving along a straight horizontal road. The initial velocity of the vehicle is 20 ms^{-1}.

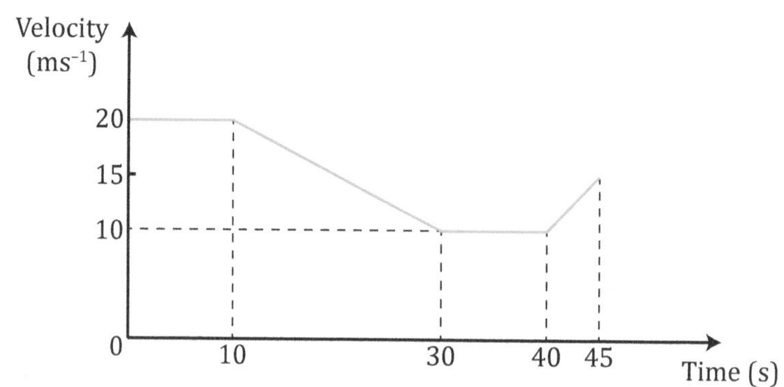

(a) Find the distance travelled whilst the car is decelerating.

(b) Find the total distance travelled whilst travelling at constant speed.

(c) During the later stage of the motion the car accelerates. Calculate the magnitude (size) of the acceleration.

(d) Calculate the total distance travelled during the motion described by the graph.

Area of trapezium = $\frac{1}{2}$(sum of the parallel sides) × distance between them.

You could alternatively, divide the shape into a triangle and a rectangle and add the two areas together. Note you will not be given the formula for the area of a trapezium so it will need to be remembered.

Answer

1 (a) Distance = Area of trapezium

$$= \frac{1}{2}(20 + 10) \times 20$$

$$= 300 \text{ m}$$

(b) Total distance whilst travelling at constant speed

$$= 20 \times 10 + 10 \times 10 = 300 \text{ m}$$

Note that you are asked for the magnitude of the acceleration so you do not need to give its direction.

(c) Acceleration = Gradient = $\frac{15 - 10}{5} = 1 \text{ ms}^{-2}$

(d) Distance travelled whilst accelerating = $\frac{1}{2}(10 + 15) \times 5 = 62.5$ m

Total distance travelled = 300 + 300 + 62.5 = 662.5 m

2 Cars A and B are travelling a long straight road. At time $t = 0$, Car A is travelling with a speed of 20 ms^{-1} and at this time it overtakes Car B travelling with a speed of 15 ms^{-1}. Car B immediately accelerates uniformly and both cars travel a distance of 600 m before Cars A and B are level and overtake each other again.

(a) Draw a velocity–time graph showing the motion of the cars from where they are first level to when they are level again.

(b) Show that the time between overtaking the first and second time is 30 s.

(c) Calculate the magnitude of the velocity of Car B after 30 s.

(d) Calculate the acceleration of Car B.

Answer

2 (a)

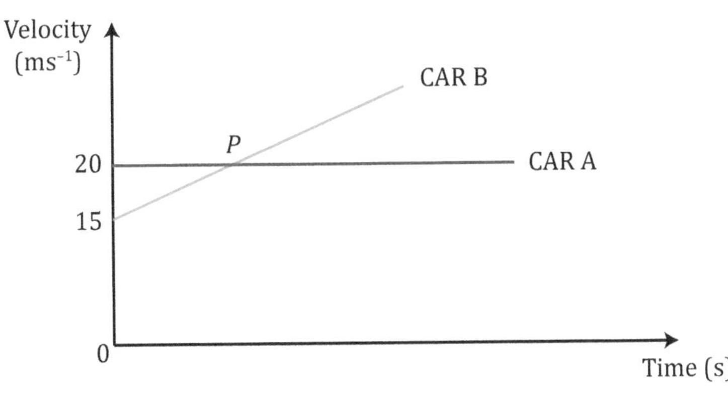

Note that the point P relates to Car B's velocity being equal to Car A's velocity, **not** where Car B overtakes Car A.

(b) Considering the motion of Car A, suppose the cars are level after time t.

The area under the velocity–time graph for Car A = 600.

Hence , $20 \times t = 600$

giving $t = 30$ s

This is the area under the graph, which is a rectangle of length 20 and width t.

(c) After 30 s the distance travelled by Car B is 600 m.

Let the velocity of Car B after 30 s = v

Area under the graph = area of a trapezium = $\frac{1}{2}(15 + v) \times 30$

Now, distance travelled = area under the graph

Hence $600 = \frac{1}{2}(15 + v) \times 30$

Solving this equation gives $v = 25\ \text{ms}^{-1}$

(d)

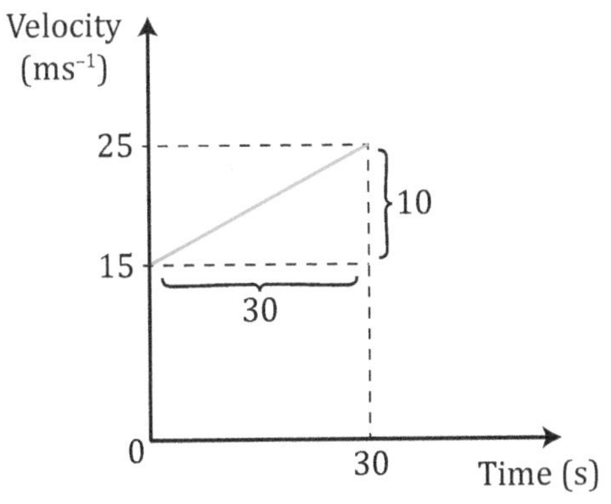

In some examination questions you will be asked to draw a velocity–time graph for motion described in a question. In some cases you will need to add some information, which you will need to calculate first in order to draw your graph.

Acceleration = Gradient = $\frac{10}{30} = 0.33\ \text{ms}^{-2}$

3 A particle starting from rest and travelling in a straight line, accelerates uniformly for 2 s and reaches a constant velocity of u ms^{-1} for 10 s, before decelerating uniformly to rest in 3 s. The total distance travelled by the particle was 50 m.

(a) Draw a velocity–time graph to show the motion of the particle.

(b) Find the value of u.

(c) Find the magnitude of the deceleration.

When drawing a velocity–time graph, ensure that the axes are labelled with quantities and units. Mark any values and letters for quantities, which need to be found, on the graph.

Answer

3 (a)

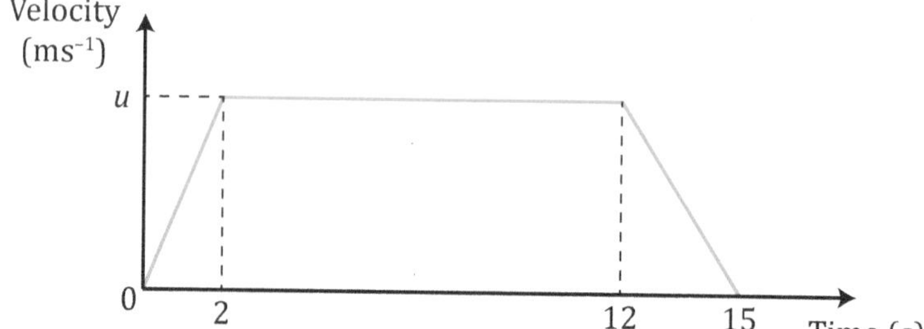

The formula for the area of a trapezium is used here.

(b) Total distance travelled = Area under the velocity–time graph

$$= \frac{1}{2}(15 + 10) \times u$$

But the total distance travelled = 50 m

Hence $50 = \frac{1}{2}(15 + 10) \times u$

so $u = 4$ ms^{-1}

(c) Deceleration $= \frac{4}{3} = 1.33$ ms $^{-2}$

Interpretation of velocity–time graphs

The diagram below shows a velocity–time graph. You must be able to interpret the graph and describe the motion it represents.

The graph has been divided into sections.

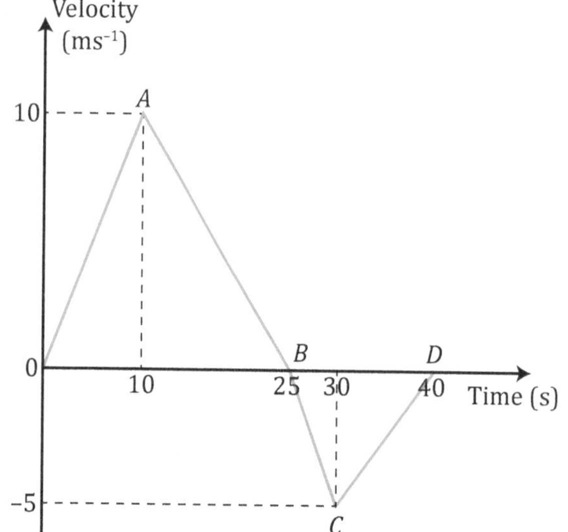

OA represents acceleration from 0 to 10 ms^{-1}.

Acceleration = gradient of *OA*

$$= \frac{10}{10}$$

$= 1$ ms^{-2}.

AB represents a negative acceleration.

Acceleration $= -\frac{10}{15}$

$= -0.67$ ms^{-2}.

Note that we omit the negative sign if it is described as a deceleration.

BC represents an acceleration, but this time because the velocity is negative, it means that the motion is in the opposite direction.

The acceleration $= -\frac{5}{5} = -1$ ms^{-2}.

Notice that because the negative acceleration is in the same direction as the velocity, it represents an acceleration rather than a deceleration.

The displacement from O to B is the area under the velocity–time graph between O and B.

Area = Area of a triangle $= \frac{1}{2} \times$ base $\times$ height $= \frac{1}{2} \times 25 \times 10 = 125$ m

The displacement from B to $D = \frac{1}{2} \times 15 \times (-5) = -37.5$ m.

Note that because the area lies below the time axis it represents a negative displacement. This means that the object is moving back in the opposite direction so it now moving nearer to O.

The displacement from O to $D = 125 - 37.5 = 87.5$ m.

The total distance travelled from O to $D = 125 + 37.5 = 162.5$ m.

Constant acceleration formulae (often called *suvat* equations)

In this section you will be looking at a set of equations that connect quantities such as velocities, distances/displacements, time and accelerations for motion under constant acceleration. Constant acceleration means that the acceleration remains at a constant value during the section of the motion being considered.

It is important to note that accelerations increase the velocity or speed of an object. A negative acceleration acts in the opposite direction to speed or velocity and will cause either of these to decrease. A negative acceleration is often referred to as a deceleration or retardation.

If a body is uniformly accelerated in a straight line, then the following equations, called the equations of motion (or *suvat* equations), can be used. The meaning of the terms used in the equations is shown in the table:

$v = u + at$

$s = ut + \frac{1}{2}at^2$

$v^2 = u^2 + 2as$

$s = \frac{1}{2}(u + v)t$

s	displacement/distance
u	initial velocity/speed
v	final velocity/speed
a	acceleration
t	time

TAKE NOTE!

You need to remember all the equations shown in this table as they will not be given.

Notice that there are four variables in each equation, so you would need to know three of them in order to find the value of the fourth variable.

Displacement, initial velocity, final velocity and acceleration are all vector quantities, which means they have both a magnitude (i.e. size) and a direction.

Normally the direction is taken as positive from left to right, so for example, a ball moving from right to left would have a negative velocity.

Note that in some questions the velocities in the above equations can be replaced by speeds.

14.2 Solving problems using the constant acceleration formulae (*suvat* equations)

The equations of motion can be used to solve problems that involve constant acceleration as the following examples show.

Examples

4 A toy car is given an initial velocity of 0.25 ms^{-1}. Due to resistance, the deceleration is 0.25 ms^{-2}. Find the distance travelled before the toy comes to rest.

Answer

4 First list the letters and their values when they are known.

Note here that you are told that the deceleration is 0.25 ms^{-2}. This is an acceleration of – 0.25 ms^{-2} when used in the equations of motion.

$s = ?,\ u = 0.25\ ms^{-1},\ v = 0\ ms^{-1},\ a = -\ 0.25\ ms^{-2}$

Using $v^2 = u^2 + 2as$ we have

$$0^2 = 0.25^2 + 2(-0.05)s$$

$$-0.0625 = -0.10\ s$$

$$s = 0.625\ m$$

Note you need to use one of the equations where you know the all the values of the letters except the one you need to find.

5 A particle is given an initial velocity of 4 ms^{-1} and is subject to a constant deceleration which brings the particle to rest in 5 seconds. Find the distance travelled by the particle.

Answer

5 $s = ?,\ u = 4\ ms^{-1},\ v = 0\ ms^{-1},\ t = 5\ s,$

Using $s = \frac{1}{2}(u + v)t$

$$= \frac{1}{2}(4 + 0)5$$

$$= 10\ m$$

TAKE NOTE!

Always write the equation of motion you are using before adding the numbers.

6 A particle moves in a straight line and has its speed measured at points A and B. At point A, its speed is 20 ms^{-1} and at point B its speed is 32 ms^{-1}. The distance between points A and B is 120 m.

(a) Show that the acceleration of the particle is 2.6 ms ^{2}.

(b) Find the time for the particle to travel from A to B.

(c) Find the speed of the particle 20 s after passing point A.

(d) Calculate the distance of the particle from A, 30 s after it passes A.

Answer

6 (a) $s = 120$ m, $u = 20$ ms^{-1}, $v = 32$ ms^{-1}, $a = ?$

Using $v^2 = u^2 + 2as$, we obtain

$$32^2 = 20^2 + 2a \times 120$$

Solving gives $a = 2.6$ ms^{-2}

(b) Using $v = u + at$, we obtain

$$32 = 20 + 2.6t$$

Solving gives $t = 4.62$ s

(c) $u = 20$ ms^{-1}, $a = 2.6$ ms^{-2}, $t = 20$ s, $v = ?$

Using $v = u + at$, we obtain

$$v = 20 + 2.6 \times 20$$

Solving gives $v = 72$ ms^{-1}

(d) $u = 20$ ms^{-1}, $a = 2.6$ ms^{-2}, $t = 30$ s, $s = ?$

Using $s = ut + \frac{1}{2}at^2$, we obtain

$$s = 20 \times 30 + \frac{1}{2} \times 2.6 \times 30^2$$

$$s = 1770 \text{ m}$$

TIP

Always ensure that you have added the units to your answer and also ask yourself if the answer seems reasonable. For example, if you are asked to find the time and you have a negative answer, then you know the answer is wrong.

7 A car is travelling along a straight horizontal road. There are three stages to its motion.

During the first stage of the motion, it accelerates uniformly from rest with an acceleration of 1 ms^{-2} for 10 s.

During the second stage of the motion, the car travels at constant velocity for 15 s.

During the third stage of the motion, the car decelerates uniformly to rest in 5 s.

(a) Show that the velocity reached after the first stage of the motion is 10 ms^{-1}.

(b) Find the deceleration during the third stage of the motion.

(c) Sketch a velocity–time graph that shows the three stages of the motion.

(d) Calculate the total distance travelled during the three stages of motion.

Answer

7 (a) $u = 0\ ms^{-1}$, $v = ?$, $a = 1\ ms^{-2}$, $t = 10$ s.

Using $v = u + at$

$$v = 0 + 1 \times 10 = 10\ ms^{-1}$$

(b) $u = 10\ ms^{-1}$, $v = 0\ ms^{-1}$, $t = 5$ s, $a = ?$

Using $v = u + at$

$$0 = 10 + 5a$$

$a = -2\ ms^{-2}$ (note that a negative acceleration is a deceleration)

Hence deceleration = 2 ms^{-2}

(c)

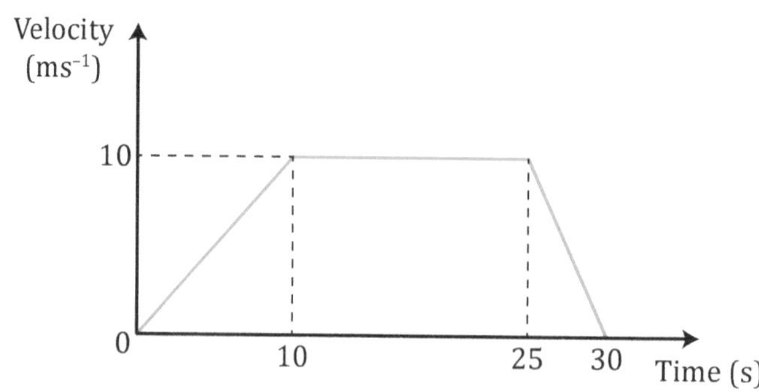

(d) Total distance travelled = Area under the velocity–time graph

$$= \frac{1}{2}(30 + 15) \times 10 = 225\ m$$

The formula for the area of a trapezium is used here, and you will need to remember it. If you cannot remember it, you can work out the areas of the two triangles and the rectangle and add them together.

Constant acceleration due to gravity for motion in a vertical direction

Bodies travelling in a vertical direction experience a constant acceleration of 9.8 ms^{-2} acting towards the centre of the earth. When travelling upwards, this acceleration opposes the motion and is −9.8 ms^{-2}. When travelling downwards, this accelerates the body and is taken as 9.8 ms^{-2}. As velocities and accelerations can act in different directions, you have to decide which direction you intend to take as the positive direction.

Note that in some questions involving the acceleration due to gravity an approximate value of 10 ms^{-2} is used rather than 9.8 ms^{-2}.

Remember to say which direction you are taking as positive in your answers.

Examples

8 A ball is thrown vertically down a well with a velocity of 5 ms^{-1}. The ball takes 6 seconds to reach the bottom of the well. Take the acceleration due to gravity, g, as 9.8 ms^{-2}.

(a) Find the velocity of the ball after 6 seconds.

(b) Find the distance travelled by the ball when it reaches the bottom of the well.

Answer

8 (a) Taking downwards as the positive direction, we have

$u = 5\ ms^{-1}, v = ?, a = g = 9.8\ ms^{-2}, t = 6\ s$

Using $v = u + at$

$$v = 5 + 9.8 \times 6 = 63.8\ ms^{-1}$$

(b) Using $s = ut + \frac{1}{2}at^2$ we have

$$s = 5 \times 6 + \frac{1}{2} \times 9.8 \times 6^2 = 206.4\ m$$

9 A ball is thrown vertically upwards with a velocity of 10 ms^{-1}. Take the value of the acceleration due to gravity, g, as 9.8 ms^{-2}.

(a) Find the maximum height reached by the ball.

(b) Find the time taken for the ball to reach its maximum height.

Answer

9 (a) Taking upwards as the positive direction, we have
$s = ?, u = 10\ ms^{-1}, v = 0\ ms^{-1}, a = g = -9.8\ ms^{-2}$

Using $v^2 = u^2 + 2as$, we obtain

$$0^2 = 10^2 + 2 \times (-9.8) \times s \text{ giving } s = 5.10\ m.$$

(b) Using $v = u + at$, we obtain $0 = 10 + (-9.8)t$ giving $t = 1.02$ s.

TAKE NOTE !

Write down all the letters with values that are known and also write the letter of the quantity you wish to find with a question mark. Then you need to choose the equation from the list. It is a good idea to write down the list at the start as it will help you to remember them.

When the ball reaches its maximum height, its velocity is zero.

If upwards is taken as positive, then the acceleration due to gravity is acting in the opposite direction so it has a negative value (i.e. −9.8).

Progress check

1. A car, initially at rest, accelerates with an acceleration of 0.9 ms^{-2}. Calculate:

   (a) The speed of the car after 10 seconds.

   (b) The distance travelled in this time.

2. A stone is projected vertically upwards with a velocity of 20 ms^{-1} from point A.

   (a) Calculate the greatest height from point A reached by the stone.

   (b) Calculate the time from when the stone is projected to when it returns to point A.

3. A stone is thrown vertically downwards from the top of a cliff with a velocity of 0.8 ms^{-1} and hits the sea 3.5 seconds later.

   (a) Calculate the speed with which the stone hits the sea.

   (b) Calculate the height of the cliff.

4. A particle is projected vertically upwards with a speed of 10 ms^{-1}.

   (a) Find the time in seconds for the particle to reach its greatest height.

   (b) Find the maximum height reached by the particle.

14.3 Using differentiation and integration with respect to time to solve simple problems involving acceleration

The graph of displacement against time shown below is not linear so the graph does not represent constant velocity. The gradient of a displacement–time graph represents the velocity so the velocity at point P is lower than that at point Q. The gradient and hence the velocity will depend on the time chosen.

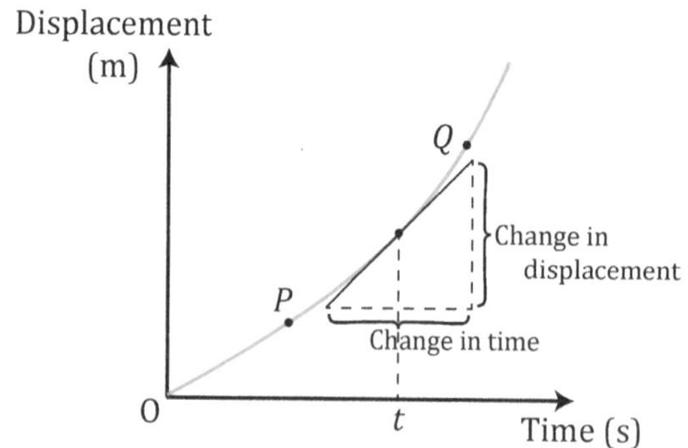

$$\text{Velocity} = \frac{\text{change in displacement}}{\text{change in time}} \quad \text{(i.e. the gradient)}$$

Finding the velocity from the displacement

The velocity at any time t is given by the gradient of the displacement–time graph.

Hence we have the important result $v = \frac{ds}{dt}$

To find the velocity numerically, the time at which the velocity is to found is substituted into the expression.

To find the velocity from the displacement, you differentiate the expression for the displacement with respect to time.

Finding the acceleration from the velocity

The acceleration at any time t is given by the gradient of the velocity–time graph.

Hence we have the important result $a = \frac{dv}{dt}$

To find the acceleration from the velocity, you differentiate the expression for the velocity with respect to time.

The diagram summarises these results. Notice that if you are given an expression for the displacement and you are asked to find the acceleration, then you will need to differentiate the displacement expression twice.

Displacement (s) → Differentiate $\frac{ds}{dt}$ → Velocity (v) → Differentiate $\frac{dv}{dt}$ → Acceleration (a)

Example

10 A particle moves along a straight line in such a way that the displacement at time t is given by:

$$s = 12t^3 - 6t^2 + 1$$

(a) Find an expression for the velocity, v, at time t.

(b) The particle is at rest twice. Find these two times.

(c) Find an expression for the acceleration, a, at time t.

Answer

10 (a) $s = 12t^3 - 6t^2 + 1$

$v = \frac{ds}{dt}$

$= 36t^2 - 12t$

Differentiating the expression for s with respect to t.

(b) When at rest, $v = 0$.

$0 = 36t^2 - 12t$

$0 = 12t(3t - 1)$

Solving gives $t = 0$ or $t = \frac{1}{3}$

(c) $v = 36t^2 - 12t$

$$a = \frac{dv}{dt}$$

$$= 72t - 12$$

Differentiating the expression for v with respect to t.

Finding the velocity from the acceleration

If you need to find the velocity from the acceleration, you integrate with respect to t.

Hence we have the important result

$$v = \int a \, dt$$

For example, if $a = 2 - t$ then $v = \int a \, dt = \int (2 - t) \, dt = 2t - \frac{t^2}{2} + c$.

Notice the inclusion of the constant of integration, c. It is necessary to find the value of c and this is done by substituting known values for v and t into the expression for v.

For example, if it is known that the object starts from rest, we can say that when $t = 0$, $v = 0$ so

$0 = 2(0) - \frac{(0)^2}{2} + c$ and solving gives $c = 0$.

The constant of integration, c, is now substituted into the expression to give

$$v = 2t - \frac{t^2}{2}$$

TIP

When integrating you must remember to include the constant of integration.

Finding the displacement from the velocity

To find the displacement from the velocity we integrate the velocity expression with respect to t.

Hence we have the important result

$$s = \int v \, dt$$

Carrying on with our example, to find the displacement we need to integrate the velocity expression, $v = 2t - \frac{t^2}{2}$ with respect to t.

Hence we have $s = \int v \, dt = \int \left(2t - \frac{t^2}{2}\right) dt = \frac{2t^2}{2} - \frac{t^3}{6} + c$

Again we need to substitute known values of s and t into the expression to find the value of the constant c.

If we know that when $t = 0$, $s = 0$, we have $0 = \frac{2(0)^2}{2} - \frac{(0)^3}{6} + c$, giving $c = 0$.

The constant of integration, c, is now substituted into the expression to give

$$s = \frac{2t^2}{2} - \frac{t^3}{6} = t^2 - \frac{t^3}{6}$$

Examples

11 A particle starts from rest and travels from O along the positive x-axis in a straight line. The particle has an acceleration, a ms^{-2}, given by

$$a = 4t - 3t^2.$$

(a) Find an expression for the velocity, v ms^{-1}, in time t.

(b) Find an expression for the displacement, s m, in time t.

Answer

11 (a) $v = \int a \, dt$

$$= \int (4t - 3t^2) \, dt$$

$$= \frac{4t^2}{2} - \frac{3t^3}{3} + c$$

$$= 2t^2 - t^3 + c$$

We need to find the value of the constant of integration, c, by substituting a pair of known values for v and t into this equation.

As the particle starts from rest, when $t = 0$, $v = 0$.

Hence we have $0 = 2(0)^2 - (0)^3 + c$

Solving gives $c = 0$.

Hence the expression for the velocity is

$$v = 2t^2 - t^3$$

(b) $s = \int v \, dt$

$$= \int (2t^2 - t^3) \, dt$$

$$= \frac{2t^3}{3} - \frac{t^4}{4} + c$$

When $t = 0$, $s = 0$.

$0 = \frac{2(0)^3}{3} - \frac{(0)^4}{4} + c$ giving $c = 0$.

Hence the expression for the displacement is

$$s = \frac{2t^3}{3} - \frac{t^4}{4}$$

12 An object accelerates from rest and at a time t seconds, its acceleration is given by

$$a = 5 - 0.1t \text{ ms}^{-2}.$$

(a) Find the velocity after 10 seconds.

(b) Show that the object travels at constant speed at $t = 50$ s.

(c) Find the distance travelled in the first 50 seconds.

Answer

> If you differentiate the expression for velocity you obtain an expression for the acceleration. To go from an expression for acceleration to an expression for velocity you integrate. Note that as there are no limits, this is an indefinite integration so a constant of integration, c, is included.

12 (a) $v = \int a \, dt$

$$= \int (5 - 0.1t) \, dt$$

$$= 5t - \frac{0.1t^2}{2} + c$$

As the object starts from rest, we know when $t = 0$, $s = 0$.

So $0 = 5(0) - \frac{0.1(0)^2}{2} + c$

Solving gives $c = 0$.

Hence we have $v = 5t - \frac{0.1t^2}{2}$

(b) If the object travels at constant speed the acceleration would be zero.

When $t = 50$, $a = 5 - 0.1t$ so $a = 5 - 0.1(50) = 0$.

Hence object travels at constant speed when $t = 50$ s.

(c) $s = \int v \, dt$

$$= \int \left(5t - \frac{0.1t^2}{2}\right) dt$$

$$= \frac{5t^2}{2} - \frac{0.1t^3}{6} + c$$

As the object starts from rest when $t = 0$, $s = 0$.

Hence $c = 0$.

So we have $s = \frac{5t^2}{2} - \frac{0.1t^3}{6}$

When $t = 50$, $s = \frac{5(50)^2}{2} - \frac{0.1(50)^3}{6}$

$$= 6250 - 2083$$

$$= 4167 \text{ m}$$

Progress check

5 A particle moves along a straight line. At time t seconds, the displacement, s metres, of the particle from the origin is given by

$$s = 12t^3 + 9$$

(a) Find an expression for the velocity of the particle at time t.

(b) Find the acceleration at time $t = 2$ seconds.

6 A particle accelerates from rest. t seconds after starting its motion it has a velocity v ms^{-1} given by $v = 0.64t^3 - 0.36t^2$.

(a) Find an expression for the acceleration at time t.

(b) Find the distance travelled after 10 seconds.

7 A lorry accelerates from rest and at time t seconds, its acceleration is given by

$$a = 3 - 0.1t \quad \text{until } t = 30.$$

(a) Find an expression in terms of t for the velocity of the lorry.

(b) Find the velocity of the lorry after 10 seconds.

(c) Explain what will happen to the lorry at $t = 30$.

(d) Find the distance travelled in the first 30 seconds.

8 A particle moves in a straight line and its velocity is v ms^{-1}, t seconds after passing the origin O where v is given by

$$v = 6t + 4.$$

Find the distance travelled between the times $t = 2$ s and $t = 5$ s.

9 A particle moves in a straight line and at time t seconds, it has velocity v ms^{-1}, where $v = 6t^2 - 2t + 8$

(a) (i) Find an expression for the acceleration of the particle at time t.

(ii) Find the acceleration of the particle when $t = 1$ second.

(b) When $t = 0$, the particle is at the origin. Find an expression for the displacement of the particle from the origin at time t.

Exam practice questions

1 An aeroplane touches down at a point A on a runway, travelling at 90 ms^{-1}. It then decelerates uniformly until it reaches a speed of 6 ms^{-1} at a point B on the runway, 2016 m from A.

(i) Find the deceleration. [3]

(ii) Find the time taken to travel from A to B. [2]

(OCR FSMQ June 2010 q6)

Answer

1 (i) $s = 2016$ m, $u = 90$ ms^{-1}, $v = 6$ ms^{-1}, and we need to find a.

Using $v^2 = u^2 + 2as$ we obtain

$$6^2 = 90^2 + 2a(2016)$$

$$36 = 8100 + 4032a$$

$$-8064 = 4032a$$

Solving gives $a = -2$ ms^{-2}

Hence deceleration $= 2$ ms^{-2}

Note that a negative acceleration is a deceleration. Once you call it a deceleration you should not include the minus sign.

(ii) $v = u + at$

Rearranging for t gives $t = \dfrac{v-u}{a}$

$$= \frac{6-90}{-2}$$

$$= 42 \text{ s}$$

Time taken $= 42$ s

---

2 A car moves from rest with constant acceleration on a straight road. When the car passes a point A it is travelling at 10 ms^{-1} and when it passes a point B further along the road it is travelling at 16 ms^{-1}.

The car takes 10 seconds to travel from A to B.

Find:

- The distance AB.
- The constant acceleration [4]

(OCR FSMQ May 2012 q4)

Answer

2 $u = 10$ ms^{-1}, $v = 16$ ms^{-1}, $t = 10$ s and we need to find s.

Using $s = \dfrac{1}{2}(u+v)t$

$$= \frac{1}{2}(10 + 16)10$$

$$= 130 \text{ m}$$

Distance AB $= 130$ m

Using $v = u + at$

Rearranging for a gives $a = \frac{v - u}{t}$

$= \frac{16 - 10}{10}$

$= 0.6\ \text{ms}^{-2}$

Constant acceleration $= 0.6\ \text{ms}^{-2}$

---

3 A speedboat accelerates from rest so that t seconds after starting its velocity, in ms^{-1}, is given by the formula $v = 0.36t^2 - 0.024t^3$.

(i) Find the acceleration at time t. [3]

(ii) Find the distance travelled in the first 10 seconds. [4]

(OCR FSMQ June 2008 q6)

Answer

3 (i) $v = 0.36t^2 - 0.024t^3$

$a = \frac{dv}{dt}$

$= 0.72t - 0.072t^2$

(ii) $s = \int_0^{10} v\,dt$

$= \int_0^{10} (0.36t^2 - 0.024t^3)\,dt$

$= \left[\frac{0.36t^3}{3} - \frac{0.024t^4}{4}\right]_0^{10}$

$= \left[0.12t^3 - 0.006t^4\right]_0^{10}$

$= [(0.12(10)^3 - 0.006(10)^4) - (0)]$

$= 60\ \text{m}$

> Remember that to differentiate you multiply by the index and then reduce the index by 1.

> To find the distance travelled between two times you integrate the velocity using these two times as the limits for the integration. To find the distance the boat travels in the first 10 seconds, we therefore integrate the velocity equation using the limits 10 and 0.

---

4 An object sinks through a thick liquid such that at time t seconds after being released on the surface the depth, s metres, is given by

$$s = 4t^2 - \frac{2t^3}{3} \qquad \text{for } 0 \le t \le 4.$$

(a) Find the formula for the velocity, v metres per second, t seconds after being released.

Hence show that the object stops sinking when $t = 4$. [4]

(b) Find:

(i) The acceleration of the object when it is released on the surface of the liquid. [4]

(ii) The greatest depth of the object. [2]

(c) On the grids provided sketch the velocity–time and acceleration–time graphs. 

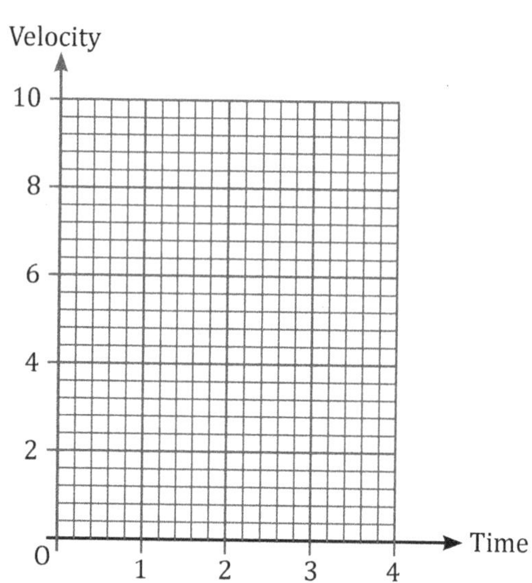

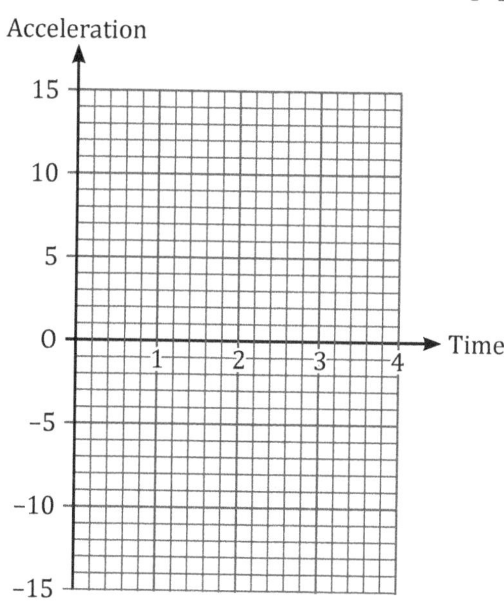

(OCR FSMQ June 2013 q12)

Answer

4 (a) $s = 4t^2 - \dfrac{2t^3}{3}$

$v = \dfrac{ds}{dt}$

$= 8t - 2t^2$

When $t = 4$ s, $v = 8(4) - 2(4)^2$

$= 0\ \text{ms}^{-1}$

So object stops sinking when $t = 4$s.

> This shows at $t = 4$, the object stops moving and is therefore stationary.

(b) (i) $v = 8t - 2t^2$

$a = \dfrac{dv}{dt}$

$= 8 - 4t$

When first released, $t = 0$ so we have

$a = 8 - 4(0)$

$= 8\ \text{ms}^{-2}$

> $t = 0$ is substituted into $a = 8 - 4t$

(ii) We need to find the maximum value of $s = 4t^2 - \frac{2t^3}{3}$

Hence, we need to differentiate and put the derivative equal to zero to determine the stationary values and hence find the maximum value.

$\frac{ds}{dt} = 8t - 2t^2$

For the stationary values $\frac{ds}{dt} = 0$

Hence $8t - 2t^2 = 0$

$2t(4 - t) = 0$

Solving gives $t = 0$ or $t = 4$.

To find the maximum value, we find the second derivative

$\frac{d^2s}{dt^2} = 8 - 4t$

When $t = 0$, $\frac{d^2s}{dt^2} = 8 - 4(0) = 8$ (this is positive so $t = 0$ gives a minimum value).

When $t = 4$, $\frac{d^2s}{dt^2} = 8 - 4(4) = -8$ (this is negative so $t = 4$ gives a maximum value).

When $t = 4$, $s = 4t^2 - \frac{2t^3}{3} = 4(4)^2 - \frac{2(4)^3}{3} = 21\frac{1}{3}$ m

Greatest depth = $21\frac{1}{3}$ m

You could also find the greatest depth by substituting $t = 4$ (i.e. the time when the object stops sinking) into the equation for the distance, s.

$s = 4t^2 - \frac{2t^3}{3}$

$= 4(4)^2 - \frac{2(4)^3}{3}$

$= 21\frac{1}{3}$m

(c) The equation of the curve is $v = 8t - 2t^2$

$v = 0$ when $t = 0$ or $t = 4$. (from part (b)).

Curve will be ∩-shaped owing to the $- 2t^2$ in the equation $v = 8t - 2t^2$.

Curve is symmetrical so the max value occurs at $t = 2$ where the value of v will be $8(2) - 2(2)^2 = 8$.

The following curve can now be sketched.

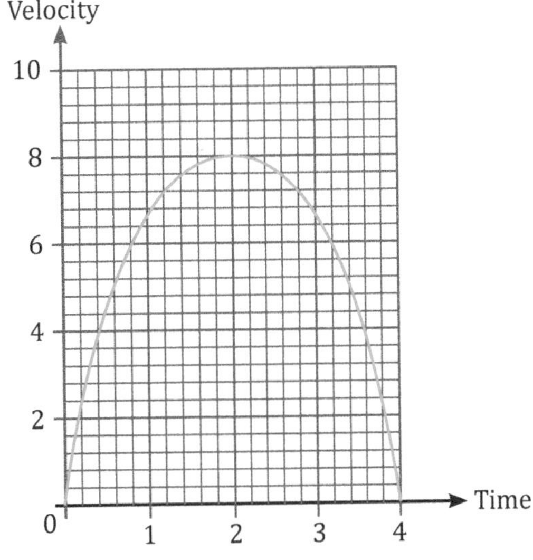

The equation for the acceleration–time curve is

$a = 8 - 4t$

This is the equation of a straight line.
When $t = 0$, $a = 8$ and when $a = 0$, $t = 2$.

Plotting these two points on the graph and joining them with a line we obtain the following.

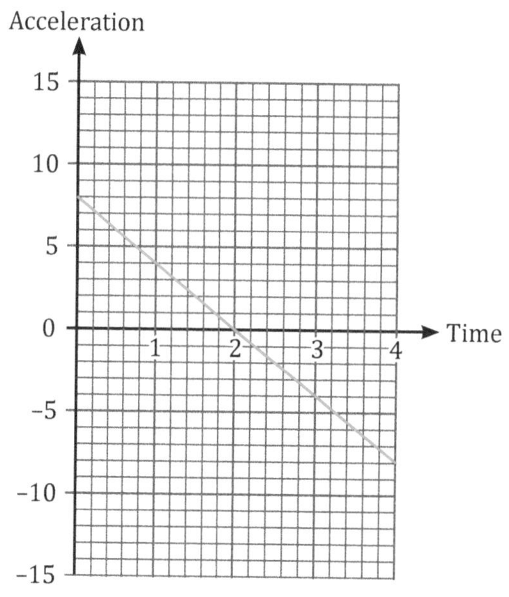

---

5 Parcels slide down a ramp. Due to resistance, the deceleration is 0.25 ms^{-2}.

(i) One parcel is given an initial velocity of 2 ms^{-1}. Find the distance travelled before the parcel comes to rest. [3]

(ii) A second parcel is given an initial velocity of 3 ms^{-1} and takes 4 seconds to reach the bottom of the ramp. Find the length of the ramp. [3]

(OCR FSMQ June 2009 q5)

Answer

If the particle starts with a certain velocity and then comes to rest it means there is a deceleration. Hence the acceleration, a, is negative in the equation of motion.

5 (i) $u = 2$ ms^{-1}, $v = 0$ ms^{-1}, $a = -0.25$ ms^{-2}, and we need to find s.

Using $v^2 = u^2 + 2as$ we have

$$0^2 = 2^2 + 2(-0.25)s$$

Solving gives $s = 8$ m

Distance before coming to rest = 8 m

(ii) $u = 3$ ms^{-1}, $a = -0.25$ ms^{-2}, $t = 4$ s, and we need to find s.

Using $s = ut + \frac{1}{2}at^2$ we have

$$s = 3 \times 4 + \frac{1}{2} \times (-0.25)4^2$$

$$= 10 \text{ m}$$

The length of the ramp is 10 m.

6 A train moves between two stations, taking 5 minutes for the journey. The velocity of the train may be modelled by the equation $v = 60(t^4 - 10t^3 + 25t^2)$ where v is measured in metres per minute and t is measured in minutes.

Calculate the distance between the two stations. [5]

(OCR FSMQ June 2010 q8)

Answer

6 $v = 60(t^4 - 10t^3 + 25t^2)$

$$s = \int_0^5 v\,dt$$

$$= \int_0^5 60(t^4 - 10t^3 + 25t^2)\,dt$$

$$= 60\int_0^5 (t^4 - 10t^3 + 25t^2)\,dt$$

$$= 60\left[\frac{t^5}{5} - \frac{10t^4}{4} + \frac{25t^3}{3}\right]_0^5$$

$$= 60\left[\left(\frac{5^5}{5} - \frac{10(5)^4}{4} + \frac{25(5)^3}{3}\right) - \left(\frac{0^5}{5} - \frac{10(0)^4}{4} + \frac{25(0)^3}{3}\right)\right]$$

$= 6250$ metres

7 A particle moves in a straight line. Its velocity, v ms^{-1}, t seconds after passing a point O is given by the equation

$$v = 6 + 3t^2.$$

Find the distance travelled between the times $t = 1$ and $t = 3$.

(OCR FSMQ June 2007 q2)

Answer

7 $v = 6 + 3t^2$

$$s = \int v\,dt$$

$$= \int (6 + 3t^2)\,dt$$

$$= 6t + t^3 + c$$

When $t = 0$, $s = 0$, so we have

$$0 = 6(0) + (0)^3 + c$$

Hence, $c = 0$.

So we have $s = 6t + t^3$

When $t = 1$, $s = 6(1) + (1)^3$

$= 7$ m

Another way to do this part would be to integrate the velocity but this time using a definite integral and using the limits 1 and 3. Either method is acceptable.

When $t = 3$, $s = 6(3) + (3)^3$

$= 45$ m

Hence distance travelled between $t = 1$ and $t = 3$ is $45 - 7 = 38$ m

Note there is also the alternative method which involves integrating using the limits 3 and 1.

$$\text{So } s = \int_1^3 (6 + 3t^2)\, dt$$

$$= \left[6t + t^3\right]_1^3$$

$$= [(18 + 27) - (6 + 1)]$$

$$= 38 \text{ m}$$

Test yourself

1 The initial speed of a particle is 5 ms^{-1} and it is subjected to a constant acceleration of 10 ms^{-2}.

(a) Find the speed after 6 seconds.

(b) Find the distance travelled in this time.

2 A car starting from rest accelerates uniformly at 0.9 ms^{-2} for 5 seconds.

It then maintains a constant speed for 20 seconds before being uniformly decelerated for 8 seconds before coming to rest.

(a) Sketch a velocity–time graph for the motion of the car.

(b) Find the maximum velocity reached by the car.

(c) Find the deceleration of the car.

(d) Find the total distance travelled by the car.

3 A car travels in a straight line and t seconds after passing a point P it has a velocity given by $v = 64 - \frac{1}{27}t^3$.

The particle comes to rest at point Q.

(a) Show that the car comes to rest after $t = 12$ s.

(b) Calculate the distance PQ.

4 The initial speed to a particle is 10 ms^{-1} after passing a point A and it is subjected to a constant acceleration of $(2t + 3)$ ms^{-2}.

Calculate:

(a) The speed of the particle after 3 seconds, and

(b) The distance the particle travels 3 seconds after passing point A.

5 A particle moving in a straight line under constant acceleration has its speed measured at points A and B. At point A, its speed is 20 ms^{-1} and at point B its speed is 32 ms^{-1}.
The distance between points A and B is 120 m.

(a) Show that the acceleration of the particle is 2.6 ms^{-2}.

(b) Find the time for the particle to travel from A to B.

(c) Find the speed of the particle 20 s after passing point A.

(d) Calculate the distance from A, 30 s after it passes A.

(e) Sketch a velocity–time graph for the journey from A to B.

Topic summary

Displacement/distance–time graphs

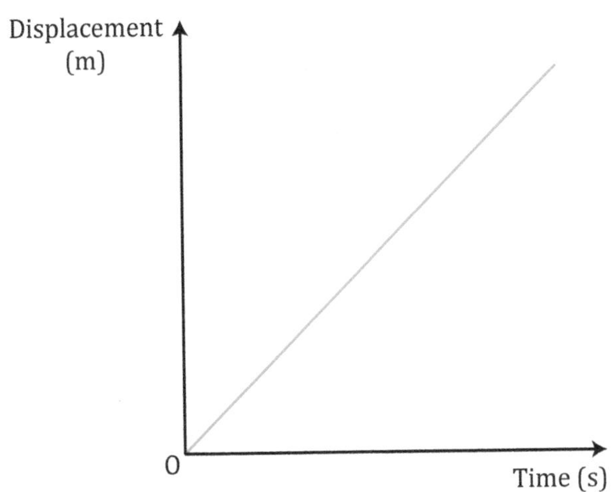

Displacement
(m)
0
Time (s)

The gradient represents velocity or speed.

A horizontal line has zero gradient and represents a body at rest.

Velocity–time graphs

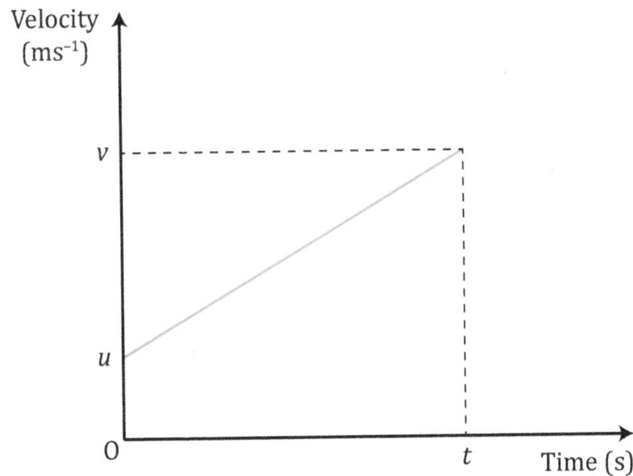

Velocity
(ms-1)
0
Time (s)

The gradient represents acceleration.

The area under the line/curve represents the distance or displacement.

A horizontal line represents constant velocity.

Constant acceleration formulae

The following equations of motion should only be used if it is known that the motion is under constant acceleration.

$v = u + at$

$s = ut + \frac{1}{2}at^2$

$v^2 = u^2 + 2as$

$s = \frac{1}{2}(u + v)t$

s = displacement/distance
u = initial velocity/speed
v = final velocity/speed
a = acceleration
t = time

Finding acceleration and displacement from acceleration

Note that if the acceleration is not constant the equations of motion cannot be used so we use calculus to find s, v, or a.

Displacement (s) → Differentiate $\frac{ds}{dt}$ → Velocity (v) → Differentiate $\frac{dv}{dt}$ → Acceleration (a)

Hence, $v = \frac{ds}{dt}$ and $a = \frac{dv}{dt}$

Finding velocity and displacement from acceleration

If you need to work backwards through the diagram shown in the previous section then you will need to reverse the effect of differentiating by integrating, as the diagram below shows.

Displacement (s) ← Integrate $s = \int v\,dt$ ← Velocity (v) ← Integrate $v = \int a\,dt$ ← Acceleration (a)

Hence, $s = \int v\,dt$ and $v = \int a\,dt$

Remember to include a constant of integration, c, if there are no limits when integrating.

Topic 1 Answers

Progress checks

1. (a) $6x + 15$
   (b) $-2x - 12$
   (c) $8x^2 + 24x + 32$
   (d) $-24x + 54$
   (e) $-15x + 27$
   (f) $-4x^2 - 4x - 8$
   (g) $-3x - 5$
   (h) $-6x - 8$
   (i) $-x^2 + 4x - 8$
   (j) $4x - 20$
   (k) $-7x^2 + 28x - 14$
2. (a) $8x - 14$
   (b) $24 - 11x$
   (c) $8x - 64$
   (d) $14x$
   (e) $x^2 + 2x$
   (f) $9x^2 + 16x$
   (g) $3x^3 - 10x^2$
   (h) $4x^2 + 3xy - y^2$
3. (a) $x^2 + 7x + 10$
   (b) $x^2 - 6x - 7$
   (c) $x^2 - 16$
   (d) $15x^2 + 14x + 3$
   (e) $8x^2 - 22x + 5$
   (f) $25x^2 - 1$
   (g) $2x^2 - 32$
   (h) $12a^2 + 10ab + 2b^2$
   (i) $20x^2 + xy - y^2$
   (j) $6x^2 - 23xy + 15y^2$
4. (a) $x^2 + y^2 + 4x + 2y + 5 = 0$
   (b) $x^2 + y^2 + 10x + 6y + 34 = 0$
   (c) $x^2 + y^2 - 14x + 4y + 53 = 0$
   (d) $x^2 + y^2 - 8x + 12y + 52 = 0$
   (e) $x^2 + y^2 - 12x + 14y + 73 = 0$
   (f) $x^2 + y^2 + 4x - 10y + 36 = 0$
   (g) $x^2 + y^2 - 2x - 18y + 72 = 0$
   (h) $x^2 + y^2 + 6x - 16y + 46 = 0$
   (i) $x^2 + y^2 + 2x - 2y - 16 = 0$
5. (a) $4x$
   (b) $3xy^2$
   (c) $\frac{2}{3}abc$
   (d) $\frac{3x}{y}$
6. (a) $3ab$
   (b) $\frac{x^2}{y}$
   (c) $2q^2$
   (d) $5x^2y^2$
   (e) $\frac{5a^2c}{b}$
   (f) $\frac{(x+7)}{(x+3)}$
   (g) 1

7 (a) $4xy(3x + 2y)$

(b) $2ab(2a + 1)$

(c) $6x(4xy + 1)$

(d) $5a^2b^2(5ac^5 + b)$

8 (a) x

(b) y^2

(c) $3y$

(d) $\frac{x - 4}{2(x - 2)}$

(e) $\frac{x - 2}{x - 5}$

(f) $\frac{1}{(x - 1)}$

9 $x = 14$

10 $x = -10$

11 $x = 15$

12 $x = 40$

13 $x = 9$

14 $x = 4$

15 $x = 4$

16 (a) $x = -1$

(b) $x = 1$

(c) $x = \frac{1}{2}$

(d) $x = -2.6$

17 (a) $x = -\frac{1}{3}$

(b) $x = -\frac{4}{3}$

18 (a) $x = 20$

(b) $x = 84$

(c) $x = 54$

19 $x = 5$

20 $x = 10$

21 $x = 5$

22 $x = 12$

23 (a) $r = \sqrt{\frac{A}{\pi}}$

(b) $r = \sqrt{\frac{A}{4\pi}}$

(c) $r = \sqrt[3]{\frac{3V}{4\pi}}$

24 (a) $u = v - at$

(b) $a = \frac{v - u}{t}$

(c) $s = \frac{v^2}{2a}$

(d) $a = \frac{v^2 - u^2}{2s}$

(e) $u = \sqrt{v^2 - 2as}$

(f) $a = \frac{2(s - ut)}{t^2}$

(g) $c = y - mx$

(h) $m = \frac{y - c}{x}$

(i) $t = \frac{2s}{u + v}$

(j) $v = \sqrt{\frac{2E}{m}}$

(k) $l = \frac{V}{\pi r^2}$

(l) $r = \sqrt{\frac{V}{\pi l}}$

25 (a) $x = \frac{1}{3}$ and $y = 4\frac{2}{3}$

(b) $x = 2$ and $y = 3$

26 (a) $x = 2$ and $y = 1$

(b) $x = 1$ and $y = 2$

27 $12\sqrt{5}$

28 $7 + 2\sqrt{6}$

29 $8\sqrt{3}$

Test yourself

1 (a) $x = 7$

(b) $x = 5$

(c) $x = 4$

(d) $x = 32$

(e) $x = 25$

(f) $x = -9$

(g) $x = -2$

(h) $x = 84$

2 (a) $5x^2$

(b) $5b^2c$

(c) $\frac{(x-7)}{(x-1)}$

(d) $\frac{(x+3)}{(x-6)}$

3 (a) $18x - 7$

(b) $-2x - 8$

(c) $-x + 5$

(d) $3x - 20$

(e) $7x - 3$

(f) $13x - 37$

(g) $-3x^2 - 4x + 2$

(h) $x^3 - 4x^2 + 8x$

(i) $3a^2 + 5ab + 2b^2$

(j) $8a^2 - 10ab + 3b^2$

(k) $5x^3 - 12x^2 + 12x$

(l) $x^2 + x$

4 (a) $x^2 - 2x - 15$

(b) $4x^2 - 21x + 5$

(c) $6x^2 - 11x - 35$

(d) $81x^2 - 1$

(e) $8a^2 + 14ab - 4b^2$

(f) $10y^2 + 23y - 5$

5 (a) $V = \frac{nRT}{p}$

(b) $n = \frac{pV}{RT}$

(c) $T = \frac{pV}{nR}$

(d) $p = \frac{nRT}{V}$

6 $f = \frac{E}{h}$

7 $m = \frac{y-c}{x}$

8 (a) $\lambda = \frac{c}{f}$

(b) $V = \frac{n}{c}$

(c) $T = \frac{Q}{mc}$

(d) $V = \frac{1000n}{c}$

(e) $c = \frac{1000n}{V}$

(f) $h = \frac{E}{f}$

9 (a) $5\sqrt{3}$

(b) $\frac{1+\sqrt{5}}{4}$

(c) $7\sqrt{2}$

(d) 20

10 (a) $\frac{5\sqrt{2}}{2}$

(b) $\frac{3-\sqrt{5}}{4}$

11 $x = 2$ and $y = -3$

Topic 2 Answers

Progress check

1 (a) $x^2 + 2x + 1$

(b) $x^2 + 22x + 121$

(c) $x^2 + 26x + 169$

(d) $x^2 - 12x + 36$

(e) $x^2 - 22x + 121$

(f) $x^2 + 14x + 49$

2 (a) $x^2 + \mathbf{6x} + 9$

(b) $x^2 + \mathbf{8x} + 16$

(c) $x^2 + \mathbf{2x} + 1$

(d) $x^2 + \mathbf{12x} + 36$

(e) $x^2 + \mathbf{16x} + \mathbf{64}$

(f) $x^2 + \mathbf{10x} + \mathbf{25}$

(g) $x^2 - \mathbf{8x} + 16$

(h) $x^2 - \mathbf{10x} + 25$

(i) $x^2 - \mathbf{18x} + 81$

(j) $x^2 - \mathbf{14x} + \mathbf{49}$

(k) $x^2 - \mathbf{20x} + \mathbf{100}$

(l) $x^2 + \mathbf{24x} + \mathbf{144}$

3 (a) $(x + 2)^2 + 4$

(b) $(x + 1)^2 + 5$

(c) $(x - 3)^2 - 5$

(d) $(x - 1)^2 - 11$

(e) $(x - 5)^2 - 27$

(f) $(x - 4)^2 - 12$

(g) $(x - 3)^2 + 3$

4 (a) $(x + 1)(x + 2)$

(b) $(x + 4)(x + 2)$

(c) $(x + 3)(x + 7)$

(d) $(x + 4)(x - 1)$

(e) $(x - 3)(x + 1)$

(f) $(x - 1)(x - 2)$

(g) $(x - 5)(x + 1)$

(h) $(x + 7)(x - 2)$

(i) $(x - 1)(x - 4)$

(j) $(x + 5)(x - 2)$

5 (a) $(2x-3)(x+1)$

(b) $(2x+1)(x+4)$

(c) $(3x+1)(x+1)$

(d) $(5x-1)(x+4)$

(e) $(5x-2)(x-1)$

(f) $(4x+1)(x-1)$

(g) $(3x+5)(x+1)$

(h) $(2x+7)(x-2)$

(i) $(4x-5)(x-4)$

(j) $(x-5)(x+2)$

6 (a) $(x+1)(x+2)$

(b) $(x+5)(x+1)$

(c) $(x+3)(x+8)$

(d) $(x+1)(x+9)$

(e) $(x+5)(x+3)$

(f) $(x-1)(x-1)$

(g) $(x+6)(x-1)$

(h) $(x+7)(x-3)$

(i) $(x-3)(x-2)$

(j) $(x+10)(x-3)$

(k) $(x-3)(x+5)$

7 (a) $(2x-1)(x+1)$

(b) $(2x+1)(x+6)$

(c) $(4x+1)(x-1)$

(d) $(3x-2)(x+7)$

(e) $(5x-2)(x+4)$

(f) $(4x-3)(2x+9)$

(g) $(6x-1)(2x+5)$

(h) $(4x-1)(3x-1)$

8 (a) $(x+1)(x-1)$

(b) $(2x+5)(2x-5)$

(c) $(2c+b)(2c-b)$

(d) $(4x+7)(4x-7)$

(e) $(p+q)(p-q)$

(f) $(5x+y)(5x-y)$

(g) $(x+y)(x-y)$

(h) $(y+10)(y-10)$

(i) $(2a+1)(2a-1)$

(k) $(c+5)(c-5)$

9 (a) $x=-1$ or -2

(b) $x=-4$ or -2

(c) $x=-3$ or -7

(d) $x=-4$ or 1

(e) $x=3$ or -1

(f) $x=1$ or 2

(g) $x=5$ or -1

(h) $x=-7$ or 2

(i) $x=1$ or 4

(j) $x=-5$ or 2

10 (a) $x=7$ or 3

(b) $a=-6$ or 7

(c) $x=\frac{1}{3}$ or -4

11 (a) $x=-0.27$ or -3.73 (2 d.p.)

(b) $x=0.87$ or -2.87 (2 d.p.)

12 $x=1.29$ or -9.29 (2 d.p.)

13 (a) $b^2-4ac=-56$

As $b^2-4ac<0$, there are no real roots.

(b) $x=-0.42$ or -1.58 (2 d.p.).

Test yourself

1. $\left(x - \frac{3}{2}\right)^2 - 2$

2. (a) $(x - 4)^2 - 4$
   $a = -4$ and $b = -4$

   (b) $x = 6$ or $x = 2$

3. (a) $(x + 2)^2 + 8$
   $a = 2$ and $b = 8$

   (b) The least value of $(x + 2)^2 + 8$ is 8 and this occurs when $x = -2$

4. (i) $a = 4$ and $b = -25$

   (ii) Least value is -25 and this occurs when $x = -4$

5. (a) $(x + 1)(x + 1)$

   (b) $(x + 3)(x + 2)$

   (c) $(2x + 1)(x + 1)$

   (d) $(3x + 1)(x + 3)$

   (e) $(x - 2)(x + 1)$

   (f) $(x + 4)(x - 1)$

   (g) $(x - 3)(x + 4)$

   (h) $(x - 1)(x - 5)$

   (i) $(x - 7)(x + 5)$

6. (a) $(3x + 2)(x + 1)$

   (b) $(4x + 1)(x + 1)$

   (c) $(5x + 1)(x + 4)$

   (d) $(4x + 1)(5x + 3)$

   (e) $(3x - 1)(x + 4)$

   (f) $(5x + 1)(x - 7)$

   (g) $(x - 4)(7x - 3)$

   (h) $(2x - 1)(3x - 1)$

   (i) $(4x - 5)(x + 6)$

   (j) $(8x - 1)(x - 6)$

   (k) $(3x - 7)(4x - 1)$

   (l) $(9x - 1)(x + 10)$

7. $5(x - 2)^2 - 10$

   $a = 5$, $b = -2$ and $c = -10$

8. Coordinates of the point of contact are $(4, 8)$

Topic 3 Answers

Progress check

1. As f(3) = 0 then $(x - 3)$ is a factor of the function.
2. Remainder = –1
3. Remainder = –18
4. Remainder = 6
5. As f(1) = 0, $(x - 1)$ is a factor of $x^3 + 4x^2 + x - 6$
6. (a) $x^3 + 3x^2 + 3x + 2$

   (b) $x^3 - 7x^2 + 13x - 4$

   (c) $2x^3 + x^2 + x - 1$

   (d) $x^3 + 10x^2 + 29x + 20$

   (e) $x^3 + 2x^2 - x - 2$

   (f) $x^3 + 4x^2 - 3x - 18$

   (g) $x^3 - 5x^2 + 7x - 3$
7. f(2) = 5
8. $a = 3$
9. (i) f(2) = 0

   (ii) $x - 2$ is a factor of the function

Test yourself

1. 3
2. (a) $a = 11$

   (b) $x = -2, -1$ or -3
3. (a) (i) f(–2) = 0

   (ii) $(x + 2)$ is a factor of f(x)

   (b) $x = -2, 2$ or 1

Topic 4 Answers

Progress check

1. Amy's age is 12 years and her mother's age is 36
2. $x = 9$ and $y = 8$
3. Integers are 15, 16, 17
4. (a) $x \geq 5$
   (b) $x \leq 10$
   (c) $x > -1$
   (d) $x > 4$
   (e) $x \leq 50$
5. (a) $1 \leq x \leq 8$
   (b) $-2 \leq x \leq 5$
   (c) $1 < x \leq 8$
   (d) $-4 < x < 4$
   (e) $4 \leq x < 10$
6. (a) 3, 4, 5, 6, 7, 8, 9 10
   (b) −4, −3, −2, −1, 0
   (c) 1, 2, 3, 4, 5, 6, 7
   (d) 16, 17, 18
   (e) −2, −1, 0, 1, 2
   (f) 16, 17, 18, 19
   (g) −4, −3, −2, −1, 0, 1, 2, 3, 4
   (h) 3, 4, 5, 6, 7, 8, 9
   (i) 0, 1, 2, 3, 4, 5
   (j) 12, 13, 14, 15, 16, 17, 18
7. (a) $x \leq 3$ and $x \geq 8$
   (b) $-3 < x < 7$
   (c) $4 < x < 14$
   (d) $-4 \leq x < 5$
   (e) $x < 5$ and $x \geq 8$
   (f) $x \leq -1$ and $x > 2$
8. $14 \leq x \leq 18$
9. (a) $x > 1$
   (b) $x > 2$
   (c) $x \leq -1$
   (d) $x > -\frac{3}{4}$
   (e) $x \geq \frac{5}{4}$
   (f) $x > \frac{11}{4}$
10. $x < 2$ and $x > 4$
11. $x > -\frac{3}{2}$
12. $-2 \leq x \leq \frac{3}{5}$
13. (4, 8)
14. (−2, 3) and (−3, −2)
15. 5.85 or −0.85 (2 d.p.)

Test yourself

1. (a) $x > 3$

   (b) $x > 5$

   (c) $x \leq -16$

   (d) $x > -10$

2. (a) $x > 10$

   (b) $x < 0.4$

   (c) $x \leq 8$

3. $x < -3$ and $x > 6$

4. $-3 \leq x \leq 5$

5. (a) $3 < x \leq 7$

   (b) $-\frac{2}{3} < x < 3$

   (c) $x \leq 6$

Topic 5 Answers

Progress check

1. (a) 56
   (b) 35
   (c) 924
   (d) 21
   (e) 792
   (f) 6
2. (a) 1
   (b) 2
   (c) 3
   (d) 120
3. (a) 1
   (b) 5
   (c) 56
   (d) 252
4. $27 + 54x + 36x^2 + 8x^3$
5. $135x^2$
6. $x^5 + 10x^3 + 40x + \frac{80}{x} + \frac{80}{x^3} + \frac{32}{x^5}$
7. (a) $1 + 6x + 15x^2 + 20x^3 + 15x^4 + 6x^5 + x^6$
   (b) 1.1262 (4 d.p)
8. (i) 0.201 (3 s.f.)
   (ii) 0.0464 (3 s.f.)
9. (a) $\frac{1}{216} = 0.004\,630$
   (b) $\frac{125}{216} = 0.5787$
   (c) 0.0741 (3 s.f.)

Test yourself

1. 720
2. $1 + 18x + 135x^2 + 540x^3$
3. 0.1897 (4 s.f.)
4. 0.1746 (4 s.f.)
5. 0.3798 (4 s.f.)

Topic 6 Answers

Progress checks

1. (a) Negative
   (b) Zero
   (c) Positive
   (d) Negative
   (e) Positive
   (f) Infinite
   (g) Negative
   (h) Zero
2. (a) Gradient = 3
   (b) Gradient = $\frac{3}{2}$
   (c) Gradient = 1
   (d) Gradient = $\frac{9}{4}$
   (e) Gradient = 9
   (f) Gradient = $\frac{4}{3}$
   (g) Gradient = $\frac{1}{11}$
3. (a) (2, 5)
   (b) $\left(2, \frac{3}{2}\right)$
   (c) (−1, 0)
   (d) (−5, −1)
   (e) $(\frac{7}{2}, 6)$
   (f) $(-\frac{7}{2}, 1)$
   (g) $(\frac{3}{2}, 3)$
4. (a) 5.66
   (b) 5.83
   (c) 13.0
   (d) 6.40
   (e) 6.40
   (f) 13.0
   (g) 5.10
5. (a) A to $B = \begin{pmatrix} 3 \\ -1 \end{pmatrix}$

   C to $D = \begin{pmatrix} 3 \\ -1 \end{pmatrix}$

   Hence $AB = CD$

   (b) A to $B = \begin{pmatrix} 5 \\ 1 \end{pmatrix}$

   C to $D = \begin{pmatrix} 5 \\ 1 \end{pmatrix}$

   Hence $AB = CD$

   (c) A to $B = \begin{pmatrix} 6 \\ -1 \end{pmatrix}$

   C to $D = \begin{pmatrix} 6 \\ -1 \end{pmatrix}$

   Hence $AB = CD$

   (d) A to $B = \begin{pmatrix} 6 \\ -1 \end{pmatrix}$

   C to $D = \begin{pmatrix} 6 \\ 1 \end{pmatrix}$

   Hence $AB = CD$

   (e) A to $B = \begin{pmatrix} -2 \\ 4 \end{pmatrix}$

   C to $D = \begin{pmatrix} -4 \\ -2 \end{pmatrix}$

   Hence $AB = CD$

   (f) A to $B = \begin{pmatrix} 6 \\ 1 \end{pmatrix}$

   C to $D = \begin{pmatrix} 1 \\ 6 \end{pmatrix}$

   Hence $AB = CD$

(g) A to $B = \begin{pmatrix}1\\2\end{pmatrix}$

C to $D = \begin{pmatrix}2\\1\end{pmatrix}$

Hence $AB = CD$

6 (a) 5.83

(b) 13.0

(c) 5.39

(d) 5.39

7 (a) $m = 3, c = 2$

(b) $m = 2, c = 3$

(c) $m = \frac{2}{3}, c = 1$

(d) $m = -\frac{4}{3}, c = 3$

(e) $m = \frac{1}{2}, c = -\frac{3}{2}$

(f) $m = \frac{1}{2}, c = -\frac{4}{3}$

8 $(-2, 8)$

9 (a) Mid-point of $PQ = (0, 4)$

(b) P to $Q = \begin{pmatrix}8\\2\end{pmatrix}$ so by Pythagoras $PQ = 2\sqrt{17}$

10 (a) Length = 5.83

(b) Length = 5

(c) Length = 4.12

11 $(6, 5)$

12 $k = 6$

13 (a) Gradient = 4

(b) Gradient = $\frac{3}{2}$

(c) Gradient = $\frac{1}{4}$

(d) Gradient = $\frac{2}{3}$

14 (a) $k = 4$

(b) Mid-point = $(3, 6.5)$

15 Equation of line is $4x - 3y = -18$

16 (a) Gradient of $AB = 1$

Gradient of $BC = -1$

(b) Product of the gradients = $(1)(-1) = -1$. Hence, AB and BC are perpendicular to each other.

17 (a) $2y = -3x + 12$

(b) $3y = 2x + 5$

18 (a) Point lies on the line.

(b) Point lies on the line.

(c) Point does not lie on the line.

(d) Point lies on the line.

(e) Point does not lie on the line.

19 (a) $y = -1$

(b) $y = 5$

(c) $y = 0$

(d) $y = \frac{2}{5}$

(e) $y = 1$

(f) $y = 3$

20 (a) $x = -\frac{1}{2}$

(b) $x = 5$

(c) $x = 4$

(d) $x = -9$

(e) $x = 5$

(f) $x = -7$

(g) $x = 2$

21 $(3, -1)$

22 $(4, -1)$

23 Both lines have the same gradient and are therefore parallel so they will not intersect.

24 Coordinates of A are $(-1, 5)$

Test yourself

1 (a) Gradient of $AB = \frac{1}{3}$, Gradient of $CD = \frac{1}{3}$

As the gradients of AB and CD are the same the two lines are parallel.

(b) $x - 3y - 1 = 0$

2 (a) $k = 3$

(b) $2x - y - 7 = 0$

3 (a) Gradient of $AB = 1$

Gradient of $BC = -1$

Product of gradients = $(1)(-1) = -1$ proving that the two lines are perpendicular to each other.

(b) $AB = \sqrt{32}$ units

$BC = \sqrt{50}$ units

(c) Tan $ACB = \frac{4}{5}$

4 $3x + 2y = 17$

5 (a) $2y - x = 4$

(b) $y = -2x - 3$

6 (a) Gradient of $PQ = \frac{5}{2}$

(b) $2y - 5x = -5$

(c) Gradient of $RS = \frac{5}{2}$

$2y - 5x = 22$

(d) Coordinates of point S are $(-4, 1)$

7 (a) Gradient of $AB = -\frac{1}{2}$

(b) Gradient of $DC = -\frac{1}{2}$

Gradient of AB = gradient of DC, so lines are parallel

(c) The vector to go from A to B is $\begin{pmatrix} 4 \\ -2 \end{pmatrix}$

The vector to go from D to C is $\begin{pmatrix} 4 \\ -2 \end{pmatrix}$

These vectors are the same so the lines are the same length.

(d) The vector to go from A to D is $\begin{pmatrix} 3 \\ 3 \end{pmatrix}$.

The vector to go from B to C is $\begin{pmatrix} 3 \\ 3 \end{pmatrix}$.

These vectors are the same so the lines are both parallel and the same length.

Hence, this and the answer to parts (b) and (c) prove that $ABCD$ is a parallelogram.

8 (a) Mid-point, $M = \left(\frac{5}{2}, \frac{7}{2}\right)$

(b) Gradient of $AB = -1$

(c) Gradient of $MC = 1$

Product of gradients of lines AB and MC $= (-1)(1) = -1$

As the product of two perpendicular lines is -1 so AB and MC are perpendicular.

(d) Equation of MC is $y = x + 1$

9 (a) Gradient $= -\frac{2}{3}$

(b) S is $(0, 5)$

10 (a) Gradient of $AB = -\frac{4}{5}$

(b) See proof in worked solutions.

(c) $4y = 5x + 49$

Topic 7 Answers

Progress check

1
(a) 1
(b) 3
(c) 5
(d) 2
(e) 7
(f) 2
(g) 3
(h) 3
(i) 4
(j) $\sqrt{5}$
(k) $5\sqrt{2}$

2
(a) $x^2 + y^2 = 9$
(b) $x^2 + y^2 = 16$
(c) $x^2 + y^2 = 81$
(d) $x^2 + y^2 = 6$
(e) $x^2 + y^2 = 12$
(f) $x^2 + y^2 = 45$
(g) $x^2 + y^2 = 18$

3
(a) $x^2 + y^2 - 6x + 2y + 1 = 0$
(b) $x^2 + y^2 - 4x + 8y + 4 = 0$
(c) $x^2 + y^2 - 2x - 6y + 9 = 0$
(d) $x^2 + y^2 + 8x - 10y + 16 = 0$
(e) $x^2 + y^2 + 10x - 2y + 17 = 0$
(f) $x^2 + y^2 - 12x + 14y + 36 = 0$
(g) $x^2 + y^2 - 10x - 8y + 25 = 0$
(h) $x^2 + y^2 - 2y - 3 = 0$

Test yourself

1 Centre (4, 3) and radius = 5

2
(a) Radius = 4
(b) See proof in worked solutions.

3
(a) $x^2 + y^2 - 4x - 6y - 12 = 0$
(b) $4y + 3x - 43 = 0$

4
(a) Centre of circle is at (2, –4)
(b) See proof in worked solutions.

5
(a) (5, 3)
(b) $r = \sqrt{65}$
(c) $x^2 + y^2 - 10x - 6y - 31 = 0$

6 Radius = 6.32 and distance = 5

This distance is less than the radius of the circle, so the point lies inside the circle.

7
(a) (2, –1)
(b) $2\sqrt{2}$

Topic 8 Answers

Progress check

1. (a) $x \leq 3$

   (b) $y \geq 2$

   (c) $y \leq x$

   (d) $y \geq -2x + 8$

   (e) $y \geq \frac{1}{2}x + 3$

2. (a) Region 2

   (b) Region 5

   (c) Region 1

   (d) Region 3

   (e) Region 4

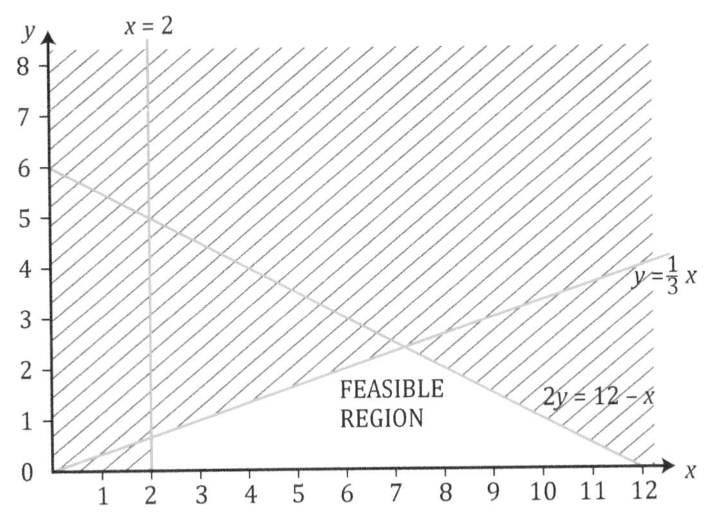

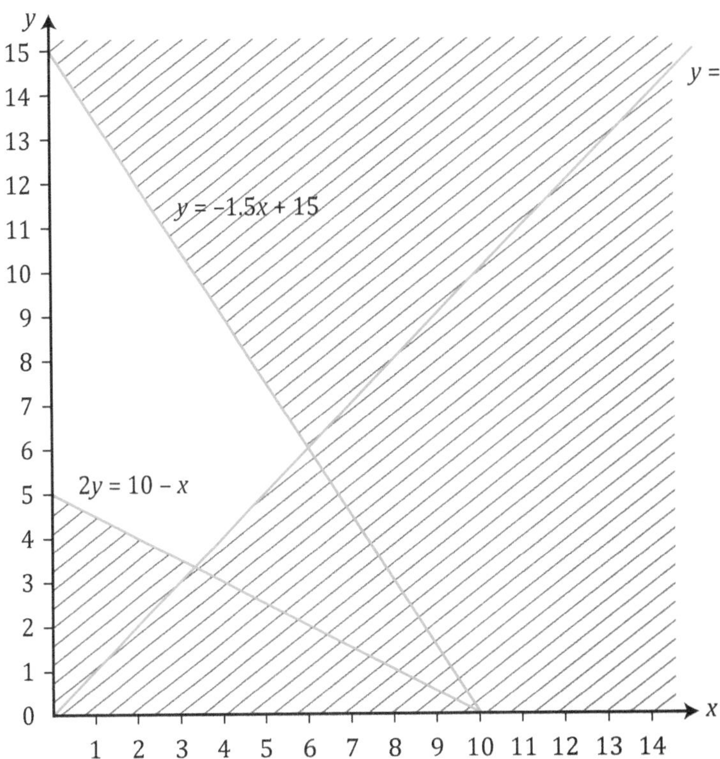

5. (a) $3x + 4y \leq 100$

   (b) $20x + 30y \leq 1500$

   (c) $y < 3x$

6. (a) $x \leq 500$

   $y \leq 500$

   $x + y \leq 800$

   $x \geq \frac{1}{3}y$

   (b) $0.8x + 0.9y$

7. $20\,000y + 15\,000x \leq 500\,000$ or $4y + 3x \leq 100$

   $y \geq 3x$

   $40x + 50y \leq 1200$

   $4x + 5y \leq 120$

Test yourself

1 (a) $x \le 150$

$y \le 120$

$x + y \le 200$

(b)

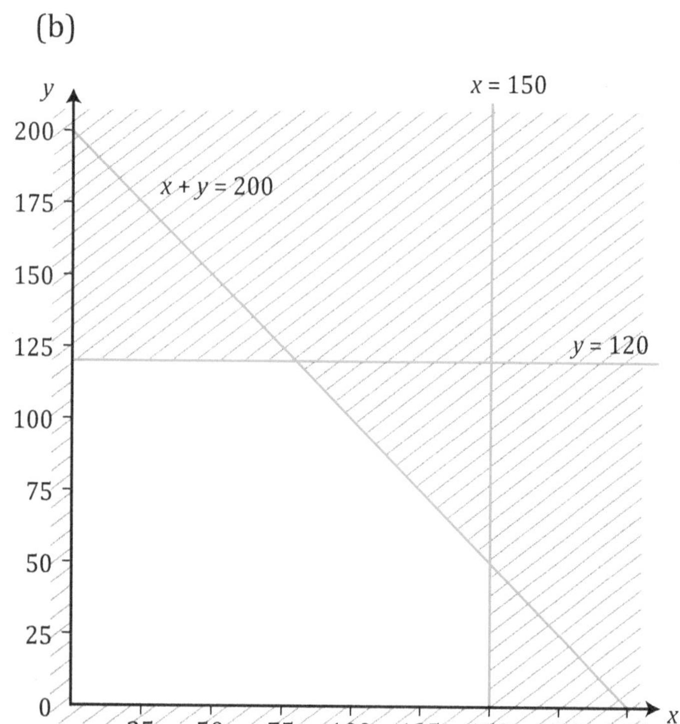

(c) 80 of bag A and 120 of bag B should be produced.

2 (a)

(b) (3, 0)

3 (a) $x + y \le 18$

(b) $8x + 3y \ge 72$

(c)

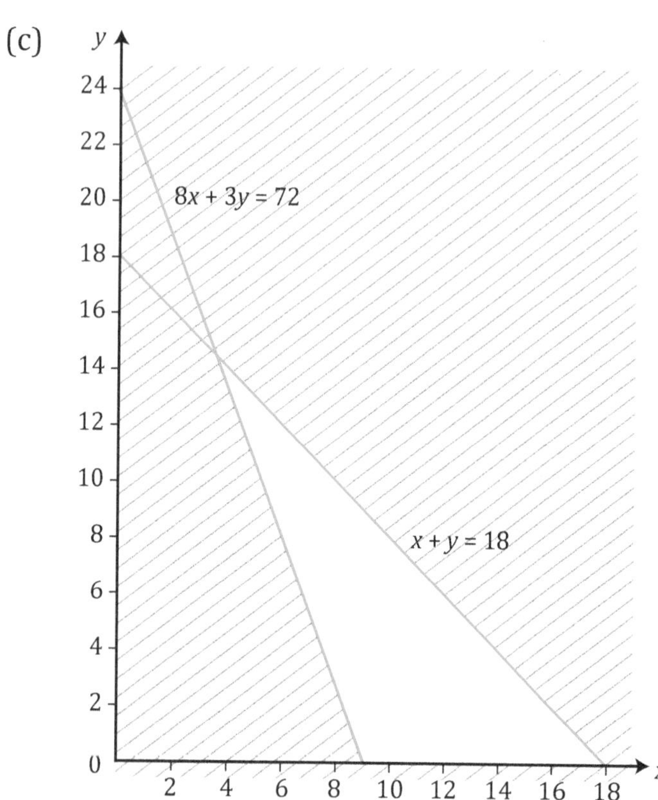

(d) $80x + 20y$

(e) 4 large tents and 14 small tents need to be used.

Topic 9 Answers

Progress checks

1 (a) 17.32 cm

(b) 9.19 cm

2 (a) 73.3°

(b) 50.3°

3 See worked solution.

4 60° and 300°

5 60° and 120°

6 153.4° or 333.4°

7 30° or 150°

8 (a) 193° or 347°

(b) 136° or 224°

(c) 68° or 248°

9 27.7°

10 (a) 80.4°

(b) 48.8 cm^2

11 (a) 225 cm^2

(b) $\frac{4}{5}$

(c) 18.0 cm

Test yourself

1 (a)

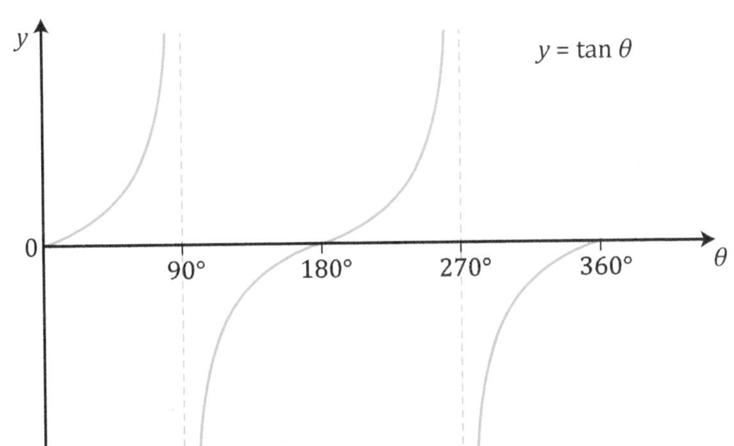

(b) 45° or 225°

2 (a) 45° or 225°

(b) 63.4° or 243.4°

3 (a) 24 cm^2

(b) 19.3 cm

4 (a) (0°, 0), (180°, 0), (360°, 0), (540°, 0), (720°, 0)

(b) (90°, 1), (270°, −1), (450°, 1), (630°, −1)

5 (a) 18.6 cm

(b) 92.5 cm^2

Topic 10 Answers

Progress check

1. 153.4° or 333.4°
2. See worked solution for proof.
3. (a) $\frac{1}{\sqrt{5}}$

   (b) See worked solution for proof.
4. 48.2° or 311.8°
5. (a) $\frac{3}{5}$

   (b) 31°
6. 14.5°, 165.5°, 221.8° or 318.2°
7. 14.2 km
8. (a) See worked solution for proof.

   (b) See worked solution for proof.

   (c) 51.5°
9. (a) 10.8 cm

   (b) 11.5 cm

   (c) 20.3°

   (d) 33.7°
10. (a)

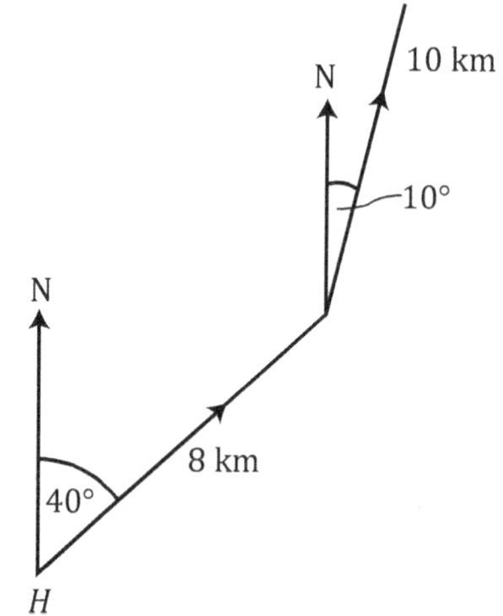

   (b) 17.4 km

   (c) 203°

Test yourself

1. 0°, 48.2°, 311.8° or 360°
2. 30°, 120°, 210°, 300°
3. (a) 48 nautical miles

   (b) 50.7 nautical miles

   (c) 215°
4. 108.4° and 288.4°
5. (a) 12 cm

   (b) VS = 16 cm, RS = 10.6 cm

   (c) 48.5°

Topic 11 Answers

Progress checks

1. (a) $\frac{dy}{dx} = 12x^2 + 12x - 3$

   (b) $\frac{dy}{dx} = 30x^4 + 32x^3 - 9x^2$

   (c) $\frac{dy}{dx} = 28x^3 + 24x^2 - 18x$

   (d) $\frac{dy}{dx} = 30x^2 - 14x - 9$

   (e) $\frac{dy}{dx} = 40x - 7$

   (f) $\frac{dy}{dx} = 10x - 7$

2. (a) $y = (x + 2)(x + 1) = x^2 + 3x + 2 \quad \frac{dy}{dx} = 2x + 3$

   (b) $y = (x + 4)(x + 2) = x^2 + 6x + 8 \quad \frac{dy}{dx} = 2x + 6$

   (c) $y = (x - 3)(x + 2) = x^2 - x - 6 \quad \frac{dy}{dx} = 2x - 1$

   (d) $y = (x - 4)(x - 2) = x^2 - 6x + 8 \quad \frac{dy}{dx} = 2x - 6$

   (e) $y = (x - 4)^2 = x^2 - 8x + 16 \quad \frac{dy}{dx} = 2x - 8$

   (f) $y = (x + 2)(x - 2) = x^2 - 4 \quad \frac{dy}{dx} = 2x$

   (g) $y = (x + 5)^2 = x^2 + 10x + 25 \quad \frac{dy}{dx} = 2x + 10$

   (h) $y = x(x^2 + 2x + 1) = x^3 + 2x^2 + x \quad \frac{dy}{dx} = 3x^2 + 4x + 1$

   (i) $y = x(3x^2 + 6x + 9) = 3x^3 + 6x^2 + 9x \quad \frac{dy}{dx} = 9x^2 + 12x + 9$

   (j) $y = x^2(x^2 + 6x + 9) = x^4 + 6x^3 + 9x^2 \quad \frac{dy}{dx} = 4x^3 + 18x^2 + 18x$

   (k) $y = (3x + 2)(2x - 5) = 6x^2 - 11x - 10 \quad \frac{dy}{dx} = 12x - 11$

   (l) $y = (5x - 1)(4x - 7) = 20x^2 - 39x + 7 \quad \frac{dy}{dx} = 40x - 39$

(m) $y = (2x + 3)^2 = 4x^2 + 12x + 9 \quad \frac{dy}{dx} = 8x + 12$

(n) $y = (3x - 2)^2 = 9x^2 - 12x + 4 \quad \frac{dy}{dx} = 18x - 12$

3 (a) $y = x^3 + 4x^2 + 4x + 1 \quad \frac{dy}{dx} = 3x^2 + 8x + 4$

(b) $y = x^3 + 4x^2 - 6x + 1 \quad \frac{dy}{dx} = 3x^2 + 8x - 6$

(c) $y = x^3 - 7x^2 + 14x - 20 \quad \frac{dy}{dx} = 3x^2 - 14x + 14$

(d) $y = 2x^3 - 3x^2 + 6x + 4 \quad \frac{dy}{dx} = 6x^2 - 6x + 6$

(e) $y = 4x^3 + 17x^2 - 27x + 9 \quad \frac{dy}{dx} = 12x^2 + 34x - 27$

(f) $y = 5x^3 + 24x^2 - 20x + 3 \quad \frac{dy}{dx} = 15x^2 + 48x - 20$

(g) $y = x^3 + 10x^2 + 31x + 30 \quad \frac{dy}{dx} = 3x^2 + 20x + 31$

(h) $y = x^3 + 18x^2 + 107x + 210 \quad \frac{dy}{dx} = 3x^2 + 36x + 107$

(i) $y = x^3 - 4x^2 + x + 6 \quad \frac{dy}{dx} = 3x^2 - 8x + 1$

(j) $y = x^3 + 4x^2 + 5x + 2 \quad \frac{dy}{dx} = 3x^2 + 8x + 5$

(k) $y = 4x^3 - 16x^2 + 13x - 3 \quad \frac{dy}{dx} = 12x^2 - 32x + 13$

(l) $y = 9x^3 + 15x^2 - 8x - 16 \quad \frac{dy}{dx} = 27x^2 + 30x - 8$

4 $y = 10x - 7$

5 $x + 20y = 202$

6 $y = 8x - 18$

7 (a) At $x = 1, \frac{dy}{dx} = -1$ and at $x = 2, \frac{dy}{dx} = 1$

(b) Tangent at $x = 1$ is $y = -x + 1$
Tangent at $x = 2$ is $y = x - 2$

(c) $\left(\frac{3}{2}, -\frac{1}{2}\right)$

Test yourself

1. (a) 2

   (b) $2y + x + 114 = 0$

2. (a) $x = -3$ or 1

   (b) Minimum point at $x = -1$

3. (a) $3x^2 - 12x + 9$

   (b) When $x = 3$, $\frac{dy}{dx} = 3(3)^2 - 12(3) + 9 = 0$

   (c) $(3, 1)$ and $(1, 5)$

   (d) $(3, 1)$ minimum point

   $(1, 5)$ maximum point

4. $(\frac{3}{2}, -5\frac{5}{8})$ minimum point

   $(-2, 8\frac{2}{3})$ maximum point

5. $(2, 9)$

Topic 12 Answers

Progress check

1. (a) $x^4 + c$

   (b) $\frac{5x^2}{2} + c$

   (c) $3x + c$

   (d) $-2x^3 + c$

   (e) $4x^4 + c$

   (f) $x + c$

2. (a) $\frac{5x^3}{3} + \frac{3x^2}{2} - 5x + c$

   (b) $\frac{7x^4}{4} - \frac{4x^3}{3} - 4x^2 - x + c$

   (c) $\frac{x^3}{6} + \frac{5x^2}{2} - 3x + c$

   (d) $\frac{x^3}{3} - \frac{x^2}{2} - 6x + c$

   (e) $\frac{x^3}{3} - 3x^2 + 9x + c$

   (f) $\frac{x^4}{4} - 2x^3 - \frac{5x^2}{2} + c$

3. (a) $x^4 + c$

   (b) $2x^3 + c$

   (c) $x^2 + x + c$

   (d) $\frac{8x^3}{3} + 2x^2 - x + c$

   (e) $x^5 + x^4 - 3x^2 + c$

   (f) $\frac{x^3}{3} + 2x^2 - 5x + c$

   (g) $\frac{x^3}{3} + 3x^2 + 5x + c$

   (h) $\frac{x^3}{3} - x + c$

   (i) $\frac{2x^3}{3} - \frac{3x^2}{2} - 5x + c$

   (j) $\frac{x^3}{3} + 5x^2 + 25x + c$

   (k) $\frac{x^3}{3} + \frac{x^2}{2} + c$

(l) $\frac{x^4}{2}+\frac{x^3}{3}+c$

(m) $x^6+4x^5-2x^3-\frac{x^2}{2}+9x+c$

4 $\frac{x^4}{16}-\frac{x^3}{6}+c$

5 (a) x^5-2x^3+9x+c

(b) $2x^4-2x^3+5x^2+5x+c$

(c) $16x-4x^2+\frac{x^3}{3}+c$

(d) $\frac{x^5}{15}+c$

(e) $\frac{x^3}{6}+\frac{x^2}{6}+c$

6 (a) x^3+c

(b) $4x^4+c$

(c) $\frac{x^3}{9}+c$

(d) $5x+c$

7 $y=2x^2+5x-9$

8 $y=2x^3+5x^2+2x-8$

9 (a) $y=x^2-2x-8$

(b) $(-2, 0)$ and $(4, 0)$

(c) $(1, -9)$

Test yourself

1 $y=4x-x^2-x^3+1$

2 (a) $2x^2-\frac{3x^4}{4}+c$

(b) $\frac{3x^4}{2}-\frac{10x^3}{3}+x^2+c$

(c) $\frac{x^3}{6}-\frac{x^2}{2}+\frac{x}{2}+c$

3 $5t^5-3t^4+5t^3-\frac{9t^2}{2}+2t+c$

4 $\frac{2x^3}{45}-4x+c$

5 $2t^3-t^2+t+c$

6 $y=5x^3+4x^2+x-7$

7 (a) $y=3x-x^2$

(b) $(3, 0)$

Topic 13 Answers

Progress check

1 6

2 23

3 0.0417 (3 s.f.)

4 See worked solution for proof.

5 57

6 35.8 (3 s.f.)

7 36

8 (a)

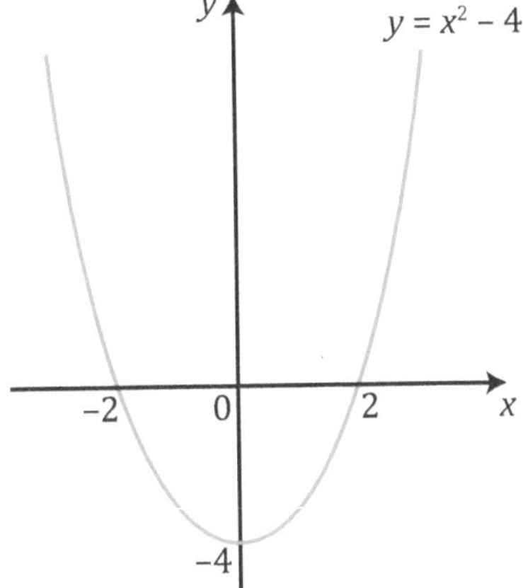

(b) $\int_2^3 (x^2 - 4)\, dx = \frac{7}{3}$

$\int_0^2 (x^2 - 4)\, dx = -\frac{16}{3}$

(c) The positive value represents the area above the *x*-axis and the negative value represents the area below the *x*-axis.

9 (a) *A* is (–3, 0) and *B* is (2, 5)

(b) 20.8 (3 s.f.)

Test yourself

1 120

2 36

3 (a) $-1\frac{1}{3}$

(b) The negative sign means that the area is below the *x*-axis.

4 - 31.5

5 $\frac{4}{3}$ or $1\frac{1}{3}$

6 (a) -6

(b) $-\frac{4}{3}$

(c) 68

Topic 14 Answers

Progress check

1 (a) 9 ms^{-1}

(b) 45 m

2 (a) 20.4 m

(b) 4.1 s

3 (a) 35.1 ms^{-1}

(b) 62.8 m

4 (a) 1.02 s

(b) 5.1 m

5 (a) $36t^2$

(b) 144 ms^{-2}

6 (a) $1.92t^2 - 0.72t$

(b) 1480 m

7 (a) $v = 3t - \frac{0.1t^2}{2}$

(b) 25 ms^{-1}

(c) See worked solution.

(d) 900 m

8 75 m

9 (a) (i) $12t - 2$

(ii) 10 ms^{-2}

(b) $s = 2t^3 - t^2 + 8t$

Test yourself

1 (a) 65 ms^{-1}

(b) 210 m

2 (a)

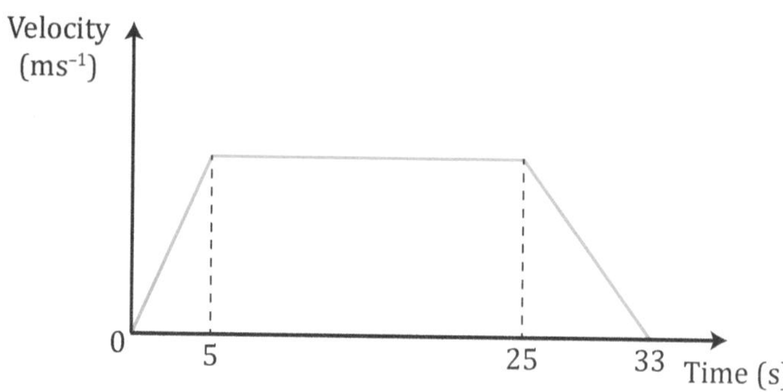

(b) 4.5 ms^{-1}

(c) 0.56 ms^{-2}

(d) 119.25 m

3 (a) 12 s (b) 576 m

4 (a) 28 ms^{-1} (b) 52.5 m

5 (a) 2.6 ms^{-2} (b) 4.62 s

(c) 72 ms^{-1} (d) 1770 m

(e)

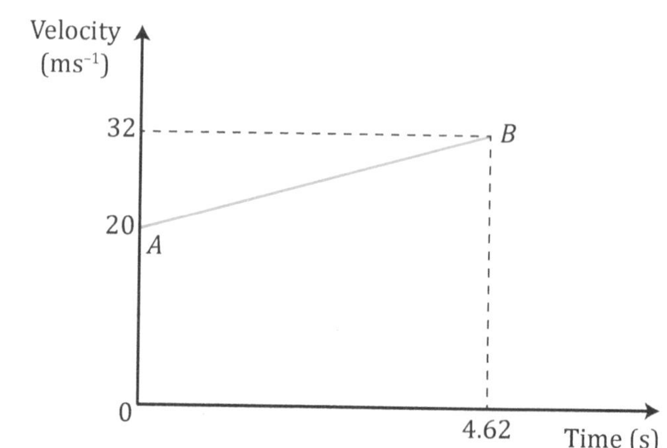